THE
NEW UNIVERSE

THE
NEW
UNIVERSE

A BIOGRAPHY OF THE WORLDS IN WHICH WE LIVE

By

Baker Brownell

PROFESSOR OF CONTEMPORARY THOUGHT, NORTHWESTERN UNIVERSITY

NEW YORK

D. VAN NOSTRAND COMPANY, Inc., 250 FOURTH AVENUE

A NOTE

*T*HE *new universe in more ways than one is relative to each observer, and what may be strange and difficult to one may be too soft and complaisant to another. The universe brewed in the kettle of this book presumes an interested and rather well acquainted taste for current problems and ideas. But it will vary somewhat in the difficulty of its parts. Where the college text book will often have a curve of difficulty almost at a dead level, or graded books of music and the arts will have a curve that grows symmetrically to the volume's close, this book is rather realistic in the order of its difficulty and like the world or a man's life is hardest at the two ends. For most persons Chapter II will be the peak of difficulty for the entire book; beyond that lies so much of Italy as this book affords.*

*T*HE *structure of the book, as outlined in the table of contents, is the structure of a syllabus, first printed in 1923, for a course in Problems of Contemporary Thought opened to upper classmen at Northwestern University, Chicago, in September 1923, with various lecturers assisting. The use of this structural outline of the book as well as the organization and treatment of the material is original with the author.*

*T*O *Dr. Edwin E. Slosson, who persuaded me to write on the world in general, this book is due. For criticism of the book in manuscript I am indebted to: Professor W. Lee Lewis, Dr. Edwin E. Slosson, Dr. M. Luckiesh — Chapter II; Professor Forest Moulton, Professor W. D. MacMillan — Chapter III; Professor Alfred Povah — Chapter IV; Professor A. R. Gilliland — Chapter V; Professor Ferdinand Schevill — Chapter VII; Professor H. S. Philbrick — Chapter VIII; Mr. Theron Locke, Mr. Lewis Hanke, Professor Earl Dean Howard — Chapters IX; X; XI; Professor Franklyn Bliss Snyder — Chapter XII; Mr. Elias Lyman Jr. — Chapter XIII; Dean Shailer Mathews — Chapter XIV; Professor Delton Howard — Chapters XV; XVI; Professor A. W. Moore — Chapter XVII; and to Mr. Ervine Metzl, Mr. John Mills, Director H. F. Harrington, Mr. Leland Case, Mrs. Helena Maxwell Brownell, Professor E. A. Ross, Miss Zona Gale, Mr. Tiffany Blake, Professor W. K. Smart and to students and associates with me in these problems, whose encouragement and continued interest have been invaluable. In justice to them, however, it should be made clear that they are in no way responsible for the material herein.*

CHICAGO, MAY 22, 1926   Baker Brownell

Contents

vii

Contents

BOOK II
Studies in Social Policy
The World of Human Conduct and Practical Action

APPENDIX

Table of Key Ideas

BOOK ONE

Studies in Matter

The World as Scientific Fact

"And I will thread a thread through my poems
that time and events are compact,"
— Walt Whitman

CHAPTER ONE

The Whole World

THE parts of modern thinking have grown faster than the whole. The knots, nodes, the cartilage and limbs of the new knowledge and opinion have gone beyond their general symmetry and form. Big hands, big feet, a new voice every hour are the modern era's appropriate endowment; but they are not coördinated. They twist and scatter in all directions, or bend foolishly in the wrong place like a scarecrow.

The parts are mighty, but the whole of the modern world is still a frail and muddled failure. Science, for example, the "practical" and the "spirit" all are of one body, but few admit it. They are segregated; they lie in nodes and isolations, and indifference still surrounds them. They are set off provincially and made at mutual odds for the sake of minor clarity and convenience. Science, the "practical," the "spirit" all are wagers for one stake of universal size, but few ask what it is. They are ways to that strange and intimate perplexity that is called "the real," but few ask how or where.

Through ancient dust and problems science shuffles contentedly along, so long as there are ruts to guide it. New worlds are bursting open over the horizon's rim; the flare and thrust of new realities and new modes of thinking on them disturb the atmosphere, but science on the whole has not yet noticed them. There is a deep worn methodology to say where it shall go; it tramps on massively and lets it go at that.

To new tools the practical and social pressures of the world have set man's hands. He works them feverishly; he works and hurries about new means to living; and never finds what living is.

In the spirit are new songs to sing, new being to wonder at. Poetries, religions, music, bright enjoyments spring like haphazard flowers from the earth, but he blunders on them with heavy feet. Man creates divinely, and stares and flounders then upon his works like a stupid child. It is a great world that he has come upon, but dangerously perturbed and self-destructive.

Though knowledge no doubt is cellular in structure and has its rightful separations and divisions and its tough walls between the chambers of reality, those walls have lost their meaning in many cases as an organic function of the whole. They are overgrown and sclerotic and inflexible; their time has passed and they had better be destroyed.

For knowledge after all is one; thinking is one; living is one; being is one; and the world — without an unfair loading of the scales for monism — has at least some sort of inner unity. It is one in being, if in nothing else, and our compartments in it, our walls and subdivisions may be little more than clots and congelations on the surface of that magma. Knowledge may be cellular, but the wax of the honeycomb is only to support the honey and to make it more available. It is a convenience. There is but one honey; the cells are made to hold it.

The modern world moves towards monasticism. Each in his own cell the specialists are building worlds, and their prayers and aspirations float out like pink and blue balloons that have no other contact with each other than the touch and jostle of hurrying towards the sky. Each in his cell called a specialized department the experts are telling their beads, manipulating their sacred formulas, sinking their souls in the ritual of their special job, and praying God to keep their eyes from wandering to the green breadth of the meadows and other casual wonders of the world.

But a world of experts and departmentalism, of purblind technicality and dogmatic scorn probably means disaster. For natural orders potentially are infinite and various, and no one can say that the work of specialists, started separately and with little thought or interest in the whole, will of itself converge into a coördinated system. As the great war shows, it well may be disruptive and divergent and mutually destructive. Our faith that nature, things in general, fate or something else will articulate for us and organize the output of the experts who are too nice minded and too narrow to do it by themselves is not well justified. Intellectually the modern world is a corral of wild horses. Each specialty kicks and bites at every other. Chemistry squeals at metaphysics. Psychology snaps at Greek. Physics kicks at English. Economics tramples art. And colleges of culture and so-called liberal arts paw and snort at commerce, while schools of commerce snort as loudly in return.

Specialists there must be in this modern world, for their work is valuable and their power to isolate a problem and to melt it down in the flaming pot of their technique could not be spared. Experts and specialists there must be to do the things assigned in this dumb world of jobs and special duties; it is the cult of expertism that is dangerous. The specialists' *Kultur* will pull disaster down upon this earth.

And in the individual, neat compartments with their watertight bulkheads are found. Men let not their right hand know what their left hand doeth, and the results are broken personalities and distraction. The results are hypocrisy and cowardice and trimming and a thick uncritical acceptance of any fad that comes. In *Who's Who* one man is somehow a great scientist, an accurate Methodist and a staunch member of the Republican party; another is a Christian minister, a captain in reserve and a southern Democrat; and so it goes. Students take their art and physics, their Tennyson and economics uncritically, and the gristle walls that separate those subjects in their minds rarely break down.

The particularism of modern thought will destroy its power; for insulated thought dies like an arm bound too long by a tourniquet. There are few specialists, there are few bureaus and departments of learning in school or college, in government or business or technological concerns that do not suffer from such insulation. Though individual exceptions are not uncommon, for many great and charming men and women still are highly specialized, the rule in general holds. The most are experts only. They have no organon. They carefully localize their interests; they assume the cant of humility and boast that they know *one* thing well. But the truth of their assertion is doubtful. Even the sea bottom is not well known to the flat-fish whose eyes are both on the same side of his head. And the unilateral vision of some scientific and departmental specialists is not well suited to any competent experience.

Soils, it is said, may be poisoned by too much of one crop. Toxins are secreted, and crops too long replanted prevent their own prosperity. The soil prohibits, as it were, too much of one thing, for specialization, vegetable or intellectual, in time is poisonous. It denies in time the dynamic unity of nature. It repudiates the flexibility of her interchange and movement, and it freezes in a specious and a special form a chance contour and a method far from final.

There are few authentic universities today. The notion of thought as a slow flame creeping from a focal core to all the parts and accidents of the world's organism is about forgotten. Our colleges of liberal arts are mechanized and split and subdivided under the hands of departmental experts. Their vital flexibility is gone, and fixed and vested interests of one sort or another quarrel for precedence. Knowledge has been Balkanized in the school and church and formal institution. It rides on petty loyalties without much loyalty or vision for the whole. The centrifugal force of modern thought over-

bears the centripetal force, and the world may shatter
with it.

There may be no United States of knowledge; there
may be no world empire of the real, one and inseparable,
but it is time to try to find one. There is separatism now,
and intellectual states' rights is a strong motive. There
are tariff walls from Illinois to Michigan. Passports must
be had to enter Indiana. Bespectacled professors at the
portals grant visas or cautiously withhold them. Jealous
experts fumble through the bags and trunks piled at
Wisconsin's line; let no unstandardized thing go by.
Too many able men are more loyal to departments now
than to the whole.

As for this book, it is a smuggling expedition in knowledge. It is a cosmic globe trotter without passports. It
will slip as quietly as possible over boundaries and all
section lines without official notice. It will try to see
America and forget the state frontiers. It will see
America first; and seeing Illinois, or Iowa or Arizona or
any other state or town or county will be but adjuncts
to that prime purpose.

It will be a book of the whole world, a tune for the new
universe, a poem, more or less, on things in general. In
everybody there is a world or two; this is but one of
them. It is an average world, a common tune, a poem
such as everyone has in him.

This rather casually constructed universe will have four
parts or shifting foci of attention: studies in matter,
which means the scientific approach to things; studies
in social policy, which means the practical approach to
things; studies in personal and æsthetic values, which
means the spiritual meaning of things; general ideas of
the world, which include the summarizing and philosophical modes by which we view the world.

Science, society, art and philosophy; each has its talent to invest; each takes its way; each finds the world
that it has eyes to see. It is a yielding and a stubborn

world that gives here, and there resists, the pressure of our thoughts and fingers and our hypotheses; and the contours that we finally mould upon it will have many factors in their composition, and numerous philosophies. But what the world is, for all that, will not be answered by this book or any other. Philosophy is not the answer to a question: It is like art, and all human activity perhaps, the formulation of an impulse and an urgency.

The first chapter suggests the point of view from which this survey of the universe is written. The next chapter will consider the structural elements of the material world. It will climb suddenly to difficulties of some altitude and then suddenly climb down again. There will be Einstein and electrons, space and ambiguous nows, radium and the atom's overcoats. For the general reader the next chapter will be the hardest reading in the book.

CHAPTER TWO

The Components of the Material World

MAN is the most moveable of animals. He can run about the continents or spend his summers at the pole. The sky no longer is his limit. The bottom of the sea is more interesting than dangerous. In ten thousand years his mobility has advanced almost geometrically. On foot ten miles an hour was good. By airplane two hundred miles an hour is now a commonplace. The radio and telegraph are parts of his mobility. Light rays are his rapid transit service. Motion is a deep obsession in man. The world that he sees reflects his predilection for motion.

A thoughtful vegetable would be less interested in motion and in space and time. In the vegetable's environment such data would be fixed and static. The cabbage next in line would be inalterably placed by some preordination. Change never could be known; only cabbage poets and philosophers could imagine it, and to them it surely is irrelevant. The passing time that men measure by their actions would be nearly nothing. For time does not pass among vegetables so it can be noticed. Age and fall frosts and the torrents of November must be a mad and sudden cataclysm. Vegetable worlds would be profoundly affected by their immobilities.

Compared with atoms and the stars, with wandering electrons and with light, man to be sure is relatively at rest. He operates upon a little, wizened earth and, there, upon a narrow film between the violence of fire and cold quietness. His daily walk is not so great as the travelling of Arcturus or the circumference of Einstein's universe, said to be 585,900,000,000,000,000,000,000 miles.[1] The stuff in him is but a minor part of things, said by De Sitter [1] to be in all one hundred billion billion times the mass of the sun; and his money or his power and liveliness will never count for much beside the total number of electrons, said to be ten to the seventy-eighth power,[1] in the world. But man acquaints himself with these and in a sense partakes of their mobilities. What he knows, he is to some extent; they join in his system.

For with man's growth and new acquaintances, with his flexibilities and new speeds, the structure of his mechanistic world has changed and warped and found new conformations. "There is news in the realm of mind," says John Dewey.[2] "The intellectual climate, the mentality, which has prevailed for three centuries is changing. The presages of this change have already shown themselves in the natural sciences . . ." Our structural ideas of things take strange forms and realignments; the so-called native, common sense approach breaks down, and the world of matter is today a synthesis of motions. It is redefined, in other words, in new terms of space and time. It is articulated anew in terms of energy and of intervals, called by Einstein space-time intervals. The structure of the world materially is no longer matter and motion. It is a kind of matter-motion called events.[3] A new universe in science and in art and human practice awaits our opening eyes.

A new universe, baffling and beautiful, where men of science tread with tenderness and fear, where unfrequented prairies reach distantly to the horizon, and strange cordilleras bind the edges down of new mysteries unheard of thirty years ago; a new continent of knowledge lies across man's path and scientists are touching it with caution, turning up with their small instruments now the joyous gold of scientific progress, now the scoria and ashes of plain defeat. They are asking strange and childlike questions of that universe and their solemn confidence of other years is not so great. What is space? What is time? What is motion? What are events? A child might answer. What are events? The best of modern minds are struggling to find out.

For events are incorporated motions, as it were; they are organic; time and change are built into them. Beside "events," the whole idea of matter, Whitehead says,[4] is but abstraction; and organisms, in which the pattern of the whole is influential in all parts, are the sole "concrete, enduring" things. He finds herein new ways to bring the mind into his general system; energy and evolution are given new organic consequence; and though his buildings may not stand the pressure of the winds of doctrine that sweep across this modern world, they indicate at least new building impulse and abandonment of old and battered styles.

They are simple and ungainly questions and nearer now to the heart and living of this universe, no doubt, than scientific questions have ever been before. They dissolve the terms and strategies of the older science, the granite frames of matter and naïve solids, the rigid plaster casts of circumstance and happenings, and they reassemble them in new and more organic form. What is a happening? What is an event? The simple question has for answer all the tortured theory and bewilderment of new found thought.

Events are organisms. They are wholes. They endure and they have a history; they develop. Concrete things are all organic; they have inner and qualitative traits; and the old ideas of mechanism, say these modern thinkers,[2] must retreat before them. It is a world no longer infinite in matter [3]; a world where Euclid's straight lines [3] can remain only as a "beautiful dream" [3]; a world where a "kind of space-time *is* the presence of gravitating matter." [3] It is all deliriously confusing, but it has some sense. Its secret is in motion. The world of this and that, these things and chances and externals, this world of "creatures" as old mystics say, these particulars and objects, boxes, waves, moons and grains of dust, are involved in the principles of change; and their wholeness is a pattern on the wind.

For change, the darling problem and the doom of the philosophers for many thousand years, has dawned at last in something of its full significance upon the modern fields of science; and motion, change's other self, finds new and deeper meaning. The dry and crackling formulas that science once could capture motion in are now less adequate. Strange space and time connections interfere, and what once was segregated more or less, neatly set off, nicely defined, turns out to be a vague and shifting part and parcel of a far greater pattern. Science has scratched the skin of motion and finds new and unexpected things. It has turned on space and time that followed it like unnoticed shadows through the centuries and finds in them strange subtleties and interests.

For motion is a space-time idea, and new insights into it must influence the other. The synthesis of space and time, or of their modes, says Pearson,[5] is change, motion, growth, evolution; and all science is description of that change or variation. But whatever it may be, motion is the deep idea in which all modern science finds its root, and a new conception of it may well integrate with one easy gesture all the scattered theories and relieve the sore distress in this modern field of thought. New times and spaces, the space-time interval between events that students say [3] is nearest to a final measurement, mean new ideas of motion; and new ideas of motion mean new worlds of what was space and time. "Space-time," says Whitehead,[4] "is nothing else than a system of pulling together assemblages into unities. But the word *event* just means one of these spatio-temporal unities." It is hard for common sense to see, but motion is at the bottom of it.

And of motion light becomes the standard and the test; and the pure speed of light measures other motions and the world of space and time. Light, burning, vibratory, golden; no one knows just what it is. In the beginning, says the ancient book, there was light; but modern men of science might more nearly say, light is the beginning.

To light, fastest of movers, the new universe is hung.
It is the rod of measurement. It is the maximum of
speed. For time, they say, is zero on one light wave and
events on it are simultaneous. With the absolutes of
space, of time, of simultaneity, of matter, of substance, of
mass, cracked and scattered and abandoned, the material
world loses most of its familiar landmarks. Light remains, through all the flux and change of circumstance,
fixed in its speed to any one observer; and time shifts to
match it. Light is the wonder and test of this world's
material reality. It is the acme of all motions.

Light is the baffling emptiness that fills man's daily
living with all its zest and dynamism. Its golden essence
permeates the stuff and process that scientists call real.
Its fire burns deep in the sources of our life. Light is the
test and exponent of motion; and all motions and all
bodies, whatever else they are or do, must look to it to
justify their natures and to place them accurately in the
pattern of the world.

For motion is presumably a relation between bodies.
More than that few dare to say, for motion and body are
but names. Science can describe behavior of a body in
expert terms, but body and motion have become for it
more like abstractions than concrete things. Of bodies,
says Russell,[6] "we know so little that we cannot even be
sure that they are anything: they *may* be merely groups of
events in other places, those events which we should
naturally regard as their effect." Science can describe
the order in which things happen, but it cannot say what
happening and motion is, unless it be that order. We can
picture no motion that is not some body moving. But
the new science sometimes ignores this. It may accuse a
small, defenseless electron of being bodyless though full
of go. It may argue that body and motion are mere
conventions separated from each other only by our arti-

fice, and it will claim, in the quantum theory, that the real thing is "action" or "the effect of energy operating for a very short time." They are quanta of energy that seem at basis discontinuous. They are events or near-events that seem the minimum of reality.[7]

Pieces of energy, the littlest event, atoms of action; the men of science nowadays speak with solemn childishness, or what would seem child's language to learned ones a score of years ago, and there is no one wise enough to tell what energy or motion mean. They speak portentously of tensors and of dim and terrible equations, but the blithe vitality of things that we call motion slips elusively away.

Motion involves change; in the science of mechanics are long formulas for the ways that bodies change and shift their relative positions in the world, but change is only a word that begs the question for motion. And position would have small meaning were there no chance for change. It is a bad hole that scientists have fallen into. Though everything may move it still is difficult to universalize man's unique motility. Scientists have built a world of motions around man's nature, but what motion may be is hard to say.

It is involved in space and time; and the space world and the time world are real to us largely because space-time is a measurement for motions. They are standards, far better than the sense of effort or less measurable experiences could be, for the description of our motions. In terms of time and space ten miles an hour means more or less the same to all. But the same motion measured by one's effort might be incomprehensible to some persons. Even the discovery of objective attitudes and of time and space points of view may be laid to man's social impulse to find a continuity between his actions now and those tomorrow. Whatever it may be, motion is involved in space and time. And space and time would surely be most difficult to comprehend were we not highly moveable animals.

Is it man's nature that science after all is explicating? There is no good answer, for the new science sits on the brink of metaphysics, and the old, bluff certainties and assumptions that once were loud in domination of the field grow little and decline. The go-getter science of an earlier day has passed its prime. There is a thoughtful interlude. There is a philosophic dusk and mystery, and old problems rise like new ones persistent for an answer.

The stalwart old science is gone. Its naïve realism and objectivity is not so confident as before. The conflict and contrast between the objective and the subjective are less bitter than they were. Whitehead,[8] Dewey,[9] and others are thrusting mind and value into a scientific order that once was purely mechanistic. They are breaking down abstract dichotomies that had become too falsely prepossessing. For subject, object are approaches to reality; they are different slants on what must be the same thing, and the modern scientist usually lets it go at that. In his struggle for fixed and objective standards of measurements, he has come to learn that about the only fixed measure in our world is the ways in which we think of things. Science must be rational, and if the world is not, then science has lost its one big chance. Its prime hypothesis is baseless. To our minds motion without bodies is meaningless, and without bodies space and time are equally meaningless. The infinite extension of space with nothing in it is only rapturous nonsense. The eternity before anything happened and after everything has happened is sweet dreams and nothing more. Space and time, body and motion are fixed descriptive terms for the plurality of things that we call the world. They are principles of that plurality. They are terms above the pigeonholes in chaos. They are standards made, and suitable more or less to the mind's use. And a mind in an immobile, vegetable body, incompetent to make a distance in a time or to change one environment for another, would find them rather meaningless and nothing.

Space, time, motion; they are terrible simplicities that man can never hope to know except in shallow parts. They are ways of ordering a universe, perhaps; they are lines of our analysis, and the burning bits of meaning that we find therein may well adjust their character and pattern to our advancing need.

Space and time are relationships between bodies. They are a kind of order so that between any two bodies there is always theoretically space for another.[9] Motion, too, is a successive order or continuum relative to several bodies. If there is absolute motion, says Einstein, we cannot know it.[10] And if there is absolute space and time, we cannot know it. As we know them, they are settings for our experience of things. Experience is always relative and finite.

Locating things is one of the huge complications of a world where a man's power to move about is of primary interest. His increased mobility has enlarged his field. It has multiplied the pluralities of his universe. It has made the problems of where and when more difficult.

From the small end of a microscope to the large end of a telescope is a long way, and the number of things along it is vastly greater than the naked eye can see. Before the spyglass came we had about 5,000 stars. Now 300 million stars are visible. Man has moved himself, visually at least, to all of those things. He has extended his sensitivity down the length of electrified wires and Hertzian waves. He has extended his hitting power sixty miles on the end of a nine-inch shell. He can move in a thousand places that were inaccessible a few years ago. His motility, actual and tacit, increases the possible things in his experience. He must account for those things. He must locate them in reference to each other or fall hopelessly into a welter and confusion.

All this has put strain upon his locating facilities. The efficiency of his space and time has been heavily tested. What did well enough for the blur and guess of his un-aided senses is hardly accurate for modern experimental science. When fifteen miles an hour was unholy speed for railroad trains, and communities of wholesome citizens resolved strenuously against it, the measurement of time and of the speed that bodies change their state was limited to a few crude perceptions in which a tenth of a second was extremely fine. But today the speed of light is casually compared with the speed of discharged electrons leaving their former place of business, where a tenth-sec-ond would be an age. To know about such things means that we must locate them. Where they are, relatively to each other, how many and at what time is the greater part of any scientific problem. To know a thing is to measure it.

There is more to locate than there once was. The de-mands of modern experimental science have rather over-reached the accommodations of Euclidian geometry and the classical absolutes of space and time. These old for-malities have their limits of application. The modern world seems to have reached those limits, even space and time may change their styles.

For space and time are a form of reference. With a world or two more of things to refer to, the system may need readjustment.[11] By means of the space-time sys-tem, any event, anywhere, any time may be indexed and filed away in the universal catalogue. The location of any one thing in reference to every other known thing may be definitely described. The space-time system is a way we have of making all things finite and particular. And we thereby save our minds from hopeless muddle. Location is the first step in any practical or intellectual action on a thing. Space-time is our system of location.

Length or distance is the first dimension in this sys-tem of reference. Breadth, or plane surface, is the second.

Depth, or body volume, is the third. Time and the quantity of change is the fourth.[12] A space-time interval, Russell explains,[12] has in fact replaced the shift and miscellany of space *and* time as a real reference and manner of location. Though events may have more dimensions, our minds are not used to using them. Four seem to be enough. We may safely say that existing things, for human purposes, have no more.

Were there no change possible in those relations, the entire space-time continuum would be irrelevant. Were there none of this that is called motion, we could use no form of reference of this sort. We would be unaware of it. Psychologically as well as mechanically, there would be no space and time.

The increase in man's mobility has made important the new problems of reference. His biological development has given sanction to a set of problems, the validity of which is mathematical and physical. The multiplication of objects in his perceptual environment and the refinement of their relations has made demands on the old system of location that are hard to satisfy. Experimental science has at last brought about the review and reinspection of our naïve notions of space and time. Space and time must be overhauled. The repair job seems to be in charge of Albert Einstein of Berlin.

It began with De Sitter, a Dutchman, Lorentz, another Dutchman, Fizeau, Fresnel, Michelson, of Chicago, and others.[13] As a traveller in space and time they found that light is emphatically unique. For light is the fastest thing in the world, and it travels at the same speed regardless of the speed of its source.[14] Einstein calls this the "Principle of the Constancy of the Velocity of Light." [15] It is a fact that has pushed old time and space out of the house forever and upset our established notions of the universe.

The second principle in the new doctrine of space and time is the better known principle of relativity. "In different systems moving uniformly and rectilinearly with respect to each other, all natural processes take place in exactly the same way," says the scientist.[16] And for that reason the apple that Johnnie drops from the upper berth of the Pullman car upon the sleeping gentleman below strikes that gentleman in exactly the same place whether the car be in motion or at rest. This well known principle seems to conflict with assertions that the speed of light is constant regardless of the speed of its source. Einstein resolved that conflict and cracked space in the operation.

Imagine a ship steaming down the bay. A man on the ship is exactly half way between the bow and the stern. He rolls two balls down the deck at the same time with the same strength. One ball he rolls forward, the other aft. It is obvious on the ship that the first ball will arrive at the bow of the ship at about the same time that the second ball arrives at the stern. It is obvious that so far as the man on the ship is concerned, the balls are travelling at the same speed. It is also obvious that a man on shore observing the speed of the balls would differ from the man on the ship. The man on shore would say that the ball that rolled forward moved faster than the ball that rolled aft. He would say that the speed of the first ball was its original speed plus the speed of the ship and the speed of the other ball was the original speed minus the speed of the ship. Both men would be right. Their difference is only in the body to which they refer for measurement. In the one case it was the ship, in the other, the shore.

That was all very well for many years. It was the old principle of relativity. It applied to all moving things. Then came some disturbing experiments on æther and on light. They showed that regardless of the motion of its source, light *in vacuo* always travels 186,300 miles a

second, and as for æther, it gave no signs of existence.
Light, in other words,[17] is a rather different affair from
the balls on the ship's deck. The balls had one speed for
the man on the ship and different speeds for the man on
shore. They partook of the speed of the ship. But light
from the ship would have exactly the same speed in all
directions. It would not partake of the speed of the ship,
and to the man aboard and to the man ashore it would
have the same velocity. Stars may move towards us or
away, but their light comes to us at the same speed. As
the scientists used to say, light belongs to the æther once
it leaves its source; and it is æther, not the speed of that
source, that determines the velocity of light.

But the æther, brought in to save the situation, has
not panned out well. If all æther, "filling all space" (to
use the old figure) is at rest relative to itself, light travelling in this medium might well have, like other waves, a
constant speed regardless of the speed of its source. This
fixed æther would drift past (as trees on the bank slide
past a moving boat) as the earth moved through space,
and experiments with light on earth could show it. But
the æther-drift experiments of Michelson and Morley [18]
did not show it, and it became clear that there is no æther
or that some of it drifts along with the earth instead of
past it. The contrast between the balls on the ship and
the light on the ship is as hard to understand as ever, for
light shows no signs of a differential motion of its ætherial
medium; it is constant, and so, æther or no æther, the
conflict remains.[19] For in regard to the earth, light travels
in the earth's field of reference; it shows no plus or minus
due to the earth's motion; it is in accord with the old
principle of relativity. But the same light in regard to
other fields of reference moving differently would show
the same constant speed to them as to the earth. Therein
is the paradox and the conflict. The speed of light is
persistently a constant regardless of where one observes
it or of the speed of its source.

The fact is astonishing. It seems to contradict the old principle of relativity. It seems to be subject to a different law from balls and bullets, and other moving things. To this Einstein answers that it is not the speed of light that is at fault nor the principle of relativity but our conventional notion of time. He accepts the two laws, proved by experiment, of the constancy of the speed of light and the principle of relativity. But he attacks the old idea of the simultaneous.

We have assumed all these centuries that now is the same now for every atom in the universe. We have always thought that simultaneity is absolute. If the two balls strike the two ends of the ship respectively at the same instant, we have assumed that such an instant is the same for the man on ship or the man on shore and for every other man.[22] It is this absolute simultaneity that Einstein questions.

Here it is that the classical ideas of absolute space and time collapse. For Einstein insists that we can know space and time only by observation, and that light as the fastest of all things subject to experimental science, and with a velocity that is constant regardless of the source, not only defines the relation between space and time, but determines their nature. From a concept in logic, Einstein reduces space-time to a specimen, as it were, for observation. Its validity in his theory is less logical than observational.

Two events at equal distances from the observer are simultaneous, says Einstein, when light rays from them reach the observer at the same time. To protests at this desecration of the absolute "now," he would answer, "How else can you know them to be simultaneous? The now is real scientifically only so far as it is observable." There is no other answer. Classical space and time has collapsed.

For it follows that an observer at rest in regard to the two events may observe them to be simultaneous whereas an observer moving from the mid-point towards one of the events will observe that one sooner than the other. Simultaneity, and with it all space and time, depends on the motion of the observer. That is fundamental. It is the child of a synthesis of the old principle of relativity and the law of the constancy of the speed of light.

To say that the velocity of light is the same for all observers is rather ambiguous, however, and it may be wrong. The velocity of light relative to each observer always appears the same to *him*, and equal to its constant velocity in its medium, says L. Bolton. But the velocity of light relative to each observer does not appear the same to *other observers*. "Consider a light beam AB having its source at A, and let there be two observers, O, O', the former of whom may be supposed to be stationary relatively to A, while the latter moves in the direction of the beam with a velocity V relatively to the former observer. The velocity of light *in vacuo* being 300,000 kilometres per second, O makes out the velocity relative to himself to be 300,000 kilometres per second, and O' also makes out the velocity relative to himself to be the same, but O computes the velocity of light relative to O' to be 300,000 kilometres per second minus V, and O' computes the velocity of light relative to O to be 300,000 kilometres per second plus V. The reason why O and O' make out the velocity to be the same, each relative to himself, is because their relative motion affects their measurements of lengths and time. These measurements adjust themselves automatically in such a way as to give the same numerical value to the relative velocity in both their cases." [20] It affects not only their measurements, Einstein would add, it affects time itself, for lengths and time are what one measures them to be, and light is the yard stick.

Einstein's theory of relativity holds to the law of the absolute constancy of the speed of light. It holds to the principle of relativity. But it denies the absolute constancy of time and space. Time and space depend on the state of motion of the body of reference. They are not valid according to a law within themselves. They are hung to light. They have a finite standard. The nature of light conditions their nature.

"Before the advent of the theory of relativity," says Einstein, "it had always tacitly been assumed in physics that the statement of time had an absolute significance, i.e. that it is independent of the state of motion of the body of reference. But . . . this assumption is incompatible with the most natural definition of simultaneity; if we discard this assumption, then the conflict between the law of the propagation of light *in vacuo* and the principle of relativity disappears." [21]

Suppose again the moving ship, a very long one. Two lights flash respectively from the bow and the stern of the ship so that the man on shore observes them simultaneously. Then to the man in the middle of the ship, they will not be simultaneous. The bow flash will be slightly sooner. As the light travels at a constant speed regardless of the motion of the source, its velocity relative to the shore will be unaffected by the movement of the ship, and the two lights that are simultaneous to the man on shore will give the man on ship time to move towards the bow beam of light and see the bow light sooner. Bullets shot by the same operation that flashed the lights would have the opposite result, for the bullet partakes of the speed of its source. To the man on shore, the bow bullet would be the later. To the man on ship, the bullets might be simultaneous.

And the answer is the epitaph of Father Time and his sister Space. The solution of the conflict, says Einstein, is in that definition of simultaneity.[22] The now is not absolute. It is variable. It is relative to the motion of different objects of reference. It means farewell forever to nineteenth century space and time.

If Professor Michelson and others had not puttered round with high speed things like light, or if Herr Einstein, Lorentz, Minkowski and others had been less concerned in very small matters of fact, this new and disconcerting universe might never have been noticed. But the revolution is now upon us. A new space and time, a new gravity, a new inertia and mass, a new cosmos have marched in. It may not affect next week's grocery bill. But it will give the new generation something to think about.

Æther was the first to go. The æther-drift experiments of Michelson and his associates showed that it is not needed. As a medium of light, it acts very much like nothing. Therefore it probably is nothing. Though D. C. Miller has been making vigorous efforts to bring the æther back through recent experiments on Mount Wilson,[23] it is not unlikely that the old imponderable stuff has been put away for good or is so much altered that its own mother would not know it. With its departure the impulse to treat space and time as if they were containers, a kind of half empty carton for the world, received a setback. The scientist's innocent confidence in space and time was shaken. He began to suffer from philosophy.

Inertia, gravity and mass, said Einstein, could be expressed in terms of constantly accelerated motion. Abolish gravity, for example, but put a man in a closed elevator and start it upward at a constantly accelerating rate and he will have all the effects of gravity.[24] Thus mass may be put in terms of motion; and at the speed of light, its unique limiting condition, the mass of any body would be infinite; for matter may be curdled motion of a sort, and mass a function of velocity.[25] From other fields the electrons and Planck's ultimate little quanta of action are coming fast to prove it. Bent light rays and space warped in gravitational fields have entered science's domain, and the conception of a curved universe is studied gravely. It may be curved, says Einstein,[26] because space, its limiting condition, is not laid out on quite straight lines. It may be finite because curved space, analogously to the surface of a sphere, may come back in itself. Calculation of lines of force indicate that the total quantity of matter in the world is limited. The universe may be boundless, though finite, because a curved surface, as of a sphere, is boundless so far as the surface is concerned.[27] The new universe has departed somewhat from the straight lines so long fashionable. But the nature of its curves is not yet known.

Every event — and all bodies so far as we know them are events — has its world line plotted on this four dimensional universe.[28] It has its distance factor, its surface factor, its depth factor, its time factor. When the coördinates of two events differ just a little, the events are adjacent; the space-time interval is not great.

By injecting this temporal quality into statements of events, Einstein makes it possible for an observer anywhere under any condition, says Luckiesh,[29] "to obtain the same apparent measurement of space. For example, the length of a rod would be determined to be the same whether measured on the Earth or on any other celestial body by the same observer and measuring device. This does not mean that the length of the rod is the *same* in all cases and it does not imply that any of the measurements reveal the *true* length. Constancy of length and true length have no meaning in this great generalization and unification. To two observers moving uniformly with respect to each other (one on Mars and the other on Earth) the rod does not appear of the same length, but Einstein provides a means for those two observers moving with a uniform relative velocity to arrive at the same mathematical statement of the phenomena."

It becomes a strange and dizzy world for those whose imagery and way of thinking have been built from childhood on the firm and final forms, presumably, of space, of time, of matter, mass and gravitation. It becomes a rubbery world; all things and bodies are events and their measurement in mass, in size, in shape, in time, in gravitation depends upon their total set of circumstances in each case, upon the character of their organization and their motion. It is an organic concept of physical reality. It is a new world ceremony of which light is the grand master with the high silk hat. The primary intervals in this rubbery world are the space-time intervals between events; and these intervals are determined [30] relatively to the speed of light, the motion of the body to be measured and other reciprocities. It is a world where two events called simultaneous in one part of space-time may be successive in another and in reversed succession in still another. It is a world where shape and size and mass of things may vary with the point of view and the relativities of motion. It is a world in which the so-called force of gravity is not a "force" at all but a twist and warping of space-time in the vicinity of "matter" such that "bodies" take on new behaviors as they approach each other.[31] The new world has a strange bonelessness about it. It is a terminology for events. Physical realities are events.

Events may be in close succession. They may be so close that between each two there is always theoretically another. Such a series of events might give us the impression of a solid body persisting in time.[32] Perceptually matter, as well as motion, it may be, is built up like a movie thriller from a dense series of events. When the world line of an event intersects the world line of an observer, the event is manifested as a physical phenomenon. That is the pattern of experience. It is a physical interpretation of the relation between bodies.

With space warped, with time a fourth dimension, with mass increasing with velocity, with simultaneity relative to the motion of the observer, with most of the absolutes of the material world collapsing like the monarchies of Europe and with light alone left as a universal standard, it may be expected that the old ultimates of matter and energy will not be left untouched. They are not untouched, but their disintegration came about independently. It came rather earlier than that of space and time. It was engineered by a different group of men.

For the founders of the theory of relativity inspect the universe as a whole, more or less, in order to know the structure of its parts. They deal in stellar distances and the course of planets. They prove their case by a bent light ray observed in an eclipse, or a whim of Mercury. The other group inspect the world's minutest parts in order to know the whole. They assume endless repetition of phenomena and an infinitely aggregative world. Their colleagues assume its well nigh endless divisibility.

Neither has dared question the logical constancy of that world, although Eddington suggests it. They fear irrational things no doubt and dread to ungear man's experience from reality. The world that man knows may be his own selection from several samples.

In any case the little hard absolutes of matter are gone, and with them the old fashioned materialist. Like space and time, the atom has caved in, and its crash was great. We are told to readjust our thinking to the new materialism. We are told that bodies are *passé*, that events perform their functions. The old continuities are gone: matter, a persistent solid something; energy, a stream as it were of motion having more or less depth; space, a continuous kind of nothing; æther, are replaced by new continuities. Their full import no one can guess.

Relativity, says Bertrand Russell, has given continuity to physics as evolution gave continuity to biology. But it is a new continuity. And the modern theories of matter are also new continuities. The old absolutes, the ultimate solidities, the atoms, Kaisers, kings, Pittsburgh-plus, æther, even our "nows" that gave our world in-

telligible, though external, continuity have dropped
away. The electronic theory of matter has plunged out
like a wild horse. No one knows, least of all itself, where
it is going.

The modern idea of a substance having its own laws
probably began with modern experimental science and
one of the Bacons. Home rule for matter was a crucial
moment in the history of human progress. With that de-
cided, men turned with confidence to experiment and
observation. They were assured that what structure
matter had was *bona fide* and valid in itself. By removing
supernatural and scholastic interference in the laws of
nature, they made the modern world possible. Confusing
it might be, but its principles were at least immutable.

Science is based on the hypothesis that the so-called
material world is absolutely valid in itself. It is a closed
system on which other worlds of discourse, the arts, the
spirit, the social values, cannot interact. It is still based
on that hypothesis, but within its field, huge changes have
taken place. The little absolutes that were components of
that world, space, time, matter, energy are in a new solution. Matter, the hard boiled stuff of our common sense,
has suffered most of all.

Today the structure of matter is known to be electrical.
With the discovery of radium and a keener observation of
electricity, the idea of matter was transformed. There are
three existences, says Soddy,[33] matter, electricity, and
energy. But matter as we usually think of it, has dis-
solved under analysis into energy or "action." And
energy is often expressed in terms of electricity, mathematics, tensors and other awe inspiring names.

The atom, once a satisfying little lump of ultimate
solidity, has become a communistic gang of electrons acting as one unit. As the molecule was and is the limit of

the physical division of matter, the atom within the molecule, was and still is the limit of the chemical division of matter. But far within the atom is the limit of electrical division of matter. That, just now, is the electron and the proton, or hydrogen nucleus. There are signs that the analysis will go further.

They are small things. Ten billion times a bird shot, says Professor Millikan,[34] is as big as the earth. Ten billion times an atom is less than a yard across. Ten billion times the nucleus of an atom is only a pin point. In this ten billionth of a pin point there may be as many as 384 electrons.

They are small but very fast. Some of them will travel 99 compared with light as par at one hundred. That is within one per cent of the absolute speed limit of this universe, and some may travel even faster. The study of the behavior of these small, fast electrical somethings is an inspection of the inner structure of all matter.

What is the machinery of an atom? Scientists have explained one atom, the hydrogen atom, with a fair degree of certainty. It is the simplest of atoms. Other atoms are too complex for even modern mathematics. The time will come, no doubt, but at present the atom is too big for us.

Atoms are built like the solar system. They are mostly emptiness shot through with badly tangled forces. There is room in one for much travelling. Enlarge the nucleus of an atom to the size of the sun and the electrons gyrating around it would be as far away as the planets. Atoms, say the scientists from Rutherford to Bohr, are negative electrons cycling around a positive nucleus. The radius of an electron's orbit is about half a hundred-millionth of a centimeter. Around that orbit it travels — in the case of hydrogen — about 1400 miles every second. It makes the round trip of its orbit, or its year, seven billion times in every millionth of a second.

NOTE: This planetary hypothesis as to the atom's nature has been abandoned by Heisenberg and Schrodinger. At best it is but a pictorial presentation of an abstract and difficult set of relationships.

What is an electron? It is the vehicle of a negative electrical charge. Perhaps it is the charge. It travels around the nucleus of the atom. Sometimes it is knocked off or otherwise is free. It has mass, but its mass is inconsiderable compared with the mass of the nucleus.[35] It has size — perhaps.

All electrons are exactly alike. No matter to what kind of atom they belong, they are still alike in charge and in all other measurable characteristics. With the nuclei of the atoms, the electrons constitute the basic world stuff. There are 600,000,000,000,000,000,000,000,000 electrons in one gram of matter. Someone has called them the building stones of the universe.

It would seem that what qualitative differences the elements may possess must lie in the atomic nuclei around which the electrons rotate. But the nuclei too, turn out to be wholly electrical in nature. Where electrons are negatively charged, the nucleus is always positive and holds the rotating electrons in their orbits — more or less — by the electrical "tractations." The nuclei of each element have a characteristic positive charge which varies according to the element. The hydrogen nucleus, for example, can hold ("hold" is metaphorical) but one electron rotating about it and it has the least mass.[36] Helium comes next with two electrons while the nucleus of uranium can hold 92 planetary electrons.

What are these nuclei? They are electrical organizations always with an excess positive charge. They are more or less complex according to the element in question. They are built up probably from combinations of helium nuclei or from helium and hydrogen nuclei along with some cancelled electrons. As the helium nucleus is probably in turn built up from four hydrogen nuclei and two electrons, it would appear that all matter is composed of two kinds of electrical entities, the negative electron and the positive hydrogen nucleus.

By this astonishing mathematical and experimental

analysis, the qualitative differences between the elements are resolved into quantitative terms of number and arrangement. The significance of that resolution is no less than tremendous.

How are electrons arranged about the nucleus? There are some 92 patterns in about nine groups. Each pattern means one of the 92 elements. Each group represents periodic recurrences of qualitative similarities between those elements. The electrons rotate as if on the surfaces of concentric shells about the nucleus. The heavier elements have more "shells" up to about eight, as a limit. Their nuclei, where by far the greater part of their mass lies, are more complex and carry more excess units of positive charge as a balance to the large number of electrons in the various shells. In the stars, perhaps, there are stripped nuclei, packed to enormous density, without planetary electrons, but on the earth we know of none. The electrons, maneuver over the surface of these imaginary shells in almost incalculable complexities.

Sometimes the nucleus of a so-called radio-active atom shoots out of itself one of its component helium nuclei. It takes electrons along with it. The atom's system is upset; it has a "spell," and when it readjusts itself, it finds it is no longer the atom that it was. It is another element, lower in weight, lesser in energy, and in general, nearer that graveyard of all elements, their seeming goal, hydrogen.

The radioactive elements are undergoing this transmutation of the elements naturally.[36] They are shooting out helium and ending up as lead. But transmutation has been accomplished artificially. Rutherford knocked some hydrogen out of nitrogen. Hydrogen no doubt can be built up into helium. Alchemy has come back.

Light rays come from energy discharged when electrons in the outer shells are disturbed; X-rays, or Roentgen rays, from the inner rings, and radioactivity primarily from the nucleus. When rays are emitted, the atom loses

NOTE: That the electrons rotate around the nucleus is of course conjectural.

that much energy. It is a downward process, with no hint of power to rebuild except from outside source.

And now come ultra X-rays to complicate and rearrange our knowledge of the world. They are more penetrating by far than any other known rays, and their American interpreter, Millikan,[37] finds their source seemingly in the general cosmos. In the transformations of an atom's nucleus, rays are emitted and these perhaps are some of them. Hydrogen perhaps builds up to helium, a nucleus perhaps captures a new electron, and these rays result from that spectacular and minute performance. It offers new suggestions, and new hope to cosmic pessimists, that the world of cosmic and atomic process that hitherto ran down to graves in hydrogen, so far as science knew, may here be building up again, with "matter" born anew.

If there be a cosmic building up, however, it well may be that man could never know it. For his experience may be unilateral, and realities in it may be involved only in an energy release, or an "event," that at the end leaves the world lower in potential than before. We are keyed to motions; we experience release of energy, and a true building up may be beyond our ken.

But sad as this downward process theoretically may be, it is presumably the source at last of all our active world, of our energy releases, of our "something doing" in this outside universe. It is all the biography of h, say Planck and Bohr and Sommerfeld, quantum specialists, and h is one quantum. This little h, now so important, is the circumference of the smallest orbit of an electron around an atom's nucleus *times* the electron's velocity *times* its mass [38]; and though the multiplying is much, the result, h, is small. A million million, million, million times h would be a short duration of energy, called "action," just noticeable to our senses. This small h seems to be the natural unit of what is called action. It is a fundamental constant. There can be no less, and any more must be in even multiples.

For an electron gyrating in the second ring around an atom's nucleus has two quanta or $2h$; in the third orbit, three quanta, and so on, and all increase or decrease in a thing's "action" is not continuous but in these little jumps. When an electron for some reason jumps from one ring to the next ring inward it has, as it arrives, some kinetic energy to spare. When it jumps from a $2h$ orbit to a $1h$ orbit, there is $1h$ released for action somewhere else. That released quantum becomes a wave of light to go forth into the world or elsewhere to do its work. What the atom loses in energy at least comes out in doing something in this world. It may run down, but it's a lively world while it lasts.

Our atoms, it would seem, are slowly bleeding to death. Unless the universe itself, as someone suggests,[39] moves in huge cycles with the general down process of this universe followed by the up process of another, we may expect that the heights of potential energy must eventually be levelled, and all action and with it all matter, "cease and desist."

But the universal dispersion of energy will not come soon. In an ordinary brick there is enough atomic energy unreleased to blow two million dreadnoughts one thousand meters into the air. A few bricks properly administered should keep civilization running for some years.

The instability of the new universe is obvious, but underlying these theories there is faith in a fundamental continuity in existence which as yet remains undisturbed. This is evident in the doctrines of the conservation of energy, and of matter; though battered and changed, they still in some sense hold. Faith in continuity is bound up in the assumption that natural phenomena are orderly, consistent and measurable. Our ideas of natural process and of organization are deeply involved in these assumptions. Of the authority for these assumptions, whether based on something other than our own mental requirements and valuations, we cannot be sure.

Five big ideas, like whales in the ocean, have been sighted in this chapter. They are: relativity of space, time, and motion, electrical structure of matter, the quantitative basis of the elements, transmutation of the elements, conservation. A sixth, the quantum theory of energy, is, at present, very deep in the water.

The Forms of the Material World

THERE are more specific things than this world but few things more interesting. As a going concern it has been a moderate success for some time and it has good prospects for the future. As an organization it is as delicately adjusted as an Elgin watch. It ticks on, as good stem winders do; here, without resetting or regulation from without.

This rather reliable world shows signs on the whole of an accurate structure, and to the scientist at least, what happens in it is always an exact result of what that structure is. In a world mainly of events science, the drill sergeant, finds system and measures for marching, regimented facts and general orders to direct them. It finds a world of concrete happenings, and it infers from their uniformities, and for other reasons perhaps less scientific, that all situations and all events have one structural base. It retires from events and the concrete this or that which it observes, to matter and motion, space and time for a structural foundation. And in recent years, with a universe overhauled by new experts of the relativist and trans-atomic schools, science finds in the speed of light, in discrete quanta of action, in the electrical nature of matter, in electrons and their activites, in "events," a structure even more remote. They are this world's components, and their organization is the structure of the world of matter. What happens, events and their successions, is the process of the world. The order of structure is primary; its continuity is logical and it inheres in all events. The order of process is temporal and dynamic;

its continuity is successive; it is revealed through change and complication.

But the casual pell mell of events is the only field in which the scientist may observe structural continuities, and universal change and instability are the only ways in which the order of process is revealed. All structure, as Dewey says,[1] is structure of something; "it is a character of events"; and what is true in structure or in process, is true only in concrete situations and happenings. Important phantoms dominate events, and abstract continuities which scientists can neither touch nor feel are called matter, electricity, the laws of things, change, evolution. In the solvent of skepticism they lose their intrinsic realities no doubt, but they remain for science the primary frame of things on which events flutter and shift like clothes drying on an oaken rail. The structure of the universe is a conception of form and organization. The process of the universe is a conception of development; it is a demonstration of natural structure; it is historical and particular. The theory of relativity and the electronic theory are mainly conceptions of structure. The theories of stellar evolution, of the formation of soils, of the origin of species are mainly conceptions of process. In nature the two are not separated, and in thought they cannot be separated long. Events, like explosions, synthesize them in bright conflagrations.

Process is irreversible. It clicks forward on a ratchet that prevents return. No situation can be perfectly repeated. Something is lost; something sinks into the mire of the past; it cannot be recovered. Events demobilize when they are over, and to reorganize them takes more than the energy available that they leave behind. Science cannot say that process some day will be over and that change will end, for the losses in events as they go by may not be losses in the world's facility for change. Science does say that things do not repeat themselves; and if they did we could not know it, and time itself, or one-way time at least, would be vacated. Process is directive. It is not a symmetrical series of events.[2] The river never can turn back.

This irreversibility of process is founded even in the nature of the molecule itself. For the energy that goes into one event cannot be saved whole for the energy of the next. Some is distracted into heat [3] and friction and molecular vibration that disperse in low potentials the energy once available for work. They call it Carnot's principle, or the second law of thermodynamics, and it shows that only a frictionless, non-absorbing engine could be perfectly reversible.[4] In a world that is neither frictionless nor non-absorbing such an engine, or any other reversible process, is impossible. For events, to science, are like engines: They are vehicles of energy that take up motion at one end and release it at the other in a form determined by their special nature. They take up energy, but they release never quite the same amount in forms available for further work. Some energy is scattered in wasted heat; it is a commission charged off to the process, and the difference in potential, which is all that counts, is a little less after than it was before. So far as available energy is concerned process always seems to be downhill. Energies will spread out. They seep through the walls of long and narrow lines of process. The natural world absorbs them on all sides. It is not prejudiced for one.

Though time, to be sure, may not be always one-way time, nor process always irreversible, though evolutionary and progressive orders of events, such as we find deep in the necessities of our experience, may be, as Lewis [4] suggests, only an incidental cosmos arising from our one-way source of energy from the sun, the world clicks on, for us at least, down its inevitable ratchet road, and what happens in it happens irreversibly. For us things move one way. They stream on without a turning.

This streaming of events in one direction seems to be nature's only predilection in the world's architecture, and though that streaming too may be a metaphor read in from its analogy to human life, the world that man reports, at any rate, is a process in development. It evolves. It stands on its preceding situation. It incorporates experience, as it were, in its next formation. Up or down, dead or alive are indifferent matters in this cosmic process; the evolution of the universe may not be edifying or purposive or getting anywhere, but it does evolve. By Carnot's principle, if no other, it cannot merely oscillate.

The streaming on of cosmic process has reportorial possibilities that man would be slow to find merely in oscillations. The world is always news. For ages men have walked their nightly beats among the stars, and astronomers with glass and camera still cover the sky for notes of interest. Sometimes a big story breaks, a new star blazes suddenly in Perseus, and a shrewd Scotch cub is first to take the scoop into the office. A more local kind of story is handled by geologists who appropriate the earth for their domain. The biologists have copyrighted life. Psychologists report exclusively on minds. Anthropologists dig among the bones and battle axes of departed men for new scandals as to human origin, and historians hold man's written records for further revelations. They come with much authority and specialties, but they all alike are cosmic journalists and their record for today will probably be something else tomorrow. They particularize their fields, but it is all one field and presumably one process. No matter where they look at it, there is but one marching on of events.

Stellar process, solar process, geological process; the machines turn in a huge silence that is hard for man to analyze. They are distinguished from each other only by their progressive localization. What is solar is also stellar; what is geological is also in the solar system; and for that matter what is living or a part of human action is also geological. The heavens are telling more or less about our sun and its small earth; for the earth after all is a

minor resident of the heavens, and an earth-born baby
reaching for its toes is a participant in the streaming of
stars. The geologist pounding rocks is inspecting a
planetary architecture on which man is a moist and
sticky bit of mould. On nature's scale man is a mere drop-
let of water that catches the glisten of suns. He can see
a good deal, but he cannot do much about such things as
stellar process.

For stellar process is a matter of the milky way and
streams of stars, of light-centuries and the distribution of
matter in this universe. Its bedtime stories are about the
childhood of suns. Poets and mathematicians speculate
on how much world there is and how many stars. Our
leading celestial mechanics such as Moulton, our stellar
statisticians such as van Rhijn and Sears and the Dutch
star gazer, Kapteyn, make ponderous estimates of the
quantity of stars. They predict the crop of suns, magnitude by magnitude, and there is much wonder, though
they no doubt are two thirds right.

About 35 billion stars inhabit this universe, says a heav-
enly census taker.[5] They are sprayed upon the sky like
milk. They hang in clouds and globules, and the fogs that
blur the night of space south of the equator or along the
milky way are clusters and festoons of suns. Towards the
milky way one seventieth of the stars perhaps are visible. Towards the poles of that milky galaxy perhaps one
fourth are visible. They have swarmed upon a disk rimmed
by the milky way. Within 20 degrees of the plane of the
milky way, say the star tellers, there are 95 per cent of
the stars. In the polar regions between 90° and 40° there
are fewer than one per cent. Our material universe of
stars, it would seem, is disc shaped. It is a cosmic grindstone, and we, from a tiny bit of grit somewhere within
look outward towards the rim indicated by the milky
way and see many stars, or we look towards the axle and
see fewer.

If shape can be claimed for a thing that presumably

has no external relations, the general galaxy has shape, and for that the celestial grindstone is as good a word as any. A capital of 35 billion stars, in whatever shape, would seem sufficient to start the universal business, and though Moulton [6] and others hypothetically assume an infinite series of super-galaxies one within the other, or in groups, with some discontinuities between them but with space, time and presumably gravitation as healthy as ever, it is not clear that anything is gained thereby but an indefinite postponement. Eventually, if not now, matter by its own postulate has limits, and that applies to a universe, it would seem, as well as to apples or a cake of soap. A world limited in quantity but without external relations is paradoxical enough. Only an Einstein's nihilism in respect to absolute space and time, curved space, a greatest length in nature,[7] or some other equally unconventional attack can solve it.

Thirty-five billion stars, or one billion as others say, are a good deal of a universe, but they have room within for exercise without much bumping. Our sun's nearest neighbor among the stars is about as far away no doubt as the average star from its next neighbor, but the distance amounts to 25,000,000,000,000 miles. If the sun were a grain of sand one hundredth of an inch in diameter, and the earth a corpuscular speck one inch away, the nearest star would be another grain of sand about five miles away. For all its billions of stars the universe is not very dense.[8] Its population is inconceivably sparse. It is granular, but its grains — micro' or telescopically — are relatively a long way apart. Everything is mostly nothing, it would seem, and man does well to notice it at all.

Star streams dominate these cosmic deserts, and nebulae and stars seem to segregate in their own preserves according to their stellar type. Crossing through each other like traffic on a street, Kapteyn found two great streams of stars.[9] An order of a sort, not random mo-

tion, and selective distribution is evident even in the
world of stars; and a system of an enormous kind dominates this largest aggregate of matter. The disk of our
galaxy has a general structure. It has a process of its
own. The grindstone works.

Stars are the small change of the galaxy and star stuffs
shift and change from vague and formless nebulae or
other cosmic goods to round stars and back to nebulae
again. Stars come and go through wide time like tran-
sients in an old hotel. They travel on the average 600
million miles per year. Each will collide some time, evap-
orate, or otherwise annul its state of being and its present form.[10] Double stars, triple stars, variable and temporary stars, spectroscopic plural stars, red, white, blue,
red again, green, gaseous, maybe liquid, solid, bright,
dead, cold, hot, big, little, getting smaller, getting bigger;[11] they range from the unsystematic stuff of nebulae,
thinner than one hundred-thousandth of the density of
our atmosphere, to cold rigidities and to solid, earth-like
spheres; they vary like flowers in a July garden.

Stars have an evolution. They have youth, say some
astronomers, maturity, old age. They collide sometimes
in mighty conjugations and new stars are born. Young
stars are giants by this theory[12] but neither dense nor
hot. Middle aged stars are dense and very hot. Old stars
are very dense and not so hot. It is a massive epic where
cosmic seasons march in regular routine, though many
experts call it out of date. It is a story of contraction and
internal pressures, for contraction of a star, or of a snow-
ball under pressure, makes it warmer.[13] Stars move from
youth to age and there await a crash or a near-crash or
some other cosmic operation — bound sometime to come
— and rejuvenation.

Nebulae are the matrices of stars; then — though doctors disagree — in the order of youth to age follow red
stars, white stars, blue stars, yellow stars, red stars.
There is first the incredible diffusion of a gaseous nebula

somewhat luminous and cool.[14] Under gravitational attraction this condenses and as condensation proceeds
the form and brilliancy, the color, temperature, velocity,
and even the chemical constitution change progressively
from type to type. Billions of years are involved in the
progression, but the stars are far from changeless.

Eight types of stars are specified at Harvard in this
evolutionary procession said to be from youth to age. [15]
From the gaseous nebula comes, first, the type called
youngest, and their nature is still simple, innocent and
spectroscopically nebulous. They are found only in the
milky way and the clouds of Magellan.[16] Then come,
say some astronomers — Hale says astronomers in
general — the big, red stars like Betelgeuse and Antares,
while others say the helium stars are next. The helium
stars are smaller, presumably, than they once were, not
so rare, much hotter. They have radiated heat and with
the loss of heat they have contracted, and by contraction
— according to a paradoxical law enunciated by Lane —
they become hotter than before. They are gaseous, white,
and their spectra show a variety of certain elements but
perhaps no compounds and no metals. They browse along
the milky way in the outer pastures of our universe. No
helium star is nearer than seventy years of travelling by
light. Next come the hydrogen stars. They are still
less rare and still very hot. Sirius is a hydrogen star, two
and one-half times more massive but twenty-one times
more luminous than our sun.

Stars with calcium prominent in the spectrum follow
the hydrogen stars. In these the limits of gaseous contraction have been reached. Lane's law is abrogated;
liquids and solids — though recent thought opposes this
— appear progressively down the scale; molecular compounds and metals are more and more prominent, and
the star becomes not only smaller, denser, but also cooler.
With the stars next in line this crisis is passed. They are
yellowish in color. They are hot, but not so hot as they

were once. They are a little more than middle aged. Our sun is such a star; so are Procyon and Capella, and there are many like them. Next are the stars, with Arcturus as a beautiful example, where the metals rise to greater prominence in the spectrum and hydrogen declines. The hypothesis has symmetry and grace, and many like to keep it, though its founder, Russell, has left it far behind.

Stars an age older than these are red, bright, and in them compounds first appear. These stars are cooling off; they are losing the warmth and vivacity of youth, though some say they have not reached it. On these red stars it is positively chilly, no doubt, with the thermometer low enough to tolerate iron and iron oxides as a gas almost ready to freeze, maybe, into liquid or into solid iron. Poor old Antares, a red star, has by this diagnosis only a billion or so years more to live.[16] The next stars in line are all faint and deep red in color. They are the carbon stars. Their cycle is about over. They will ride mutely at terrible rates across the far meadows of the universe awaiting life, a reviving crash perhaps, collision, heat, new love, rejuvenation.

But there are other theories of the growth of stars; for age, after all, may be unsound as the measure of their status, and seniority may have no prestige in the skies. MacMillan,[17] for example, discards age and contraction as the dominating principles of stellar evolution. Mass and atomic dissipation are for him far more important, and a star that swims by lucky chance across sky areas of cosmic plankton, or nebular material, will gather to itself new life, new mass and new illumination.

A star's energy, says MacMillan,[17] "is a function of its mass, and the energy is derived from a breakdown of the atom itself due to the excessive violence of the conditions imposed upon it by the gravitational stresses." At the expense of their own masses the stars and suns radiate their energy; for the atom's organism is destroyed,

MacMillan thinks, under the terrific stresses within the greater stars, and free negative electrons and positive nuclei, thereby released, sometimes collide, lose their property of mass, at least in the gravitational sense, and liberate a corresponding energy and radiation. Atoms under stress may dissipate themselves in radiance, and under right conditions may be evolved again from radiant energy, says this imaginative scientist; and stars may wax as they enter richer fields of nebular material, and wane once more on leaving them.

They are thrilling stars and atoms that he provides, and his ways of gathering up the radiance lost in space into new atoms and new stars, and of turning from belief in cosmic mechanism that is running down to a cyclical conception of existence from atomic forms to radiance and back again is vastly interesting though still unproved. His atoms have new resources; his stars glint with new reserves.

Man has classified the stars like fowls at a poultry show, but the stars stream on without too much respect for his analysis. Their cycles it would seem are ageless but not unchanging; their universe shifts and spreads in many strange directions. Even the one-way drift and process of the universe is questioned by Einsteinian experts such as G. N. Lewis,[17] past and future are alike; and atoms having had their fling, MacMillan says, have ways of coming back. The youth of Sirius presumably is not an absolute beginning. It is a consequence no doubt of some collision, some catastrophe or some less striking change; and a previous cycle, perhaps on to old age, and even more anterior cycles, preceded it. We can assign no starting point for time; its limit is established in another way, and age within the stellar and solar processes means little more than the designation of some phase in the stellar routine. To the parts of the process we can assign age relative to other parts; of the whole no absolute age is conceivable. As relational conceptions space, time, even quantity, cannot easily apply externally to the whole of material existence. The entire problem must be reassembled in the light of the new physics and the new space and time.

What sets the tempo of the universal process only the future scientist will dare guess. Stars seem to move through youth to middle age on to senility in repetitive cycles. Be they cycles of age or cycles of mass the idea is the same. They grow perennially in crops. They come in millions like Fords from the factory, with minor individualities but with a general likeness that cannot be denied. There is endless repetition and multiplicity in natural process, all things drift on the same stream at about the same speed, and the stream never turns back. The change in the chemistries of the stars with advancing age at a tempo fixed perhaps by the natural transmutation of the elements suggests an essential continuity of process in all material existence. If we knew the electron we could know, no doubt, the universe. If we knew one light wave we could know the world and time and space.

By consensus Doctors Chamberlin and Moulton are perhaps our leading stellar obstetricians. On the birth of stars, and particularly on little still born mishaps such as our earth, they are experts far surpassing the old fashioned family doctors, Kant and Laplace. Their close acquaintance with some little things, such as the molecule and the mechanics of gases, has given them a precedence in this practice that their predecessors cannot question. If Laplace had persuaded the molecule to agree with him, his family history of the solar system, with the sun condensing from a nebula and leaving concentric rings behind, which in turn condensed into the respective planets with motions inherited from the parent, might be acceptable today. But Laplace, sad to say, could not cultivate the molecule's acquaintance or know the real mechanics of peanut meteors or of suns. And Laplace's theory rapidly is fading out. The planetesimal hypothesis is replacing it.

Our solar system is largely sun with eight particles called planets cycling around it in almost circular orbits.[18] All together the planets and various other subsidiaries called moons, planetoids, comets and meteors make up less than one seven-hundredth of the mass of the system.[19] The sun supplies the other six hundred and ninety-nine parts. Compared with the planets the sun has about the ratio of a campus coed to eight Maryanna chocolates, and the wonder is, not that the planets are so large, but that they are there at all. For the sun is an intense thing radiating with personal magnetism, and what might have happened to the planets is not pleasant to discuss. It has terrific storms and tempers that hoist vast masses of its flaming gas 200 miles per second into space for 20,000 or for 600,000 miles.[20] It has dark vortices called sun spots from time to time, in which the earth could move unnoticed, that may be solar cyclones or darker gases flowing down from higher levels. On top the sun has fluid structure; its inside is not known.

The apparent surface of the sun is called the photosphere,[21] and it is gas or liquid maybe under a pressure and a mighty heat. It is the seat of solar radiation that would melt, says Moulton, every hour a layer of ice 2,200 feet thick over all the surface of the sun, or on every square yard do the work of 70,000 horses. Its temperature is 10,000 degrees Fahrenheit or more. It sends to the earth some two billionths of its radiative energy and makes us what we are.[22] Parts of the photosphere seem to rotate faster than other parts, and this would indicate that the sun is fluid and that a day on the sun, or one rotation period, is shorter at the equator than near the pole.

Overlying the sun's photosphere is the reversing layer.[23] It is about 500 miles deep and is composed of cooler gases. They make black absorption lines in the spectrum that are suddenly reversed to bright lines when radiation from the photosphere is cut off by an eclipse. Iron, sodium and heavy metals are some of the gases of the reversing layer.

Above the reversing layer is the chromosphere of the sun 5,000 to 10,000 miles in depth. It is made scarlet by incandescent hydrogen and calcium, and there is helium there in huge amount to perplex man with its mysterious simplicity. Beyond the chromosphere, and even lighter, is the corona. It is exceeding rare, with a dust particle once in every fourteen cubic yards, and with small and scattered clouds of gas more or less between. It is a pearly zone about the sun 300,000 or 3,000,000 miles in depth, and its streamers reach five million miles or more beyond. An element, perhaps, is there, not yet found on earth, called coronium. In all the sun and in its vivid envelopes of gas 37 other elements are known to exist. They range from lead, silver, iron to silicon, carbon and hydrogen. There is much of interest and there is much unknown in this average middle-aged star that we call *the* sun.

Only an incident in the sun's system is eight small potatoes, called planets, circumgyrating at distances from 36 million to 2,791 million miles from the central sun. One of the minor potatoes of this octet is our earth. It is not much as things go, but it is all we have; and the manner of its formation is bound to have a local interest in our provincial minds that cannot be entirely ignored. Here enter Professors Chamberlin and Moulton, of Chicago, with their planetesimal hypothesis. How was the earth made? The old liquid earth with a crust around it is not taken so seriously as once. Chamberlin and Moulton have a different earth on view.

We are stuff of the sun, and all this earth and the things upon it once were stewing in that central luminary. A few accretions swept from space may be from other

sources, but children of the sun we are in all intents and
purpose. This earth was thrust away under the stress of
a visitor's attraction. We were an ejection from the sun
such as scientists see during eclipse storming into space
hundreds of miles per second. As a knot of flaming gas,
a roman candle light, this earth first started on its planetary course; and the wandering stranger that occasioned
it is lost now in the depths of heaven. It was a dark star
perhaps and silent that swept down into the solar field
so that things began to happen. We cannot know him —
but he has done his work.

For what the moon does daily to the earth in the form
of tides as it swings athwart our field of gravitation, the
mysterious stranger did with terrible intenseness to our
sun.[24] It is the old story of a star and its collision or near-
collision with another, in the course of time.[25] Had the
stranger hit us square the heat of impact would have
dispersed both in an enormous nebula of gas. But he
swung near and then away again, and the sun bulged and
spouted flame into intervening space and was left a sun,
focus of a spiral nebula. The solar tides broke loose but
the sun was not destroyed.

As the stranger approached — let us name him Genesis — fiery prominences on the sun belched forth, one
from the side directly towards the stranger, another
from the side diametrically across.[26] These first eruptive
tides fell back, presumably, into the sun. As the stranger
came still nearer other belchings from the sun took place,
but these did not fall back clear to the sun. They acquired a tangential motion from the stranger's influence
and by a well known law of celestial mechanics, revolved
in regular orbits round the sun. They perhaps became the
inner planets including earth. As the stranger reached the
climax of his journey towards the sun, other and still
larger eruptions stormed up from the solar photosphere.
These became the larger, outer planets of the solar system,
and it may be that after these the inner planets came.

Our system had two parents then, though one has left
for parts unknown. He came, and a spiral nebula revolv-
ing round this central sun was formed. He went away,
and the solar system ever since has been picking up the
pieces. Presumably the integration of that nebular material, its first expansion and its cooling, its coalitions
into knots and nuclei of solid and of liquid stuff is the
foundation process of our earth. We are a mass, one
three hundred thousandths of the sun, or one three-
thousandths of one per cent, shot from the sun by a
release of solar gravitation, and we have fallen into an
orbital motion around the sun some 92 million miles
away. It was an exciting birthday but too hot to witness.

From the solar nebula to Mount Marcy, the Mississippi
river and the Tribune tower is a long way, however, and
much has happened along the road. How did the earth,
our *terra firma*, come from these far fields of flame swept
gas? For the solar nebula was evoked from the sun, says
Chamberlin,[27] and was "a little more than a streaming,
knotty pair of arms of nebulous matter shot out from
the sun and curved into spiral appendages about it by
the joint pull of itself and a passing star." From this
vague stuff our earth developed.

In the knots is the story of the earth's accretion.[28]
After emergence from the sun, says Chamberlin, most of
the nebulous matter, through sudden expansion, radiation, cooling and condensation, was gathered into knots,
"the collecting-centers of the future planets, planetoids,
and satellites, or into planetesimals, the food on which
these knots subsequently fed." And the earth knot was
among them.

It was a knot measuring 30 per cent, it may be, of the
present earth and it was rotating from its first ejection
from the sun. It cooled and solids came as well as liquids,
and with these as a gravitational and magnetic nucleus
collection could begin. As it swept through space around
the sun it gathered up gas molecules and liquids as well

as solid meteors and planetesimals; even now some twenty
million meteors are captured daily by the earth. Thus
grew the earth, bit by bit, meteor by meteor, and by
planetesimal dust; big enough to take a rotund form with
iron, maybe, in its heart, and a rigidity of steel; big enough
to fill the seas and to catch, make and hold an atmosphere.
The lithosphere, the hydrosphere, the atmosphere, land,
sea and air, the "geologic triumvirate" was formed, and
the earth's work began.

Men who have made collections of the earth's juvenilia
say that it began as a small lithosphere, a small atmosphere and a small hydrosphere, perhaps, growing up
together.[29] Acting upon each other the winds and waters
of the earth and the giant lifts and extrusions of the rocks
built up slowly the surface of today. A range of temperature that keeps the water for the most part midway between a gas and a solid rock-like ice is essential to this
work.[30] Other factors enter, for the earth is old: Some,
calculating by the rate of radiation from the sun, say
20,000,000 years; some, figuring by the salt carried to the
ocean, say 90,000,000 years; others find by radio-active
degenerations an age of 1,250,000,000 years; still others
say the older rocks are 2,000,000,000 years or more of
age.[31] At any rate much has been at work to make us
what we are. Through all that time three great geologic
factors have wrought jointly their effects: They are land,
water, air.

One fourth of the earth's surface is bowed up; three
fourths are bowed down; the continents are the one; the
seas fill the hollows of the other, and have always filled
them, very likely, since the earth was small and young.
It is a virile globe, under conflicting stresses. It is ever
hoisting continents anew out of the sea where otherwise
the rains and wind would carry them for good in a few

million years. It is elastic, and it bulges at the equator,
now more, now less, as time goes on.[32] Gravity "shapes"
it towards a perfect sphere. Rotation flattens it at the
poles; there is equatorial bulging; and when the rate of
that rotation changes, the flattening must suit itself to
the new speed. Today the equatorial bulge is more than
thirteen miles. Tomorrow it will be less if rotation rates
decline and more if they advance. The surface of this
elastic globe gives and takes. Under stress it sags and
swells; its segments shear across each other with the jar
of earthquakes. Under stress and deformation continents
bulge up, rocks melt in the pressure, and lava flows with
volcanic thunders.

Some things retard the earth's rotation; some increase
it. The fall of meteors upon the earth, the accession of
new planetesimals to increase its bulk, the tides all retard it. The shrinkage of this planetary aggregate, the
shake-down of the young earth, the crystallization and
the increasing density of the interior down to its core of
heavy stuffs make rotation faster and the day a little
shorter. Through all its history the earth has shifted
speed a little, now maybe faster, now slower, and its
shape has changed in conformity with its motion. When
the equator bulges, tensions come there and compressions
come about the poles. Continents bow up. The lighter
segments of the earth are crumpled upward to relieve
the strain. The history of dry land begins.

Nature is a long unwinding, and the history of this
earth has many chapters still unwritten. There are three
eons of our planetary progress, say Chamberlin and
Salisbury:[33] the formative eon of birth and adolescence,
the extrusive eon of transition, the gradational eon of
relative maturity. In the first eon there were six stages:
1, the nuclear or nebular stage, 2, the atmosphereless
stage, 3, the initial volcanic stage, 4, the initial atmos-
pheric stage, 5, the initial hydrospheric stage, 6, the
initial life stage. These stages overlap, some are doubtful,

and 3, 4, 5 were no doubt more or less contemporary. In the second eon there is one era called, 7, the archeozoic, or most ancient life stage. Here geologists first can substitute observation for hypothesis, for archean rocks are the oldest in the records. In the third eon there are, 8, the proterozoic era, 9, the paleozoic era, 10, the mesozoic era, 11, the cenozoic era, respectively the first life, old life, middle life and late life eras. These are the eleven chapters of the history of our globe, and they have many subdivisions running from archaic granites and Cambrian measures, layer by layer, thirty huge steps in time, or more, to the pliocene and more recent strata of the rock. It is a story two billion years, five billion years, eight billion years or more long. The rocks tell it layer by layer as the ages pass. The life whose forms and skeletons lie scattered down the hill of time tell the story of evolutionary change. It is a story of development and change, of accumulation age after age, and of growth and struggle. The past of the earth is lighted by many lamps.

The rocks are no more this earth than the seas and atmosphere. Their priority is doubtful. Their significance in the building of this planet is hardly greater than the work of wind and water. But the rocks are readable; they retain the past; they show title, place and time of natural processes age by age, as the fluid members of the geologic triumvirate cannot. The rocks can tell their story where sea and air are mute.

Some rocks are born of fire. Some are born of water. The one is igneous rock. The other is sedimentary rock. Fire rock may be primeval stuff left from the building of this planet or a cooling from yesterday's volcano. Sedimentary rock is always secondary. It is a rebuilding of the planet's surface from water-born fragments of a former state. The waters, or more rarely the air, lay it down layer on layer, age on age, and between the leaves are many specimens of the past. It is accretionary rock, and time is the chief contributor. Igneous rock is the work of heat and fusion.

The granites are igneous rocks. Feldspar, porphyry,
quartz, obsidian, basalt, gabbro are igneous rocks. Lava
and tuff and the dusts of volcanoes are igneous. The rocks
with silica predominate, the granites and the feldspars,
are the acid rocks. They were made, presumably, nearer
the surface of the lithosphere whence the irons and magnesium have been withdrawn to some extent towards the
deeper centers of the earth. The basalts and the gabbros
are those deeper rocks and they are basic.[34]

In the cauldrons of the earth new rocks are brewed.
Some cool slowly, some under great pressure. Some cool
rapidly, some under less pressure. Some release their
gases in mighty bubbles as they cool. In some the gas
is pent. In some the gas erupts with volcanic force; it
hurls rock dust and lava over the countryside. In all
igneous rocks feldspar in some form is usually found.[35]
Its combinations of silica, alumina, potash, soda and lime,
is the staff of our rocks' existence, but it has many forms.

Deep rocks cooling slowly underground are in general
completely crystalline. The interlocking crystals of a
granite — where the quartz, the feldspar, the dark iron-
tinted hornblende, the glittering mica are interwoven in
the texture of the stone — have made a tough and enduring monument to this earth's constructive power.[36]
Other rocks have consolidated more rapidly. They have
cooled in thrusts and dykes; they have intruded themselves into surrounding layers of cold rocks. They have
cooled on the margins of the magma-basins, the cauldrons
of this planet, like sugar on the sides of a candy kettle.
They look sometimes like common white stone or dark
stone, for that is what we mean by stone, but there are
crystals there too small to see. The microscope on feldspar, for example, shows rods and other forms of crystals
minutely meshed together without distinction. Still
other rocks have cooled quickly. The glasses and the
obsidians, the lavas and the dusts that are half igneous,
half sedimentary, and the fire rocks that have not crys-

tallized are there to show it. Where segments of the earth shear across each other, where crumpling comes or a falling planetesimal concentrates its impact, where there is pressure and heat the earth sets up its cauldrons. The rocks stew in the earth's kettles. New batches are always ready.

In the sediment and ooze of the sea bottom the second order of the rocks began, for water is but little less than fire the power that builds the stony plating of this earth. Sea ooze and lake muds, the mire of ancient swamps, the rain-soaked dust of planetesimals, the wet grist from glacier mills and the depositions of the streams that work across the ages while continents rise under them and wear away again beneath their shuffling feet, all these are the raw stuffs of the layer rocks. They are the sedimentary rocks laid there by water in myriad laminations. Today the ocean floor is laying down, no doubt, the mountain tops of tomorrow, and the River Thames, older than the island of England, is carrying down the fill for a new Europe.

The limestones and the shales and sandstones are the sedimentary rocks. Pressure and cementation are their consolidating agents. The breaking down of igneous and other rocks or the detritus from organic action furnishes their materials. The silts and clays, mainly of aluminum silicate, are compressed into the shales and slates.[37] The broken quartzes, and silica, are cemented into sandstones. The lime remains of plants and animals, their stiffenings and weapons, their shells, armour, skeletons, sunk to the bottom of the sea make limestones.[38] Microscopic bits of organic history compose the chalk cliffs of England and the limestone strata on which northern Illinois is built. They are massive cemeteries. They are magazines of death.

There are organic rocks called coal and peat left from the tropic swamps, and there are iron ore beds thrown down by organic action as well as by the leach of streams and springs. Rock salt and gypsum are among the minor rocks. Conglomerate and metamorphic rocks are other secondaries; the one rehashed from older, ill assorted fragments; the other changed by heat back to a crystalline form. Marble is no doubt a metamorphic limestone. There are other rocks. The air throws down a sediment of snow in northern lands which consolidates into ice rock ten thousand feet thick on the surface of Greenland. The rock makers have a large repertory that runs from fire to ice and from hot cauldrons of the central earth to the cold deeps of the sea. The earth is built of several things and in numerous ways.

The sedimentary series of rocks is the time table of the ages. For it is usually safe to say that the stratum above the stratum below is younger. Down thousands of feet through these rocky leaves of time, geologists have prodded faithfully. They have tabulated the ages of the earth. They have placed the rocks in accurate priorities. Between the ancient leaves of rock are specimens of life. Age by age, step by step, they are revealed. The recessive relics of the animals and plants that grew and flourished on this earth are there in correct order. From the simpler fossils embedded in the older, lower rocks to the organic complexities of later times in the upper rocks it is a long story. It is a story of growth, struggle, adaptation, death, evolution, and there are many stopping places on the way from past to present. Millions and hundreds of millions of years are caught in those old sediments. A century is one inch thick, a thousand years is half a minute's climb. Discontinuities break the order here and there; non-conformities intervene between the sediments, showing when the sea was gone. There are ups and downs in long oscillations; there is sedimentation and the building of rock under the seas, then erosion, chemical and physical, and the wearing down of rock when the sea for the time has retreated. Most of America has been sunk half a dozen times. The earth bulges, but the winds and waters scour off the bulge. Geology is a history of rock cycles.

What wears away this earth? The mobile spheres of air and water turn upon the sphere of stone and wear its roughness and protrusions down. It is called erosion, but it really is the earth's internal friction and the continuous readjustment of chemical and dynamic factors in this planetary outfit. It is the shell of water and the shell of air rubbing on the shell of outer stone. The powers that make the swells and sags in the rock surface of the earth have no small part in the restlessness of winds and waters that will wear those swellings down. It all comes largely from the "force" of gravity and from rotation. They raise and they tear down. Destroying agents become builders; the builders destroy, and the process shambles on.

For the sedimentary rocks, laid in massive series through the ages, are children of the fluid wind. They are wind rocks, in a way, as well as water rocks; for the erosive agents of the earth alone can make them possible, and without winds erosion would be trifling. The continents would be rainless deserts. The rivers would be empty. Vapor would rise above the tropic seas — if it could rise at all — if there were seas — and fall back whence it came. Bitter heat and bitter cold would separate the day from night, the tropic zones from other regions of the earth, and fall from spring. Without the distributing winds this earth would be violently static, violently extreme and little change of surface or development could take place.

The winds bear the burdens of the rain into the great interiors. They give the rivers their first push. They make the degradation of the continents a persistent and ever present fact. And gravity and the earth's rotation are their sponsors. For the primary genesis of the winds is the rise of heated air from the earth's equator and the displacement of it by cool and heavier airs rushing in from either side.[39] The tropic air expands with heat. It is charged with vapors from the warm sea. It rises and drifts away northward and southward, and the great trade winds blow in below to take its place.[40] Gravity and the sun's heating power set the atmosphere in circulation, while the earth's rotation causes its deflection eastward.

It is a huge force that raises moisture to the skies and carries it to the far ends of the earth. It is equivalent, according to an expert estimate, to 300 billion horse-power constantly in operation.[41] And it is a huge energy that is released again when that rain falls and the rivers run their courses to the seas. The power of many hundred million horses is always pawing at the land and carrying it down to the ocean. It is wearing down the Mississippi drainage area one foot, it is said, in 6,000 years, the Danube area one foot in 6,846 years, the Rhone area one foot in 1,528 years, the Hoang Ho area one foot in 1,464 years, the Po area one foot in 729 years.[42] So the cycle goes. The winds, the rain, the ice, the streams, the sea again; the continents wear down under the scuffling of waters, and the discharge of the streams builds new beds of rocks for future continents.

There is no still thing in the world that stands insulated from the stream of change and endless process, or if there is, science cannot offer it to man's intelligence. The air swings across the earth in giant circulations. The sea pours itself upon the mountain tops and runs back. Even the rocks grow old, wear away and start anew. They are all fluids of a sort. They are mobile; they are unstable; that is what this planetary process means.

On the thin frontiers where water, air and rock have met and mixed in a geologic no-man's land there has appeared a dirty film of stuff made of all three that we call soil. It is detritus of the weathered rocks not yet carried to the sea, and it contains the air and water left

there by the winds and rains as they go by. It comes
from the mixtures and mobilities of geologic matter.
There is rock there in large percentages. There is water
up to thirty and forty per cent. There is air up to 25 per
cent. There is organic scrap and leavings and their decay,
called humus, up to five and six per cent.[43] Soil is a synthesis of the sea, the atmosphere and the rocks. It is
minor mongrel stuff bred of frontier clashes. It bulks
little, but its significance to man is great. For man
is the child of soil. He is bred from the dust of the
earth.

The natural shift and transposition of the matter of
the earth is worked into the soil. There are air and rock
dust in the sea; there are dust and water in the air; there
are air and water in the rock. They interpenetrate, and
soil is little more than a more effective mixture. The sea
pours through the air and soaks through the soil. The
water that falls on land alone in ten or fifteen thousand
years is more than all the seas now hold.[44] The ocean
migrates through the air once in ten millennia or so, and
the atmosphere and rocks translate themselves across new
forms, no doubt, at hardly lesser rates. Soil is a focus of
this flux, and growth in the soil has something of that
spirit.

A fourth geologic feature, neither air nor rock nor water, enters at this time in the earth's process. It is a
fragile smear of something here and there that we call
protoplasm, and —?! —?!! — it lives. The colloids of the
soils have broken down a path for it, for their membranes
between the granules of the soil have been "osmosing,"
or at least "imbibing," very likely these many years. The
earth's temperatures — strange and wondrous fact —
vary, where this jelly came, not more than a few score
degrees; the semi-fluid stuff dare neither freeze nor boil.
The time is right; the mixture is made; land, air and water
join hands in its consistency; life dawns in tiny splen-
dour on this little earth. It is a minor geological affair, but

big for us. It is a dawn no doubt repeated many times on other little shifting earths throughout the universe.

The biography of God has not been written except as science finds it in the long unwinding of natural processes. And the earnest work of men today who devote a lifetime to one hour of that biography deserves a reverence and an honest criticism no less than is accorded ancient scribes and prophets. They, not the "fundamentalists," have read the Bible in the stars. For the truth that grows there bit by bit with honest facing of the facts regardless of man's weak hopes and prejudice is the divine tale that makes us free. All natural process is in some sense evolutionary. It is biographical of the universe; it is a revelation by degrees of a world held there in man's basic presumptions. It is an unfolding by a guardian that we call Time, and though "conservative" bishops and others of this age may not agree, it is no less true that scientists as compared with Moses are preferable as biographers. Moses must have his due, and it is much, but the history and order of natural process is not a part of it.

Here the process of the universe has been reviewed from the largest aggregate of matter that our minds accommodate down to the dawn of life on this particular earth. By successive localizations an evolution can be traced, logically at least, from the general to the more or less particular, if not from first to last. It is a thrilling course of events, and treated here in terms of five main periods: the galaxy and the evolution of the stars; the sun and the evolution of the solar system; the planetesimal hypothesis, the earth and the evolution of land, sea and air; the rocks and soils; and the geology of life.

CHAPTER FOUR

The Appearance of Life in the World

A MAN'S prejudice for life is invincible, and his interest in things called living justifies the massive research of biologists and others in a field that might draw only brief attention in a perfectly impartial cosmos. For life is a novelty of the last hundred million years or so, and its importance as a factor of this universe outside of man's exuberance and wishing is not much. On the geologic scale of solar energies and rocks, and the wearing of water, the slow sediments laid down, the everlasting winds, and the earth's secretion of the seas, life is a feeble daub of gluey stuff that gets its sustenance from the mightier forces of the earth and sun in draughts that always have been small. The greatest geologic work of living things, perhaps the limestones, is not much more than five per cent of the sedimentary rocks alone, and the coal measures, the building up of soils and forests, the influence on erosion and the contributions and withdrawals of the air's carbon dioxide are not much altogether in a billion years.[1] It is all a minor chemistry and by-play in the cosmic process of a cooling sun. Life is episodical, but man is one with it, it is his peculiar chemistry, and he makes it central. It is a small whisper heard here for a moment in the lull of universal thunder. It is permitted by the balance and a momentary peace in the evolution of a planet.

On this earth life is a thin and uncertain layer, sometimes called the biosphere,[2] left, as it were, in the form of a precipitate from the interactions of the rocks (the lithosphere), the seas (the hydrosphere) and the air (the atmosphere), and always subject to their geological con-

ditions. It is a complication of the energy of the sun with
the chemical reactions and electrical phenomena of certain tender and high wrought compounds of the elements,
and it depends on a set of geological conditions that may
change greatly in the course of time. It rests on moderate
temperature conditions, fuel supplies, water circulations
and electrical and radio-active states of the earth that
must not vary much if life survives. The living thing is
an unstable and explosive compound always involved
with nitrogen, and is sensitive in extreme degree to slight
changes in environment. The living thing is an engine
with a narrow range of temperature, and intensities of
cold or heat destroy it.[3] For some hundred million years
or more this earth has kept a mild spot here and there
ranging, say, from ten degrees Fahrenheit to 200 degrees
where living things have grown, and that is wonderful
indeed amid the violence and shift of cosmic temperatures; but nothing guarantees its future.[4]

A supply of radiance, primarily from the sun, and a protection against too much of it, says Chamberlin,[5] is the first
condition that the world must meet in order to maintain
life. Light is the dynamic factor of a living thing, and
man's worship of the sun as his creator is not far fetched.[6]

A supply of carbon, oxygen, nitrogen, carbon dioxide,
water and combinations of these as well as lesser quantities of phosphorus, sulphur, iron, potash and other earths
is the second condition.[7] These are the stuffs that make
up living things, and though their junction here in numerous carbon compounds [8] may arise from certain
geologic regulations, it is in a large way fortuitous and
without preordinate entelechy. Life is a geologic fact. It
is — for science — the continuing reactions of these carbon compounds; and the "idea that a peculiar vital force
acts in the chemistry of life is extinct." [9] To science life,
as Ward says,[10] is a property of matter.

A third condition that the earth must meet, if life is
to appear, is a way to maintain the continuity of vital

action. A fourth condition is a circulatory mechanism able to bring supplies and to carry waste away; and a fifth condition is an osmotic mechanism for pumping fluids.[11] With this machinery lives can go on, and though it is incorporated now in living bodies, it remains primarily geologic and mechanical in nature and in origin. Life is a geological phenomenon.

For all their instability and flabbiness, living materials are persistent organisms more lasting than the rocks. They have found a way to conquer time that works better than granite.[12] They have come down, no doubt, in unbroken continuity from ages when this accretionary earth was young and smaller than it is today, when the air was thick with planetary dust, and the seas emerged only in pools and lakes amid the dust heaps and the slag of the new world. They have lived in closely linked inheritances while continents have sunk time and again and the hills have worn away. They have expressed in organic continuity the basic appetite for persistence that inheres in all existing things, and it is hard not to read into them mistaken teleologies and psychic motives. For man organically is older than the earth's crust. His stability, rooted in the ceaseless flux and restlessness of life, has outlived the mountains and the seven seas. The power of a live thing to focus natural actions and materials on its own organic continuity, to treat, as we say in other fields of discourse, all things in the environment as its utilities, to take up and to cast away this thing and that thing, but to maintain throughout a hundred million years or more a formal continuity and a persistent organism is geologically unique.[13] It is a bunching of energies and materials with a strange centripetal persistence in its action that we find hard not to personify and to translate at once in terms of wishes and utilities, impulses and psychic appetites. It is hard not to say that living things aim to persist or wilfully live long; but scientifically they are a process that only does persist.

They have not succeeded in being old; their chemistry
and process is such merely that they are old. This soft
colloidal stuff called protoplasm, a rose bud or a young
girl's hand, is older than the Rocky mountains or the
deeps of the Atlantic.

In the pores of the moist earth, perhaps, the things
that we call living first began a vital process that has
come without a break down a million centuries to this
day. It started in colloidal carbon compounds, gluey
stuff, albuminous, that unlike crystals in solution fail to
pass through a membrane by osmotic action; [14] and it
developed slowly. These were the basic colloids wrought
here by mixtures of some elements in the pores and pas-
sages of the soil.

As the soil waters came and went, says Chamberlin,[15]
the solutions and emulsions and suspensions borne by
them were concentrated and in part deposited. Threads
and solid films and lumps were left there and in them colloids and crystalloids must have mingled. Alternations
of deposit must have come and partial re-solution. The
plexus of films grew thicker and more membrane-like.
The pores and passageways were more and more closed.
Concentrated solutions and emulsions were more and
more liable to entrapment in the inter-grain spaces.
They were enclosed by films formed over their exposed
surfaces. The open network was converted into a cellular
reticulum.

Trillions of these crude capsules could be formed, says
Chamberlin; and their colloidal membranes, with their
captured, half colloidal content, would provide the
mechanism for osmotic action. Osmosis would begin;
the primitive exchange between the soil waters and solutions without and the colloidal content of the cells within
would start its long career,[15] and the machinery of life

would then be founded. For soil itself, according to its lovers, such as Whitney,[16] is almost living. In the capillaries of the early soil organic process may have well begun.

In nitrate laden pools or lakes or, as others say, in the early seas life also may have had its seat. Henderson shows that modern sea water in chemical composition is close to our blood serum.[17] Others more fancifully suggest that bacterial spores, hardy to the cold of interstellar space, drifted in upon the earth from other worlds, and Arrhenius says they may have been impelled here by light pressure. Be that as it may, the life process came gradually about no doubt, not with a loud creative bang. It came of a succession of short steps, not with a *presto*, life. It had a slow and painful introduction.

Five steps may have led to living things, says Osborn:[18] First was the assemblage one by one of several of the ten elements now essential to a life. They gathered in, no doubt, with hydrogen and oxygen leading and with nitrogen, carbon, phosphorus, sulphur, potassium, calcium, magnesium, iron and perhaps silicon following in order.

Second there came, says Osborn, a new form of unity in the cosmos. A mutual attraction arose, an organic unity developed, which is termed an individual or organism, and whether or not it is unique, it is significant in the origin of life.

Third is the guess that this organic grouping took place in colloidal suspensions. Some scientists are even willing to assert that living organisms in other worlds or in other arrangements still must be colloidal. For how could changeable and plastic forms that still may stay unaltered be other than colloidal?

Fourth are mysterious catalyzers or chemical coördinators [19] along with the development of plant and animal functions. This too, says Osborn, is a new coöperation in the cosmos. And fifth, along with the assemblage, mutual attraction, colloidal condition and chemical coördination, come natural selection and perhaps a trace of competition, or at least of struggle, to test out the life value of the furniture and actions of the living cell.

Such was the origin of life, say wise men who have turned their telescopes on the distant past and found there on a far horizon the margins of our living. It was a million centuries or more ago, and it was a small affair wholly subject to the natural law.

But life is not the wax or wick of the candle, it is the burning. It is not the complex nitrates and the carbon compounds in which it sits but their combustion. Life is a set of energies. It is the working of an engine, and the fuels and mechanisms, the origins and methods of construction are after all not life.

What life is cannot be photographed or weighed for it is not a substance but an action, and what it does is a better way to know life than to classify its materials. It will do with a marshmallow, for example, about what the campfire on a moonlit night will do. And an ounce of tallow, says Osterhout,[20] takes up the same amount of oxygen, sets free the same amount of heat, and produces the same amount of water and carbon dioxide, whether fed to a dog, or burned in a candle.

Life is a team of energies. It is a dynamic equilibrium that retains identity of form though always changing shape and substance. It is work done on materials, and one product of that work, so long as there is life, is carbon dioxide. It is a balance and a ratio of energies; it is their organization. Life depends, says Osterhout,[21] "upon a series of reactions which normally proceed at rates bearing a definite relation to each other."

This dynamic conception of life is raised by Osborn into a rather terrifying theory which he has christened: Tetrakinesis. For in each organism, he says, life represents the action, reaction and interaction of four complexes of physicochemical energy; namely, the energies of the inorganic environment, of the developing organism, of the germ cell, of the living environment.[22] These energies, and they are exceedingly complex, work together to make the actions of a lifetime. They are not one but four simultaneous evolutions of energy, says the proud parent of this theory; and, of the four, the energy complexes of the germ of "heredity-chromatin" far surpass all the others in detail and in possibilities.

Sunshine is the main dynamic source of life, and the ability of chlorophyll, the green of plants, to capture it by a method called photosynthesis is one of nature's triumphs. Sunshine makes the wheels of life go round. Its energy is ever present in the things that live, and an electric stream of energy from the chemical elements in the earth, the water and the air is drawn by it into the mesh of living work. For the energies of living are largely electrical in nature.[23] They are electric currents, and living matter like a multitude of batteries, sets up the streams of positive and negative ions between appropriate poles. Charged and recharged by the sun all life and its development, say many scientists, is in this sense electrical.[24]

"So this is life," the cattle man would say, visiting the turbid city, from the great plains. For life is sunshine and storage batteries; it is the electrical phenomena basic in all chemical reactions; it is energy teamed with the life elements and the sun. It is combustion, for that is basic chemistry explainable in terms of ions, electric currents, positives and negatives, electrolytes and dielectrics. It is a schedule of energies, hurried there, retarded there, according to its program, by coördinating agents called catalyzers, enzymes or other regulative bodies. Life is a pattern of energies. It is not easy to say more.

Life is a burning, but a much complicated and conserved burning. It is the consumption of fuels, like a slow

fuse down through the ages, but the products forthcoming
from that combustion are nicely coördinated and spaced.
The living cell, says Loeb,[25] "synthetizes its own complicated specific material from indifferent or non-specific
simple compounds of the surrounding medium," and in
that it differs from non-living things. It is not simple
like a lighted torch. Life is an uniquely organized burning; it is a ritualized combustion; but its difference from
the candle flame is less in principle than in degree.

Like fire life is appropriative and imperialistic. It
seizes and devours. It transforms alien energies into its
own living. To know life study the fires of the world.

Energies flow in and out of living things; their matter
changes always; but an individual, specific form remains
and is maintained so long as life remains: This, said
Cuvier, is the distinctive property of life.

To maintain this vital equilibrium and continuity
three processes are mainly necessary. They are the great
physiological processes of living things, and in degree they
are distinctive among the worlds of things and processes,
if not in outright principle. No inorganic thing has found
them in their developed form; they work only for life.
They are: metabolism, reproduction, sensitivity.

Metabolism refers to the ability of the living protoplasm to transform matter and energy, with the liberation or the storage of energy and matter in its own
protoplasmic substance as a consequence.[26] Reproduction
is the process whereby living organisms give rise to new
organisms. Sensitivity, or irritability, refers to the ability
of living things to receive and to respond to impinging
energies or stimuli. They are the physiological processes
of life; they are all aspects, in a general way, of the cell's
fundamental metabolism; and the unit of vital organization, the single cell, exhibits them in full working order.

What the cell does in life is to a large extent a story of
these processes. The world is ready for its first biography:
The story of a simple cell, but withal a living creature,
has begun.

From that primeval spark of life sprang the living con-
flagration of today. The elephants, presumably, and the
humming birds, the forests broad and sweeping, the
whales and violets, the oysters and Mr. Coolidge and
H. L. Mencken, all are combustions traced to that first
organic fire a million centuries ago. It was a single cell,
no doubt, that started all life's business, or if more than
one, there were bioidal predecessors that were not living
things, perhaps, but farther on than a colloidal jell.
Once the tree of life was firmly founded, the descent, we
may suppose, was strictly linear. It was continuous.
Though Bower says [27] "that it is quite gratuitous to
assume that all life sprang from a single source," such a
source is probable, if not in some living thing, then farther back in the earlier chemistries of the earth. All living things no doubt have come historically, as well as
embryonically from a single cell.

The cell is the unit of organized protoplasm. Without
a glass it usually is too small to see, and in higher animals
and plants millions of cells live in one community and
system that is called an individual. But the cell, no matter how specialized, has always a system of its own. It
has its bit of living protoplasm. It does its work. It lives
its life.

The cell has a body of protoplasm, and within that
body is a nucleus, like the pupil in the iris of the eye.
Within the nucleus in turn are granules or threads of
stuff called chromatin. There are further complexities,
but the chromatin in the nucleus and the nucleus in the
cell body (or cytoplasm) are the three prime parts of
every cell. As a whole the life material of the cell is called
protoplasm.[28] But protoplasm — primal living stuff and
most complex of known substances — is not homogene-

ous. It is cellular. It is organized. It is differentiated into cytoplasm, chromatin, and other varying materials with varying functions. Protoplasm is organized into systematic working units. The cell is that working unit.

With the life and works of the single cell recorded by biographers such as Wilson,[29] and the chemistry of living fairly well explored, the great word metabolism is not so terrifying and mysterious as it was. A man's metabolism is, physiologically, his life, and a Boston bandit who said, "Money or your metabolism" would be no less sinister, though less obvious, than the good old fashioned kind. Metabolism is the ceaseless change that living is, and the life of an individual plant or animal is really a complex chemical reaction extending over a period of time.

All the chemical activities of the organism, says Osterhout,[30] are included in metabolism; "they are the very essence of life." The processes of waste within the living thing are called destructive metabolism. The processes of repair are called constructive metabolism. Every living thing, man or amœba, single cell or sequoia tree, is an equilibrium between the two. Life is a balance between metabolic actions. It is a dynamic ratio between chemical instabilities. It is a poise between ceaseless waste and repair. In youth the scales tip slowly up. In age they tip slowly down.

Constructive metabolism in the living things of this world owes its potency chiefly to sunshine. Sun power drives the mechanism of green leaves. By its red and orange radiance, as well as ultra-violet, they transform and help to store energy away for all the living world to use.[31] Sunshine builds fuel, or food, enough to run all breathing things as well as modern industries. And though green plants can capture only less than one per cent of the sun's energy that comes to them, they can make up for inefficiency by expansion. One tree may show an acre of leaf surface to the light, and in each leaf millions of cells, and in the cells chlorophyll bodies, and in the chlorophyll bodies myriads of minute bits of chlorophyll, each one a little solar dynamo or engine, are working busily stowing energy away. It is constructive metabolism.

This is the job, called photosynthesis, that falls to chlorophyll. To the green workshops carbon dioxide comes, and there under the influence of sunlight it combines with water, and oxygen is given off. The leaves absorb the carbon dioxide from the air and do their work. That work — now imitated in the laboratory — is the primary constructive action of the life process.

The first product of this combination of carbon dioxide and water $(CO_2 + H_2O)$ is formalin, a poison, which is promptly changed to sugar and that in turn often to starch. Starch is the end product of the chlorophyll machine, and in starch the energy of sunshine that started to make carbon dioxide combine with water — much against their natural hopes and wishes — finds rest, comfort and storage until a time comes for more action. From starch and sugar, fats may be formed, and with nitrogen abstracted from the soil or air, proteins may be built up. The air above each acre of soil, says Osterhout's little book, contains ten million dollars worth of nitrogen.

From carbon dioxide and water, by sunshine and the machinery of chlorophyll, to the complex carbon and nitrogen compounds of living material is the course and chemistry of constructive metabolism. It is life's basic building process. On a summer day a pumpkin plant will build 25 grams of starch per square metre of leaf exposure, and a catalpa will make 45 grams of starch per metre in a day.[32] That means work and much constituent material. The vegetation of the world is a huge assimilator. It changes every year more than 130 billion pounds of carbon dioxide into organic stuff.[33] One small wheat harvest represents in assimilated materials many million tons.

Constructive metabolism is the storage of energy by living things. It is the manufacture of available foods or

First Presbyterian Church

BAY CITY, MICHIGAN

ALVIN CONVERSE SAWTELLE, Minister
1901 Center Avenue

SUNDAY, FEBRUARY 15, 1931

HARRY RUSSELL EVANS, Director of Music
2152 Sixth Street

—

THE QUARTETTE

Helen Eloise Carey	Soprano
Florence Day Ambrose	Contralto
Lyle M. Clift	Tenor
Lawrence C. Gregory	Baritone

THE CHORUS

SOPRANOS
Katherine Adie
Alice Buchius
Mrs. Kaye Buttars
Ruth Copeland
Mrs. W. E. Findley
Sarah Koch
Opal MacDonald
Johanna Mueller
Mrs. C. P. Murchison
Elizabeth Nelson
Mrs. Chase Oren
Jennie Redfield
Mrs. A. J. Runner
Belle Stone

TENORS.
F. W. Bradley
Garrett Hadcock
George MacPhail
Lyn MacPhail

ALTOS.
Elizabeth Berry
Bertha Diehl
Mary Erla Findley
Mrs. George Florence
Dorothea Gollin
Madeline Hadcock
Edith Nelson
Phylliss Nelson
Eleanor Pratt
Gwendolyn Mae Stone

BASSES.
Melvin Berry
George Dent
Donald Donnelly
Joe MacPhail
Arthur Nelson
Theodore Nelson

The Morning Service
TEN-THIRTY O'CLOCK

Organ Prelude   Communion No. 2   Guilmant

The Doxology

The Call to Worship

The Invocation

The Lord's Prayer

The Psalter   Selection 7

The Gloria Patri

Anthem

The Children's Sermon   Clean Hearts

The Children's Prayer

Hymn   82   Holy, Holy, Holy

The Scripture Lesson   Matthew 5:13-16

The Prayer of Intercession

Offertory   Offertory in D flat   St. Clair

Offertory Solo   Come Ye Blessed   J. P. Scott
                         Mr. Ewer

The Prayer of Dedication

Hymn 480   Awake, My Soul, Stretch Every Nerve

The Sermon   **THE CHRISTIAN'S MISSION**

Rev. Willis L. Gelston

The Benediction

Organ Postlude   Goronation March (from "The Prophet")

Meyerbeer

THIS EVENING

A RECEPTION

will be tendered by the young people of the church to members of the Alma College Glee Club and to students of the Central High school and the Junior College who are their special guests this evening in the church parlors, from 6 to 7 o'clock. Light refreshments will be served. All our young people and their friends are cordially invited.

PROF. ROY W. HAMILTON

Professor of English language and literature in Alma college, will give the address at the Young People's service in the Lecture room at 7 o'clock. Prof. Hamilton is sure to have something well worth while to say, especially for young people who have their life mostly ahead of them. It is sincerely to be hoped that he will have a good audience to speak to. The Young People have prepared a fine program for the evening and deserve the hearty support of the whole church.

OUR GUESTS TODAY

The Rev. Willis L. Gelston is the pastor of the Presbyterian church of Alma, Michigan.

Due to illness members of the Alma College Glee Club cannot be with us today. In their place we shall have as our guests the Presbyterian Quartette from Alma under the direction of Prof. Jess W. Ewer, professor of vocal music of the college, with Miss Grace Roberts, organist and accompanist.

We extend a most cordial welcome to each of them.

Mr. Sawtelle and the choir are conducting the morning service in the Alma church and are to be guests of Alma college at dinner at noon.

Announcements

❧ ❧

A BIT OF HISTORY

On a Sunday evening in 1886, the Rev. J. Ambrose Wight preached a sermon from his pulpit in the First Presbyterian Church of Bay City, in which he emphasized the need of a Christian college in central Michigan. At the close of the service, Mr. Alexander Folsom said to Dr. Wight that he was ready to give $50,000 toward the founding of such a college. A committee of the synod took the matter up and with the help of several other generous offers, the doors of Alma college were opened to students on Sept. 12, 1887. The First Church has always taken an active interest in the college and we welcome to our midst today its representatives.

THE WOMEN OF THE CHURCH

About 125 of them met in the Lecture room last Monday afternoon to consider the matter of unifying the women's work in the church. The sentiment in the meeting was very favorable to the idea of forming one organization and a committee of six was appointed to work out the details of such a plan and report later. The committee consists of Mrs. James A. Adie, Mrs. Harry F. Chapin, Mrs. Arthur D. DeFoe, Mrs. George L. Martin, Miss Emily B. Sidebotham, and Mrs. Paul F. Thompson.

CHURCH NIGHT

A group of about sixty people is meeting each Wednesday evening to study "Character Building," under G. L. Jenner, superintendent of schools, and "India," under the pastor. Most of them come for supper at 6:00 o'clock at 35 cents per plate. The classes meet at 7:00 and close at 8:00. All are welcome. Reservations for the supper should be made with Mrs. William Berry. The closing date for this series of Church Nights has been changed from Wednesday evening, Feb. 25, to Tuesday evening, Feb. 24. On this date, February 24, we will have the Rev. Dr. E. D. Lucas, of Lahore, Punjab, India, as the guest of the Church Night group. He will speak on India and the situation there. The evening's program will be open to all. Dr. Lucas will also address the Rotary Club at noon on this same date.

GROUP ONE

will meet Thursday at 12:30 with Mrs. John McIntosh, 209 North Chilson, for a pot-luck luncheon. Each woman will please take her own table service.

GROUPS EIGHT AND NINE

will meet Thursday at 3:00 with Mrs. Fred Lutz, 1815 McKinley.

THE WORLD'S DAY OF PRAYER

on February 20 will be observed in Bay City with a Women's meeting in Trinity church in the afternoon at 2:30 o'clock and a meeting for the general public in the First Baptist church in the evening at 7:30 o'clock.

AN ORATORICAL CONTEST

will be the feature of the Young Peoples' service next Sunday evening. Four or five of our young people will compete on the subject of "Stewardship," a subject which is being studied this year throughout the Presbyterian church. Further details of the contest will be given next week.

PLEASE!

Mrs. Barter would appreciate it very much if the contributions not yet paid for the Nov. 26th Food Sale would be sent to her before the annual meeting, as the final report must be made at that time.

fuels which may be used at once, soon, or later. It is the up process, sometimes called anabolism. Destructive metabolism is the release of energy by living things. It is the use of food or fuel to furnish action and to run the life machine. It is the push of living, and by various mechanical devices it gets various results from heat to locomotion. It is the down process, sometimes called katabolism. Both up and down metabolism in general may well be taken as the life process. It is the vital fire that is called living; but of the two kinds of metabolism the down process is more essentially the living of a thing. It is the prime combustion that is termed living energy, and without it there can be no life. "Growth, reproduction, motion, and irritability, and constructive metabolism may cease, as in a resting seed," says Osterhout,[34] "yet life may go on for many years. But when destructive metabolism ceases, life ceases."

This down process is the burning of food in the organism. It is generally the oxidation of the fuel stuffs in the living thing, and carbon dioxide is given off. What the candle does in the burning of tallow, the dog does in eating it. Tallow coöperates in his life process; he turns it into living material; he gets his "kick" out of it; and casts it away again as lifeless waste. When is the tallow living dog? The answer is: When it is burning.[34] When food is "chemically active in the process of combustion" in the organism that food is alive.

The life fires, however, are not in all respects like candle flames. They burn at lower temperatures and in watery solutions — which is not extraordinary but hardly similar to candle light. They are facilitated and controlled by enzymes and other "yeasty" things. They get their oxygen, in the case of many animals, from little carriers of iron, in man called hemoglobin, or of copper, vanadium and other things — for further reference see a horseshoe crab who uses copper. Life is a great variety of things and forms, and even chemists find it hard to pin it down

to one metabolism. But the chemical up and down of
life is rarely missed by living things. Plants make the
life energy first available, and animals by using plants
may change that fuel material to suit their needs: such is
constructive metabolism in its various forms.[35] Then the
bonfires begin. The fuels are oxidized again. Things happen. The machinery of living rattles on. Scientists call
it pompously destructive metabolism. But the young
man says, "This is the life."

That ancient dinosaur whose oral furnishings included
2,002 teeth must have encountered a problem in accurately inheriting such a dental regiment from his ancestors. For neither father, mother nor baby dinosaur —
his name was Trachodon Iguanodont Dinosaur — could
count and they were too indifferent to intellectual fail-
ings to care. Counting and the perfect coördination
between the upper 1,092 teeth and the lower 910 teeth
was not a matter for a dinosaur's brain or individual
anatomy to take care of. It was a problem for his reproductive cells or germ plasm.

The wonders and complexities of reproduction, for this
is but a minor case, make it the most spectacular, if not
most fundamental, of living processes. It is another expression of that Heraclitean principle of life, illustrated
in every day of living, whereby the forms and functions
and activities persist throughout a ceaseless change of
material content. Reproduction and the convergence of
ancestral lines point to the fact that all life is a single
system. The mystical unity of all life is hardly more
cogent than the organic unity of life that science finds.

Reproduction is not fixed in status or in form. It may
be simple — as in parts of cells that give rise to similar
parts of cells by the process of division — and thus well
nigh indistinguishable from ordinary metabolism. It may

be specialized rather more, as in cells that reproduce
other cells. It may be highly specialized, as in complex
organisms that give rise to new organisms. In each increasing specialization it carries a longer past into its
process and a higher complication of evolutionary development. As the development of more complex forms of
life is presumably a cumulative chemical process, in which
a specified order of reactions must be repeated to arrive
again at a specified result, it is only natural that an organism during the reproductive process will recapitulate
its evolutionary history in the embryo; for any other
method would introduce a discontinuity and a break in
the chemical process of development that no natural
order could withstand. This rehearsal does take place.
It is one of the clearest indications of the virtual continuity of the whole life process. It shows that the entire
field and area of living things from past to present is, in
a sense, one multifarious reaction. It is all the same affair
and process, like a grass fire burning many blades.

In most of the higher forms of life reproduction is
by the sexual method, and around that reproductive
differentiation in the germ cells and in mature organisms
has gathered a secondary set of characters and consequences that determine to a large degree the way that
plants and animals live and the forms of human institutions. Instead of neatly dividing in two after the
manner of simple asexual cells, sexed individuals make
specialties of germ cells and their development, and use
reproductive methods and gestative routines that pre-
determine in a sense the complexity of the offspring.
Cells are set aside, like queen bees, charged with the
reproduction of the entire organism, while the other cells
go about their various businesses of simple subdivision,
growth and building up the individual's anatomy.

The germ cells are male or female, for there are (Thank
God) only two sexes. That a bisexual system should
develop, rather than trisexual or octosexual systems, is

due no doubt to its rise by evolutionary elaboration from simple cell divisions, as well as from the fact that two sexes introduce a wealth of possible variation into the heredity mechanism without unbearable complications. In any case there are — as is rather generally known — two sexes and two kinds of germ cells, male and female. The one, or spermatozoon, is small and often motile, the other, the ovum, is larger and is stored with food. After the spermatozoon penetrates the egg and fertilizes it, the two fused cells, now a new individual, are called a zygote. The story of the zygote is thereafter a story of cell division. It is the rise and development of a new individual.

In cell division lie the secrets of heredity, the future of the race and the past of all the ancestral line. In the cell nucleus are granules of chromatin which now take position "in lines like beads on a thread." [36] These threads of beads are called chromosomes and for each species of animal or plant there is a definite number. Some have two; some have two hundred. Man has forty-eight.

As the cell prepares for division the chromosomes, now bent and knotty rods, move into one plane, where each chromosome splits lengthwise into two daughter chromosomes. These two move apart towards the poles of the cell where they meet other daughter chromosomes and form the two daughter nuclei. The cell then divides with a daughter nucleus assigned to each one of the two new cells. This in general, and with a myriad of delicate complications, is the division process of all cells.

But the division of the zygote, or conjoined egg and sperm cell, is of a somewhat different order. Here two nuclei, one of the sperm and one of the egg are resolved into one system. [37] The chromosomes of the sperm and of the egg first move towards the equator of the cell, where each chromosome splits lengthwise. As the daughter chromosomes move respectively to the poles to form the daughter nuclei they sort themselves in such a way that half of the chromosomes of the egg cell and half of those of the sperm cell are in one daughter nucleus, while the rest are in the other. Then the fertilized egg cell makes its first cleavage. Two cells appear where there was one before. There will be much more of that.

The cleavage of the zygote not only separates the sex cell's chromosomes so that half the chromosomes of every cell thereafter in that individual will be derived from one parent and half from the other; it also segregates the protoplasm of the cell body, so that different parts of that material are represented by special groups of cells in the developed organism.[38] They proliferate in layers called (see Conklin) the endoderm cells, the ectoderm cells, the nervous system and the notochord, the muscles and the mesoderm, and from these develop appropriate features such as organs and body parts in the mature organism. The higher forms, especially the vertebrates, have long rehearsals of their evolutionary past in embryo. They develop in sheet-like structures that gradually indent and re-enfold elaborately into the structures of the mature body.[39] They pass through many stages, and the human embryo is no exception. It has its gill slits and its tail and other ancient furniture no less than the uncultured embryos of dogs and cats.

Weismann called the hen discontinuous but her egg continuous; and that made Weismann famous. Every successful egg, said Herr Weismann, creates two things: the chicken and the germ cells in that chicken. All eggs are as old as the hen that lays them, for eggs and hen begin life together in the parent germ cell. Early in the embryo the reproductive cells for that embryo are set aside, and thereafter the chicken or other individual has little to do with them. He or she is merely the vehicle for them, the apparatus for feeding them and the instrument for placing them when they grow up in positions of advantage for the development of another generation.[40] Once the segregation of reproductive cells in the embryo is made, the nature of those germ cells and their "heredity chromatin" cannot in general be altered. That segregation is made usually in the initial stages of embryonic growth. The line is egg to egg with no chicken between.

This is Weismann's theory of the continuity of the germ plasm and the discontinuity of the somatoplasm or individual. The hen that grows and dies is a stub line off the continuous line from egg to egg. All individuals are stubs. They create no germ cells. They rarely influence them. They are created by the germ cells; but those germ cells also create the germ cells of the next generation. It is a significant theory that doubtless is generally true. It follows that an individual's acquired characteristics cannot be inherited. Experiments, despite some recent contradictions, indicate that they never are inherited.

But Lamarck still has his day, and his theory that characteristics acquired by one individual may be inherited by the following generation still has staunch if somewhat modified supporters. Kammerer finds that salamanders have a perverse way of inheriting new spots for old, when the new spots are acquired under special sun and scenery conditions during the salamander's younger years and adolescence.[40] Durkhen finds that caterpillars of a certain brand pass on to later generations some greenish tendencies acquired by the artificial use of orange light upon their pupae. Semon says that living things "remember" some experiences and pass the "memory," or record, or "engram" on to future generations (see also Plato's Phaedo). As a consequence of a stimulus imposed by the conditions of life, he says, an engram is impressed on the organism, and Bower says: [41] that the facts derived from ferns suggest the acceptance of some form of "mnemic" theory as a working hypothesis. But the inheritance of acquired characteristics, though true, perhaps, in special cases, has probably not the general validity of Weismann's doctrine of discontinuous individuals.

What the individual has dies with him, for death is the price of individuality. He is an adventitious instrument highly specialized and when his function is fulfilled death is his natural terminus. Death is a discontinuity, similar to that of any chemical change, and though we usually avoid it with much earnestness, it is the natural end to a metabolic process that will always wax and wane thus in periodic rhythm.

Had our ancestors lived their simple life of single cells without sex evolution or the strain for new advances, and been content to divide simply again and again with now and then a stimulative conjugation, death, except by outer accident or disaster, could never have evolved. For death came at that stage in evolutionary history where the individual was separated from the continuous germ plasm. Death was the price of diversity of structure and special adaptation to environment. It was the price of sex and of the biological purpose and result of sex, namely, diverse heredity, unique individuals.

For the bitter struggle to escape death from without led to the evolution of death within. The factors that evolved the individual and segregated him from the line of germ plasm left him discontinuous (physiologically) and without means of direct reproduction. In other words he dies. The machine runs and then runs down, and whether his metabolism can be improved until the wheels will run indefinitely is a problem not very near solution. The natural continuity of life lies elsewhere.

Lyell taught Darwin that the continuity of living things today means their continuity with yesterday and through

all time. That was Darwin's evolutionary secret and the
potent guess that found its confirmation in the origin
of species and the natural mechanism of the world.[41]
For the continuity of natural mechanism cannot be broken where science is concerned, and the life mechanism
including man and beast and ancient reptiles is no exception.[42] Nature does not make jumps, an aphorist has
said. A study of the gradual change of vital species and
their graded intervals shows that he is almost right.

The evolutionary process is presumably mechanical
with natural cause for every natural consequence, and it
is irreversible. For a change in form and function is a
change in chemistry; heat is dissipated; Carnot's ancient
law of irreversibility applies. Parts that are sacrificed
never are regained and simplicities once lost are virtually
gone for good. The horse cannot get back his three toed
foot, and many vertebrates have marched on straight to
extinction because they specialized too much for some
too temporary habitat and lost forever general characters
and functions that they might need again. In this sense,
says Osborn,[43] chromatin evolution is irreversible. Diversity is the result. For unique individuals and species
come of cumulative changes that never can turn back.
Evolution is centrifugal. Complexities increase and there
is no general way, except by death's control, to their re-
duction.

At the monkey trial in Tennessee, where a youth was
prosecuted for teaching evolution, Maynard Metcalf said:
Evolution means the change of an organism from one
character into a different character, and by character I
mean its structure, or its behavior or its function, or its
method of development from the egg or anything else. The
term in general means the whole series of such changes
which have taken place during hundreds of millions of
years, from very lowly beginnings.

"Evolution" arose as an explanation of the origin of
species in terms of a gradual and continuous process. It

has remained the ultimate continuum for biology and all life action. It has become a cosmical metabolism in which orders and species rise and fall symmetrically and some life seems to cycle upward towards an unknown peak.

There are inner currents and controls of evolution, and coming characters have motion and velocity of emergence. In the evolutionary process there are hints of a general organization that increases in complexity as it is investigated. Some parts or characters *evolve* more rapidly than others in geologic time, says Osborn,[44] and some *develop* more rapidly than others in the course of individual growth. Some characters are coördinated, as in plants, by catalytic chemical messengers and some, as in animals, by catalysts and by the nervous system too, but who can say what coördinates the appearance of homologous characters in widely different species? The totality of living things acts sometimes as if it were a whole with something of a nervous system. It suggests at least a unity of origin and a timed march onward by all its parts. Two million years it took the elephant to lose his lower tusks, but at that the teeth of elephants evolved much faster than those of rats.[45] As in the individual's development so in the evolution of the species there are strange accelerations or retardments and controls not accountable to environment. Life as a whole is something of an organism.

A fire reaches for fuel. A lamp wick uses oil in its environment to fill its pores. There is no psychic complement to these reactions, though the survival of the fire hangs on getting fuel. The drive and the control of evolutionary process is in general such a "struggle" on the part of living things to get what they must have. It is a struggle, and the competition often is intense, but it is no less chemical in last analysis so far as science is concerned.

The imperialism of living things, banker or stoker, wasp or antelope, that reach like fires — for they all are

fires — after fuel that they must have, is the prime
meaning of adaptation to environment. It is the chief
control of biologic evolution, and the environmental
factor though important is no more active than the adaptive mechanism provided by diverse heredity, by death
to individuals with a chance to try another generation,
and by immortal germ plasm. For in a living thing's environment conditions are imposed upon continued living
that must be met if the life combustion goes on. The reaction of an organism on its environment may be suitable
to continued living or it may be death; and in the latter
case a new product of the germ plasm may arise better
adjusted to the thing that caused the death or failure of
its predecessors. The fires of life then burn over environmental areas that before were threatening, useless or
without available fuel.

"I am fully convinced," says Darwin,[46] "that species
are not immutable, but that those belonging to what are
called the same genera are lineal descendants of some
other and generally extinct species, in the same manner
as the acknowledged varieties of any one species are the
descendents of that species. Furthermore, I am convinced that natural selection has been the most important, but not the exclusive, means of modification . . .
by the preservation and accumulation of variations,
which are beneficial under the organic and inorganic
conditions to which each creature is exposed at all periods of life."

But the gradual evolution of the species (or, as DeVries
says, their evolution by jumps [47]) when expressed in
terms of "struggle" and "selection" should not be interpreted as primarily a psychic problem. Darwin's
principle, says Osborn, "is in fact adumbrated in the survival or elimination of various forms of lifeless energy
as witnessed among the stars and planets." On the exuberance and surplus of the germ plasm and on its huge
capacity for variation the success of natural selection

depends. It is a mechanical principle that needs no unique vitalism or directive force for operation.[47] Plants die under the desert sunshine until one comes that can resist dehydration. To the plant that can withhold its watery fluids the desert is selective, but neither plant nor desert is psychically aroused thereby.

Nature is experimental. Trial and error is her dumb and massive method of selection. Trial implies diversity of form and effort. Error means extinction, and success is life.[48] In the life process many things may happen. Some carbon compound found by the groping chemistries of protoplasm may introduce tomorrow new energies and forms that will upset us utterly. But such a violence of chemical discontinuity is improbable, and advances made in vital evolution will be within our present order, not beyond it. Man will be the one to introduce the carbon compound (such as gunpowder), and though that means catastrophic discontinuity and extinction to some species, he will weave it on the whole into the fabric of living without too much abruptness. Nature is wasteful with her trials and progenies and her excess of varied forms over those that can survive. But as the age old living process matures and our geological instabilities decline there will be less waste perhaps and less fortuitous variation. The struggle for existence may entail less slaughter.

Equilibrium will not come, however, until the fuel or food supplies are balanced with the productivity of germ plasm. Wide flung stabilities must supervene upon this earth. The restlessness and fluctuation of our nervous world must cease, and that is doubtful. Perhaps we would not wish it. Even now an evolutionary balance in the world is found in certain forms; and armoured brachiopods of the old Cambrian seas are standing pat today as they stood pat thirty million years ago.[49] They are a sessile shellfish older than the oldest families of Virginia and more conservative than the editorials of the New York

Times. They have changed but little. Their type is stable. They have reached a balance and repose that nothing much disturbs. But who wants to be a sessile lamp-shell? Man has come of plastic lineage, and though the conservatives in nature are many, his is a more rest-less stock. Man has changed much; the single celled amoeba has changed little down the ages; and their re-spective policies and statesmanship are no doubt vastly different.

Man is a newcomer on the earth. His sudden rise to power has introduced a sometimes dangerous, sometimes beneficial, factor in the environments of other living things. Whether he survives or whether he will wane again while sessile shellfish live along for thirty million years beyond his grave depends on nature's new experi-ment called the individual. It is not strictly new of course, but its emphasis in modern eras is great. It is a way to find adjustment to diversities in environment. It is a vehicle for the germ plasm that is not stopped by strange topographies. It can draw life from more places and thus support more life than less developed forms. But it is still on trial. All living things are still on trial. They stand in long ranks daily for inspection, and the oldest and the youngest must daily meet the test.

What are the ages of life? First was the age of inver-tebrates and fishes called the palæozoic. Then was the age of reptiles and amphibians called the mesozoic.[49] Last is the age of mammals called the cenozoic. Fishes are twenty-five million years old. Reptiles are twelve mil-lion years old more or less. Mammals are three million years old. The mammals are only as old as the Rocky mountains, but the reptiles and amphibians are older than the Appalachian range.[49] The invertebrates are older than the coal measures and the Scottish highlands. They are as old as the archaic hills of Canada. The fish that flops under a man's foot as he extracts the hook is older by two dozen million years or so in unchanged lineage than the newcomer who caught him. And the worm is older still.

Bacteria are the oldest living forms on earth.[49] Some are large, one twentieth of a millimetre in length. Some are small, one two thousandth of a millimetre in length. They are omnipresent in the soils and surface of the earth. In the excretion of a human adult, there are daily some 33,000,000,000,000 bacteria. For all its age the bacterium is a prosperous form of life. Some can derive energy and nutrition directly from inorganic compounds, and some can live without the help, direct or indirect, of sunshine. They are uniquely primitive. Some bacteria are good for us. Others are very wicked creatures.

Next come the algæ with the evolution of the chlorophyll, and they are followed by the reach for sunlight and the growth of leaves and stems. As plants depend on bacteria to get nitrogen from raw rock compounds and the air, the animals in turn depend on plants' ability to use sunlight, to store starches and other bottled energies. Without plants the animals could never live, and so the pyramid of life ascends.

Close to early plants are protozoa of which our friend Amœba is a well known member.[49] With animals come locomotion and a new world in which going after things dominates waiting for things to come along. Individuality, initiative, experiment emerge cautiously even in the protozoa. The ciliata are motile single cells that find in their ability to move a secret that will eventually reveal most of the conscious powers and reasonings of later life.

The jelly fish and sponges, the star fish and the worms slide one after another into the reservoir of life.[50] The molluscs lumber in, and the more articulate crabs and spiders and the insects follow.

Next the vertebrates with fish first join the array, and the sharks evolve with a backbone that will serve the higher vertebrates and man. The amphibia take their liberties on shore and the common fishes start their sea routine.

From the first fishes through amphibians come the reptiles, and they were dominant on the earth from carboniferous times for a long ten million years or more. Great egg laying beasts inhabited the ancient continents. Fin backed lizards came, and on Africa, most stable of the continents, huge vegetarian reptiles, built like the hippopotamus, appeared. The turtles got their start in life, and the great dinosaurs in many forms entered existence. The *Tyrannosaurus rex*, in "speed, size, power and ferocity the most destructive life engine" ever evolved, trampled the earth. He weighed two tons and it was tons of fight for his brain took less than sixteen ounces of it.[51] There was the brachiosaurus, largest animal that the earth has known, one hundred feet in length; and there was a small lizard-like reptile that is ancestor to the birds.

But the reptiles declined three million years or so ago and only five remain, of which the turtles, snakes and lizards are best known. The stock of the cold blooded animals has lost its drive. The evolution of these forms before the mammals and the birds has become static. Their line of germ plasm has lost its great vitality. The torch that burns brightest is now elsewhere. The mammals have it.

There are whales and field mice, mastodons and tigers, horses and men to represent the mammals. One of their number, belonging to the primates, with hair and flat nails and a very grasping hand has overrun the earth like a pest of rabbits in Australia. He is called man.

Man is a placental mammal that hatches its young within the body and suckles them after birth. He is derived from a small insectivorous beast similar to the tree shrew, it is said; [51] and thence his arboreal ancestors are near the form of lemurs and the forefathers of the apes. His descent to the ground was the landing day no doubt of some primeval Columbus, for then man's history probably began.

The primates are the lemurs, monkeys, apes and man. ·
Besides the primates there are nine branches of placental
mammals. They are whales, seals, land carnivores, in-
sectivores, bats, hoofed mammals, manatees, rodents,
edentates, cousins all.[51] Most of the changes in the mammals have been in the loss of characters and in changes of
proportion. Few new characters have been gained but
the proportions of the head and the limbs have been profoundly changed. By adding teeth and by stretching or
pulling, swelling or contracting, the skeleton of a tree
shrew, says Osborn, may almost be transformed into
that of a whale. It took one million years for the horse to
lose his fifth toe and two million years more for him to
lose his second and fourth toes. The horse is as old a
job as man but in a different, and according to Jonathan
Swift, a better style. Had man concentrated on his legs
instead of on his head he might have been almost a horse
by this time.

But evolution must be distinguished from teleology
and fate. It is no preconceived idea. It is no trans-scien-
tific valuation realized in slow progress of the species
towards a moral climax. The worth of the mosquito is
no less than the worth of man under the objective glass of
science, for hypothetically, science is indifferent to values.
Evolution is merely a descriptive term for a natural one
way process. It shows signs of form and organization as
a whole but its entelechies are hardly those of Aristotle;
they are too submissive. It is progress, we may say, but
progress here is not a necessary moral or æsthetic end.
For to the declining reptiles the world has dangerously
degenerated. It is crowded with catastrophe and fearful
risk. Hideous beings ride the world, always ready with
an iron heel to crush a reptile's life. The world is a wreck
to reptiles.

But purely natural values must still be based somehow
on the significance of existence and on ability to maintain
existence in the face of competition and death. Life has

a prejudice for living. A fire burns as if it wanted to. It is continuous so long as there is fuel. A fire, like life, has a prejudice for burning; but that is metaphysical. The great fact for science is that life does go on.

Life after all is but one chapter in the universe, and this one — Chapter IV — has concerned itself chiefly with five problems of life. They are: the geological basis of life; the origin, nature and distinctive characteristics of life; metabolism; reproduction; biological evolution. The sensitivity of living things, surely a distinctive characteristic, will be discussed later under the name of mind and behavior and related subjects.

CHAPTER FIVE

Mind and Behavior

FROM the burning that is called life a strange smoke and fragrance rises. Clouds accumulate, and shadows of the fire shift across them. There are reddish lights that are neither fire nor earth nor measurable energies. They are soundless and without heat. They do nothing and they weigh nothing. They are things that seem to be, but when the flame fades out they fade and their gesturings become nothing. We can lift them out of the heat of living and hold them like pictures to look at, but we cannot lift them far. They are the things of thought.

For consciousness, whatever it may be, can hardly be an energy interacting with the energies of living things. The taste of alcohol makes no one drunk, nor can the smell of sulphur tarnish silver, and to assume that thought can intervene, like an acid or alkali, in the delicate chemistries of living is to deny the continuity of natural mechanism and to abrogate the basic hypothesis of objective science. Meanings do not move; two plus two cannot do anything; love will not liquefy or raise the temperature of water, for the mental side of things is forever divorced by hypothesis from the space-time order of matter and mechanism. To confuse them destroys both.

As the living process becomes more complicated its area of contact expands. It is affected by more things. Its sensitivity increases, and the world of meaning appropriate to it is ever more complex. For man there is more meaning in the world than for the spider; his mental scope is no doubt greater; but the content of his thought, however analyzed or caught by introspection, has never yet been observed to do anything. It has never been weighed or measured scientifically and no doubt never will. It cannot push anything or stop it. It cannot fall down-

stairs or fill a mail box. It stands aside from matter,
motion or causality, and the realities that rest on the hypothesis of science cannot accept it. To science as such
it is not real. The frame of Uncle Henry's picture may be
objectively described. The canvas may be weighed and
measured. The pigments may be analyzed and given
formulas. But Uncle Henry's likeness is none of these
and cannot interact upon them.

Psychology is deeply bifurcated, and complete separation between its epistemology and its physiology is only
a matter of time and progress. They are founded on
different orders and hypotheses, and to try to organize
them scientifically together is futile.

It is said that man thinks and that living things are
sensitive and that a difference lies therein between life
and what has never lived. It is hearsay evidence that no
doubt is true, but the difference between *homo sapiens*
and other animals and between living things and things
that do not live is more in degree than in kind. For the
processes that have to do with metabolism, reproduction
and sensitivity are continuous with natural inorganic
process, and the elaboration of simple ways of being ir-
ritable that mark the behavior of the jelly fish into the
intricate tempers of a famed soprano or the brain wrest-
lings of a philosopher is no exception. The primary sensitivity of living things is the physical basis of man's
behavior and of his complicated response to stimuli.
And that sensitivity is not much different from certain
physical and chemical responses in the inorganic world.

The difference, where there is one, is largely in the
wholeness of behavior of living things and the enrichment
and increasing correlation of their responses as they evolve.
They can use energy as an engine uses coal; they can
divide and specialize labor, and they can concentrate

the results in an action of the whole body that is new in
nature. The eye does not see; the man sees with the eye,
and the light energy used in seeing enters a tangle of
changes and conversions that affects, among other things,
the behavior of the entire organism. There is system
there and a kind of subordination and use, for use is a
concept of organization. The correlation of vital energies
into one behavior is a major mystery and problem. But
the how of an organism's behavior and its prediction is
subject to purely scientific treatment. It is a problem, as
Watson says,[1] primarily "in what the whole animal will
do from morning to night and from night to morning."

What he will do is in general what he can do, and that
depends on the mechanical and locomotive furniture
with which he is equipped. Complex as his behavior
may be, it is no more complex, presumably, than the
physical structure associated with it. He is as versatile
and as subtle as his nervous system; for a simple body
behaves simply. We may lift off behavior as it were, and
look at it apart from the body that behaves, but that is an
abstraction never made by nature. We may find behavior
scented with responsibility and moral symbolism, colored
with happiness and dislike, with clouds of meaning and
ulterior ends above it, but in that world nature makes no
intromission. Observable action and the results of action
according to the narrow categories of the natural world
is the only field in which psychology can be called a
science. Behavior is a function of physical structure.

The sponge for example is not a notably nervous animal. He has no nervous tissue, or at least very little.[2] He
lacks sensations — to judge by his behavior — and he
feels no patriotic thrills or the poignancy of love. What
the inner life and imaginative consciousness of the sponge
may be cannot be known, but his actions suggest that

he has none. Though his intellect may be profound and varied, and his philosophy Kantian with all the excruciating intricacies of the three critiques, his behavior shows no signs of it, and for all natural and causal purposes we may assume that he has no intellect or philosophy. Only by observing his behavior can we guess at his mentality, and the names and signs for mental things, so far as they have scientific bearing, are really terms and shorthand for his behavior.

Of the three kinds of nerves, the sensory nerves or the receivers, the motor nerves or the activators, and the central nerves or the adjustors, the sponge has only one, the activators, and of those exceeding few. He can transmit no nervous impulse to another part. He is incapable of a general shock and only the direct stimulation of a muscle around a water orifice will bring it into action. The sponge is nervously not integrated, and his ego is no doubt multiple and badly scattered. The sponge is no traveller. He stays put where bathers off the beaches of Key West stub their toes on him. He cannot act as a whole. He need not live as a whole, for he is not automotive. And he very likely does not think as a whole, as automotive animals always must.

Beside the loutish sponge the sea-anemone has something of the polish of a gentleman. He has a pedal disc on which he travels solemnly from one anchorage to another, and though he lacks a central nervous system or adjusting focus he has receiving nerves and activators both well developed. He can transmit a nervous impulse clear around his little tub-like body, and if some stranger touches him he will contract suddenly as a whole, spew out the waters of his interior, and reduce himself both in girth and volume.

The sea-anemone is a good example of life with a diffuse nervous system.[3] He has a mesh of nerves throughout his living substance, but he has no centralized control. Detach a tentacle, for example, and it will operate as loyally as ever if properly excited; or separate the upper half of the anemone from the lower and the pedal disc will crawl about from place to place much as before. Nerves the sea-anemone does not lack. He lacks a central station. He is awake enough, but he hasn't any brains.

First the muscles, then the activating nerves, the sensory nerves and last the central brain seems to be the evolutionary order of nervous development. In the unintelligent sponge muscles are stimulated directly and separately by appropriate things in the environment and the activating nerves, if present, are insignificant. In the sea-anemone are signs of nervous transmission and muscular correlation and the stimulus to an action may not be on the action's site. For the sea-anemone has receiving nerves as well as activators and spatial propinquity between the exciting cause and the muscular activity becomes less necessary. With further development comes centralized nervous organization, and between the stimulus and the muscular response there is no need now of propinquity either in space or in time. Complexities still increase and are compounded and behavior has new subtleties. The higher worms have brains, and even the earth worm has a three part nervous system not unlike our own. Receiving nerves reach from the earth worm's skin into his central apparatus, and motor nerves run thence out to his muscles.[4] Throughout the vertebrates the spinal cord is uniform, but the brain shows great development. From the fishes to man the hemispheres increase in size and complication, and a cerebral cortex that in lower vertebrates is concerned almost solely in the job of smelling becomes in the mammals a huge headquarters for all the senses, for "voluntary" action and reserve "experience." In man the cerebral cortex weighs some thirteen grams and is composed of 9,200,000-000 nerve cells more or less. In that nine billion lies the reason for a college education.

But nerves are accessory to actions, and psychic

terms should not be thrust into the physical mechanism. The sea-anemone, says Parker, has no sensations distinct from the reception of a stimulus and the speedy activation to muscular response, but how does Professor Parker know? For sensations *per se* have no more physical place in higher organisms than in the sea-anemone. Psychic terms do not mix well in the physical phenomena, and though delayed responses and a mulling over of stimuli in the nervous centers is no doubt true of higher animals, sensation, intellect, thought, memory and the like are not good terms to describe adjusting mechanism and its operation. They are not physical terms nor purely scientific in their category. They are not behavior.

What a sponge does is hardly a chronicle of adventure. He rides no chargers to the fray; flying to the pole is not among his aspirations. He can bend his skeletons a little and he can close his water ports against too swift a flood. His performances are few, so far as overt actions are concerned, and what he does he does repeatedly and separately with various parts of his body.

In this respect man is different from the sponge, for he does a multitude of things and he does them with his whole body. Though this can hardly be a mark of superiority, perhaps, except in our own prejudice, it is no doubt preferable for us to the repetitive simplicities of the sponge. His unity of living is a repetition of performance and of structure in all his major parts. Man's wholeness is diversity of function and of structure and the organization of his parts into one going concern.

And the going part of it is one of the secrets of their difference. For man is a locomotive animal and compared with the sponge the slowest and the laziest of gentlemen is a scintillating live wire. To run about successfully an animal must be highly organized. He must act as a whole. He must have diversity of structure and function joined with wholeness of accomplishment. He must have coordinating powers and he must organize a control of

himself and his activities that in sessile things is hardly
necessary. And the more he runs about the more necessary this is. When the sponge elected to sit down all
through the ages the nature of his "mind" was by that
election largely predetermined. He has been unable to
make those broadening contacts that come of travel.
And the sponge today remains conservative and rigidly
provincial.

The mobility of man has much to do with the nature of
his thinking, and though things might not be different
if man were fixed and immobile they would seem different.
Of most of them he would never be aware. They would
merge and blur, and the ancient and honorable institution of thinking might never be founded. The articulate
world of reason and of science, their termini and the
wholeness of things are more or less a function of man's
locomotive power. They are, as it were, an organic consequence of the wholeness of his behavior.

To nerves and to ductless glands man owes mainly
the wholeness of his living. They are his coördinators,
and locomotion as a whole without them would be impossible.

Nerves are of course the liveliest machinery in the
process of behavior, and their systems become more
complicated and lively from sponges down to pianists
and poets. Their function, as James says,[5] "is to bring
each part into harmonious coöperation with every other,"
but of their physiology we know only too little.[6]

For new research in this field psychology is no doubt
waiting. Already Charles M. Child, for instance, can
make a head grow where a tail belongs by increasing
through experiment the "rate of living" in that region.
By altering conditions he can produce a smaller brain,
an extra head or eyes and establish "physiological gra-

dients"[6] determining the order of development. Though
nerves now are less fashionable than they were before
girls were athletes they remain important. Without them
organic relationship would be impossible. They make
for coördinated behavior, and one action on the part of
a diverse bag of organs, limbs and members called a
human body would be, without them, out of the question. Nerves take account of time and build it somehow
into the physique. They establish zero hours for general
action, and on that hour the general action begins.

But nerves and their electrolytic currents are not the
sole coördinators. Glands are quite the thing today, and
everybody seems to have them. Their work is chemical
and their vehicles for the exportation of their products
are the streaming fluids of our living bulk.[7] There is the
thyroid gland secreting thyroxin. This helps to control
growth. Its deficiency makes for general slowness. Its
excess makes for too much life and restlessness. The para-
thyroid glands seem to restrain the nervous system from
overactivity and breakdown. The adrenal glands act
in crises to stimulate the muscles to long effort. They are
the "anger glands." The pituitary gland affects the
growth of the skeleton and the connective tissue. It
affects metabolism and our tolerance to sugars. It stimulates the growth of sex glands and affects the tone of the
visceral muscles. The pineal and thymus glands seem to
retard the growth of sex glands until puberty. The puberty glands composed of interstitial cells within the sex
glands, have to do with the secondary sexual characteristics of the male and female and affect the individual's
general vitality and youthfulness. The glands (ductless)
are character makers. Without them the world would
lack much that is interesting.

But, important as they are, the nerves and glands
are not the whole of man's wholeness of behavior. His
living has an architectural wholeness that underlies even
these coördinators. His behavior is not atomic; it is

integral. His life is one life, dynamically as well as temporally, and over-analysis is likely to be false analysis.

Atomism, psychic as well as physical, seems to have seen its best days, and belief in analytic ultimates of mind as well as of matter is losing hold. Nature behaves in wholes. Its realities are aggregative not individual; and though our analyses may push legitimately far beyond the natural frontiers of bodies and behaviors down to theoretic and explanatory components it is not clear that nature itself acts on such principles of rational subdivision. An electron is valid enough as a focus of numerous interesting affairs in the mechanistic order, but an electron alone and isolated, as it were, in a bottle would be presumably unreal.

Psychic atomism is no better off. The old sensationalism of Hume and Locke is merely theoretical. Such simple and isolated psychic atoms do not exist and the stuff of experience is more nearly, as Dewey says,[8] "adaptive courses of action, habits, active functions, connections of doing and undergoing, sensori-motor coordinations." A sensation in these terms is a point of readjustment in the life process, and experience — which man preserves and lower animals generally do not — is an aggregation and a wholeness derived from many sources. In psychic and epistemological fields atomism will not do, and under the narrow categories of science where the behaviorist operates it is even less efficient.

For behavior implicates the whole man, and what he does now is not a unit in itself, like piece work from a factory bench, but a part in a "behaving" process that is conterminal with his life. When Titchener says[9] that the psychologist seeks to analyse mental experience into its simplest components, that he takes a particular consciousness and works over it again and again, process by process until his analysis can go no further, he exhibits in one sentence the entire museum of faults that modern scientists find in the old introspective psychology. For consciousness without material mechanism is not in scientific strictness a process at all; nor can a particular consciousness be recognized by objective observation; while an analysis of consciousness into psychic atoms and components may be an interesting exercise but not closely attached to the reality. Behavior is a whole.[10] It can be objectively observed. It is strictly limited under scientific categories. Behaviorism in that respect is a purification of psychological method and a more complete separation of the science from the mother stock of philosophy and morals.

Though the real is broader than science, no doubt, and the absolutes of science are true in only one dimension of the world, science in its field remains science, and despite protesting introspectionists, things that cannot be observed in common, that are unmeasurable by common standards and that possess neither matter nor mechanism are hardly scientific. For the "mental" and the physical by hypothesis cannot interact.[11] Neither are they parallel processes like the double track to Omaha. Only one is process. Only one is subject to general observation, experiment and measure. Only one has nature's continuity in space and time. "Mind" is not parallel to nature nor can it interact with nature; it is another order and dimension. The two are different points of view. They are abstractions, as it were, on different principles. They are attitudes; they are postures; and to try to relate them causally in interaction, or architecturally in parallelism, is dangerous and unnecessary.

Science must give up its psychic correlates, if it would be science, and living behavior must be interpreted in

terms of action and material. Conklin gives a list of
parallels between the psychical and physiological; and
like others who attempt it, he unintentionally suggests
the superfluity of the former. All living things, says Conklin,[12] have differential sensitivity; and this in higher
animals and in psychic terms is called the special senses
and sensations. All living things have mechanical re-
flexes and tropisms, and these in psychic terms become
inherited instincts and acquired habits. Organic memory,
or the results of previous experience in the general protoplasm, becomes the registration of experience in nerve
centers and association tracts and is called — psychically
— the associative memory. Adaptive responses, or the
results of elimination of useless responses through trial
and error in all living things, become in higher forms, he
says, the results of trial and error plus associative memory, i.e., experience, or, psychically, intelligence and reason. Varied responses are — psychically — inhibition,
choice, will. Identity, or the continuity of individual organization in all living things, is psychically the continuity of psychic life, or consciousness. And subjective
phenomena, if any, accompanying lower processes become, in psychic terms and in higher forms, feelings and
emotions. The latter part of this program of mental
development is obviously strained to suit a system and
there is a blithe mixing of mind and mechanism that
surely is not based on biological observation, but the program suggests at least the biological background of
behavior and its development. The difference between
the lower and the higher animals is not between the mechanical and the psychical. It is, scientifically, the difference between a relatively simple mechanism and a more
complex one. It is a difference in measurable behavior.

Even the image, that fortress of the introspectionists,
is called by Watson [13] implicit behavior; and if by image
is meant a centrally aroused sensation free from the outer
mechanism of the body, the image as a scientific fact,

Watson would say, does not exist. That is strong medicine for psychology, for with the image must go its other psychic relatives such as memory and will. They are but parts of a man's whole behavior. They are implicit or overt actions; they are delayed or immediate responses to stimuli, and their pictorial and intrinsic aspect as ideas or "thought content" have no place in the behaving mechanism. "Consciousness," says Watson,[14] as he roars to the attack on the old psychology of James, Wundt, Titchener, Angell, Judd and McDougall, is not the proper "subject matter of psychology." For consciousness "is neither a definable nor a usable concept;" it is merely another word for the 'soul' of more ancient times. The proper subject of psychology — and here Dr. Watson becomes more amiable and seductive — is "behavior" or the activities of the whole human being. It is a wild and bloodthirsty battle, but the behaviorists will win.

The hub of modern psychology and of all behavior mechanism is in stimulus and response. To light energy, to sound and other things that indicate an environment ever on the move we have a differential sensitivity; and, to the scientist, "good" behavior means adjustment to that moving. The one is stimulus; the other is response. Stimulus, says Watson,[15] is "any object in the general environment or any change in the tissues themselves." Response is the "system of organized activity" in any animal. And adjustment is the alteration of the physiological state of an organism so that the stimulus no longer arouses reaction. Life is a long line of instabilities and their resolutions. Hunger sets in and the muscles of the stomach contract. The stomach is filled with food, the contractions cease, and hunger for the time is quieted. Life is a procession of hungers of one kind or another, and their satiations. Often they are called problems.

But the range of stimuli changes as life goes on, and things that disturbed our childhood no longer raise reactions, while things that leave a baby quite serene find alert response in later years. The black and ponderous gesture of a fat man's shadow no longer scares the man of forty-five, and the sweet writhing of a little coral snake may interest and amuse a child of three. From "without" come stimuli that we call the outer world and from "within," from all our muscles and our viscera, come other stimuli that we call quite inconsistently our personal affairs. Whether this difference between the outer and the inner has any right to serious consideration is hard to say, but in either case and in either field the range of stimuli shifts and, until maturity at least, greatly increases.

Responses, too, change and develop. The training of a man tells in his actions, and learned responses are eventually greater in number by far than those unlearned. Instincts, so called, are unlearned responses.[16] They are a part of our birthday furniture, or at least of earliest infancy, and they include responses that habit or life experiences have not made. There are external responses and the "ordinary doings of the human being," and there are internal responses of our muscular and glandular systems that are no less important though more difficult to see. When men can describe the correlations of stimuli and responses so that knowledge of one will give knowledge of the other the main problem of psychology will be solved.

The experience of life pays dividends. It earns a profit and its encounter with the past helps to assure the future. A man's behavior after a drenching by experience is usually different from what it was before. He has "learned" something. He has made an adjustment. He is a different man. He has "conditioned" or helped to "condition" some stimulus or response.[17] He can condition a response to a stimulus by substituting a new response to that stimulus. He may reach for fire the first time; but he may learn to draw away the second. He can condition a stimulus to a response by substituting a new stimulus to that response. He may fall in love with impecunious Mary, but he may eventually love and marry the wealthy Jane. There are many learned or conditioned responses in a man's behavior. There are fewer unlearned or unconditioned responses given him at birth. Man adjusts his responses or behavior to the demands of the environment. Usually a learned response is a better adjustment. But not always.

How is response conditioned? Throughout life and in all animals, says Watson, this substitution of new responses to old stimuli takes place. Today the little dog makes baby Harold laugh and play. Tomorrow the same little dog will make him scream and run. Harold will have a new response because the little dog bit him playfully on the ear this morning. It is the same little dog no doubt, but it is not the same to Harold. Harold has acquired a learned response to it. He has met an experience somewhat contradictory to and discontinuous with the response that nature first prepared for it. It is an experience suddenly made complicated. The vaguely pleasant little woolly bouncing thing is also painful, namely, to his ear, and Harold responds in a manner more in adjustment to the new stimulus. Nature assumes consistency in experience and when a stimulus turns out to be different from expectations the difference in turn will be presumed to be persistent and a conditioned response will rise to meet it. It is typical of all experience. An animal's ability to readjust itself rapidly to the inconsistencies of experience is said to be the measure of its intelligence. By a flexible adjustment and conditioning of responses it can create, as it were, a continuity of behavior in the face of discontinuity and upset in environment. Solving problems is an aspect of vital continuity.

As a means of measuring human performance of this

kind "tests" have been devised and administered to considerable parts of the human race by experts such as Terman, W. S. Monroe, Walter Dill Scott [18] and others; averages have been found of human problem solving power; aptitudes and vocational facilities have been recorded, and a significant effort made to find and to correlate the measurable characteristics of human behavior and to predict its course in any instance. It is a complex and difficult problem and the general grading of mankind will always be as dangerous and imperfect an experiment in the future as it has been in the past, but tests of ability in specific responses are a different matter, and their results in industry and education, in war and in the professions will be of value. They are based tacitly on ''behaviorism,'' and they assume that a man's reaction to a given set of conditions will always be appropriate to the mechanism with which he is equipped.

Differences in structure and in early training, says Watson,[19] will account for all differences in later behavior. Habits are learned even in embryonic life; for the learning process is an aspect of the life process; while inherited behavior, or instinct, is less significant and is dropped by Watson as unnecessary. As a corollary of the way man is put together, he says, and of the material out of which he is made — he must act (until learning has reshaped him) as he does act. Such remarks are very hard on poor Psyche.

At birth the child has love, fear and rage behavior; [20] he sneezes, hiccoughs, feeds, grasps, defecates, urinates, smiles, cries; he has trunk and leg movements, circulation and respiration, erection and other sex organ responses, defensive movements, vocal responses and the Babinski reflex; and on this behavior basis is built up, by the process of conditioning, the huge complexity of his later life. They flow from the source of the stream of human activity; they are unlearned responses, and the entire process of adjustment works in this material.

Emotions from this point of view are visceral reactions,[21] and though overt behavior is a factor in them they are predominately glandular and visceral responses that have not been articulated or put in words. Emotions are a surplus of reaction. They are a margin of potential, as it were, the reserve accumulated over the driving needs of the moment, and they break out sometimes into strange and impracticable paths.[22] To some objects, "charged" with emotions, as the cross or a fraternity pin, the flag or K. K. K., the dim beating of a tom-tom or the nude rhythmics of a chorus girl, there are accessory responses not wholly necessary to the practical needs of efficient action. They are responses for themselves, as it were, without direct use in the adjustment of the organism to the specific situation. They are behavior that runs away from the close utilities of efficient habit and zooms in strangely unnecessary aspirations, loops and excesses. It is emotion. It is spiritual dynamics.

At birth there are three types of emotional reactions. Fear behavior, rage behavior and love behavior have their beginnings then, thinks Watson,[23] and long and meticulous experiment with babies seems to prove it. Two stimuli call unlearned fear from infants: They are loud sounds and loss of support. One stimulus calls out unlearned rage: It is the hampering and obstruction of bodily movement. Four stimuli bring unlearned love: They are stroking, tickling, gentle rocking, patting. These seven stimuli, more or less, are the overt excitants to man's emotional life, and the "conditioning" of them and their responses results in all the complexities of mature emotional behavior. They are mainly visceral types of behavior from the jump and breathlessness of fear and the heart throb of love to the increase in blood sugar of rage.

But our emotions are not simple long. We learn to hate, to love, to fear the multitudes in our environment and much of that behavior is foolish and ill placed. To little Albert, less than a year in age, a white rat was presented. It was a friendly rat and Albert had played

with it for weeks and liked it. This time, however, a loud
noise was made behind his head just as he touched the rat,
and Albert jumped violently, fell forward and buried
his face in the bed. This rat-with-noise experiment was
repeated, and then days later the rat without noise was
put before him. Did little Albert love the friendly rat
as he had loved it once? He did not; he feared it. His
response was changed, and when the rat appeared he
began to cry, he fell over and raised himself on all fours
and crawled rapidly away. Thus, says Watson, are the
complexities of our mature emotional life developed. The
early months of life and the early years are of critical
importance in the temperamental direction of a child.
They should not be left to the caprice and notions of
unskilled maids nor to careless and uneducated parents.
In those months our emotional habits are laid down and
the unverbalized behavior of our lives, which Freud calls
complexes, suppressed desires and the like, finds its first
momentum.

For modern life is caught in meshes and entanglements
and new demands that are too complicated for a simple
unlearned man. "Natural" response alone and the behavior "that God gave us" at birth is not enough for
survival in this new wilderness that we are entering. We
have learned more in the last 150 years, someone has
said, than in all our history preceding, and on learning
and on learned responses will fall increasingly the extra
load of civilization in the future. Strange storms assail
the nervous systems of our people. Hysterics and break-
downs and psychopathic oddities jut through the urbane
surfaces of our life. They indicate a change and complication in our environment, a restlessness and shifting of the
stable things to which man was adjusted, that are fast
and hard to follow. When men take from nature the con-

trol of their environment and administer it themselves, when they seize powers beyond their former grasp, they create their own major problem. It is the problem of cities. It is the dangerous fruit of conquest, for man has conquered the "natural" environment — within his puny limits; and it remains for him to conquer the environment of his own making. He has changed the things without faster than the things within. He has laid burdens on himself that may break his back.

This is Freud's instigation, although he may not know it, to a psychology of inhibition and blockade in urban man, of the "conditioning" and mis-conditioning of natural responses, of civilized life and the burden of society and of man's learned and mis-learned behavior in response thereto. The dream is his technique, and though his method is rather more interpretive than scientific, it has value as a comment on modern mental life and the effect of customs, social pressures and blockades upon it. For convenience' sake, in securing social order the sex stimuli and responses of humankind have been shackled and much put upon. No men and few women behave sexually as nature made them. They are overlaid with inhibitions and diversions and newly learned responses. They are "conditioned" and reconditioned and suppressed, and though the results may make for social order, they are disastrous oftentimes to the individual. These are the facts that underlie a Freudian psychology. With the dream as his instrument and probe he psycho-analyzes these effects in modern life. Christian civilizations have never faced frankly the sex life of mankind, and because of it they may come near to disaster. They have feared its alien smoke and burning, and they have turned away as if it were not there. If Sigmund Freud, a Jew, can force it into Christian statesmanship his service to mankind and to the Christian church will be invaluable.

Man is the greatest of wishers, and with the increasing

schisms between his external conduct and the impulses of his native life, those wishes become more complicated and more pressing. They are an unexpressed rebuttal of outer strictures and conformities, and they find release not always in overt behavior and action but sometimes in dreams, hysterias, "complexes" and the like.

A wish, says Holt,[25] is "a course of action which some mechanism of the body is set to carry out," and a dream is a fulfilment of the wish. This is the Freudian key to all interpretation of dreams. It is his approach to a profound and literary analysis of an urgent human problem. The wish that modern life cannot fulfil — often but not always sexual — finds a dream adjustment. In phantasy and ghosts, and in implicit change in mechanism no doubt, man works out his suppressed desires. A dream, says Freud,[26] is always the fulfilment of a wish.

It follows then that dreams may be interpreted to reveal man's conquered impulse, and though distorted and hidden under odd symbolisms and verbalities they do, in the analyses of Freud, Jung, and Brill and others, reveal it. They reveal vanquished tendencies to action in the increasing complication and conflict of an individual's development. They are a census of dead soldiers and imprisoned wishes that marched out hopefully towards fulfilment and were thrust back out of action by superior forces. Dreams are a substitute, as it were, for overt life.

"One morning," says Freud [27] of one of his colleagues, "sleep was particularly sweet. The woman called into the room: 'Mr. Joe, get up, you must go to the hospital.' Whereupon the sleeper dreamt of a room in the hospital, a bed in which he was lying, and a chart pinned over his head reading: 'Joe H . . . . . cand. med. 22 years old.' He said to himself in the dream: 'If I am already at the hospital, I don't have to go there,' turned over and slept on. He had thus frankly admitted to himself his motive for dreaming." And so it goes: We dream our dreams and in them live in some symbolic form or other the life crowded beyond the frontiers of reality by more impressive interests. They are the lost causes of our minds. They are the reservoirs of what we must forget.[28]

And words are like dreams. They are responses, more or less implicit, to impinging stimuli. They are substitutes for things and short cuts for more overt behaviors. They are learned responses to complicated stimuli that are themselves sometimes the sound or sight of words. Words from the scientific point of view are mechanistic stimuli or responses to which "meaning" as a psychic and immaterial context has no observable relation. Words to the natural scientist are not "word contents"; they are not intrinsic meanings and appreciations; they are links in the human mechanism. They are factors in behavior, and they do very well for him as such without subjective incandescences.

Words, says Watson,[29] are substitutes for objects and situations, and thus begins a promising theory of symbols on a mechanistic basis. For every object there is a verbal substitute to which a man responds much as if it were the thing itself. For all the world there are words, and the word world in a man can be manipulated with facility. It is a muscular affair eventually, built up much as our highly coördinated manual habits are built, and carried on from visual and auditory stimuli, or what not, to the complicated muscular or kinæsthetic stimuli and responses of the larynx, the musculature of the chest and throat and face and the behavior of the viscera. These are physiological vocabularies, and streams of habitual responses in them set to the stimulus of a well known word or other thing are our memories.

And to the scientific purist thinking is but word behavior kept subvocal. Thought, says the behaviorist, is nothing but talking to ourselves, and "muscular habits" learned in overt speech are responsible for implicit or internal speech. [30] To those horrified by this muscularizing of thought it should be made clear that what one thinks about is different from the operation of thinking. Though thinking may well be muscular as the behaviorist insists, the so-called "content" of thinking, whether it be "$2 + 2 = 4$" or beefsteak, is not a matter of muscular behavior. Thinking belongs in the closed system of physical mechanism into which no "psychic" or incorporeal things dare intrude, but things to think about are many and diverse and are limited to no special order of reality.

Whether expressed overtly in speech or behind the walls of outer action in thought words are responses or stimuli, as the case may be, in our behavior mechanism. As stimuli in place of "things" words are the critical discovery in man's civilization, and his ability to manipulate them instead of the objects that they symbolize is a primary economy of life that gives us precedence over all other animals. Long trains of "thought" may be carried on implicitly that, worked out in overt action, would take a hundred years, and conclusions may be made in a few seconds that otherwise would take months of painful action and physical experiment.

Words are a condensation of the trial and error method used by Nature through all her evolutionary processes. They are a way of making trials without the expenditure of too much energy and time. They are a way of testing errors in possible behavior without too hard a penalty. Words are a way of making rapid, tentative adjustments to a new environmental situation and of fixing on the right adjustment without preliminary waste and disaster. Through words we profit by experience and retain in "memory" long lines of tacit responses that will save a repetition when the stimulus comes again. Thought is an inexpensive way of making experiments. It makes a working model of a possible adjustment to the environ-

ment, and if the model does not work it can be discarded
for a better one without disastrous waste.

Man's so-called intelligence is an epitome of natural
evolutionary method. Trial and error, selection, and survival of the fittest, both physically and logically, underlie
what we term intellectual behavior. Thought wastes
less, perhaps; it is faster; it is quieter; it may be more
efficient, but it remains the same in principle as the
evolutionary process of change and development and
selection through all the material world. That world,
indeed, acts (metaphorically) rather like a great intelligence; it behaves (metaphorically) not as if it were guided
by a "mind" but as if it were a "mind." For a man's
thinking, which we appreciate somewhat as a whole,
would look a good deal like the natural processes of
change and development and evolution if we could observe it in its parts. If nature were observable as a whole
or if thought were observable in its parts the two might
not be dissimilar.

For thought processes are not different in principle
from the other mechanisms of the world, and their activating factors are no less material and naturalistic.
"Meaning," "ideas," "thought content" are not incorporeal somethings located somehow in our thinking
operations with power to push them one way or another.
They have no location either in time or space and they
have no power to enter the natural system on which
science, by hypothesis, is based.[31] They are, simply, the
things that thought and words refer to, and the validity
of their relationships lies in their own respective fields
of discourse and not in any way on man's process of
thinking about them. The tendency to locate the "meaning of an idea" or the "content of a thought" as if it
were somewhere within or near our physical mechanism,
the predisposition to treat the "things in our minds" as
if they were bodyless beings that interact as individuals
somehow in our physical behavior, the habit of separating

"thoughts" from the things that they refer to, on the one hand, and from the mechanism of our behavior, on the other, and leaving them like a slice of ham dropped out of a sandwich, is myth making and most unscientific. Words, images, thoughts and the like are references to things of various kinds both material and immaterial. They are substitutes for a more explicit and outright action towards those things. They are, scientifically, ways of behaving, and they involve in no causal way the things themselves. They are, regardless of their so-called "content," an organic part of man's behavior process.

Broadly speaking, actions are designated intelligent, says Angell,[32] "when they disclose the ability to adjust quickly and successfully to new and variable conditions." They are liberal responses governed by the call of the present as well as by the hands and habits of the past, and their flexible adjustment to change and movement in surrounding things makes possible a living continuity across a relatively discontinuous environment. Intelligent behavior is a natural selection from numerous alternatives; it is one response from a sheaf of variables, and if it be the arrow best suited to that shot, the large number in the sheaf of alternate responses should be given credit for it. For ways to increase the variables of living things without destroying their continuity have been of critical importance through all their evolution. Ease of adjustment and the conquest of new environments is made possible by these methods — such as sex and individuality [33] and diverse chromosomes — and a life process, that without these factors making towards variation would be fixed in scope and limited in environment if not wholly extinct, can go on with them from field to field, like a grass fire, and appropriate the universe. And intelligence, like sex and individuality, is a way of increasing the variables of the life process without too much waste. They are tacit variables, as it were, without risk of too much disaster. They are tried out, not in fully expressed action but implicitly, and when one of them fails there is only forgetting; there is only a suppressed desire or a newly learned response. There is not an individual's destruction. For the intelligent individual, learning is a substitute for death.

Our so-called intelligence is a more efficient form of a wholly natural method that has been in operation, distributively, through all the course of the life process. And intelligent behavior is but a neater way of producing many variations from which the best can be naturally selected. It is more flexible. It is less a result of specialization and meticulous fitness to one environment than a generalized power to adapt itself with many variables to various environments. It is more general than specific, and its coördinations with the hand and other generalized structures of the human body are uniquely successful in the struggle for life. The habit mechanisms derived from past experience are its reservoirs, and the factor that determines the best response from alternative adjustments to a stimulus is no doubt the stimulus itself. With conditioned stimuli and learned responses, intelligent behavior is implicitly more complex than simple tropism and the like, but it is not different necessarily in principle.

The frog, it is said, is the pioneer in intellect. He can learn a thing or two, and by tremendous trying he can profit somewhat by experience. Beyond him, or "lower" in the scale of evolution such achievement is impossible, while above him, up to man, rather greater cleverness is found. The frog can modify his reactions to suit a need; [34] he can solve a problem in his simple, unaffected way; he can learn, and though the process of teaching him has an ungainly length, he eventually can choose the best of two paths in order to find food.

No memorials to the frog who discovered intellect have been erected. He deserves no thanks, for our sorrows would be less no doubt, had the variables and alternatives of intelligent behavior never been created. As the founder of that system the frog is more or less the parent of our joys and tribulations, for without alternatives of action and with no sense of choice, happiness and sorrow would very likely never be. Set like a machine to one recurrent line of action, an "unintelligent" creature is probably neither glad nor sorrowful. He merely goes along.

But the frog after all is only by convenience called the ultimate material for pedagogic effort. All life is subject to the learning process in some form. The responses of all living things are modified in some measure by the needs of the situation, and it is only a question of degree to call the frog more cultured than his "lower" relatives. He is no more a founder than a primeval cell is founder. For the adaptation of responses to the environment is essential to the continuity of the life process of the world. It is in the nature of living. It is the penetration of life stuff into all the crannies of the earth. It is the continuity of life overriding the breaks and roughness and discontinuity of the environment. It is the flame with increasing momentum consuming many fuels. To establish that continuity and to organize the fragments of environment into a relevancy and value in the life process is the primary *élan* of life, the reason for society, and the problem of intelligence.

If either "everything or nothing that men came upon in their primitive day-dream had been continuous in its own category and traceable through the labyrinth of the world, no mind and no self-consciousness need ever have appeared at all," says Santayana.[35] "The world might have been as magical as it pleased; it would have remained single, one budding sequence of forms with no transmissible substance beneath them. These forms might have had properties we now call physical and at the same time qualities we now call mental or emotional; there is nothing originally incongruous in such a mixture, chaotic and perverse as it may seem from the vantage-ground of subsequent distinctions. Existence might as easily have had any other form whatsoever as the one we discover it to have in fact. And primitive men, not having read Descartes, and not having even distinguished their waking from their dreaming life nor their passions from their environment, might well stand in the presence of facts that seem to us full of inward incongruity and contradiction; indeed, it is only because original data were of that chaotic sort that we call ourselves intelligent for having disentangled them and assigned them to distinct sequences and alternative spheres."

Towards a wholeness of life intelligent behavior is always driving, and the whole behavior of the whole man is his life's only natural unit.

To some recent Germans must be given credit for abandoning the atomism of pater Wundt and his descendants and finding once more in the wholeness of a living situation the prime unit of psychology. Theirs is the school of the Gestalt or Configuration and, though not behaviorists, they ask, "Who has experienced one sensation; who has reacted to one isolated stimulus?" And their answer is, "No one." To divide fundamental data where no natural division is, say these Gestalters, is to rob phenomena of all real character.[36] The structure of an operation involving thought is its own, and its configuration may be different from what an analysis and subdivision of the materials involved would give. It is a wholeness that may include several diverse elements, but its wholeness is not accretionary; it is organic; it is plastic.

For of psychology — and in other sciences to an extent not usually realized — Berthelot's attack on atomism holds its own. "The principal reproach that can be made against the atomic theory as against all analogous conceptions," says Berthelot as quoted by Humphrey,[37] "is that they tend to concern themselves with numerical relations between elements and not with bodies themselves, thus reducing all reactions to a unified and necessarily imaginary type. In short, they strip phenomena of all real character, and substitute for true explanation a series of symbolical considerations which are pleasing to the mind because it manipulates them with more facility than it does realities in the true sense of the term."

In support of this the configurationists in psychology, ask, "How can we see an object as a whole; how can we behave as a whole, if that wholeness is only the sum of discrete parts?" The answer of Koffka,[39] Köhler and others of the group is to deny the isolation and discreteness of the elements of a living situation.[38] A single sensation, a single stimulus, even a single response is illusory. The "behavior of the whole man," as Watson has called it, is capable of theoretical as well as experimental elaboration.

But human behavior is not wholly clear even in terms of the whole man. There are still larger cycles of behavior. The life of a family is one life. The life of society is one life. They are hardly the sum of the actions of individuals. They have a structural wholeness of their own. If individual behavior cannot be stated in terms of isolated sensation or stimulus, it is also true that the behavior of society cannot be stated fairly in terms of individual behavior. Though distributed among many individuals and species life after all is one process. A forest fire is one fire though many separate trees are burning. Like the wholeness of life it has a sweep and courage of its own.

Society has a behavior. It is a wholeness that has been too little studied. It is a unit of human living that is too often observed only through the peep holes of individual

actions. Historical topography and the march of peoples
are aspects of it, but there are others. What is the countenance of human living? Who can draw its picture?

It is a field where the hypothesis of science becomes
rather less useful and the hypotheses of value rather more.
It is a field where matter, mechanism and descriptive
fact seem to be less applicable as coördinating concepts,
and value, end and accent seem to be more. A change in
point of view and the precedence of another order usually
follow the transition from studies in matter to studies in
social policy. The world of natural fact is one way of looking at things. It is valid but not ultimate. The world of use
is another way of looking at things. Though obviously
not ultimate, it is no less valid than the world of fact.

Six problems have been discussed here in a twisting
course that has followed more the upheaved contours of
the subject than the fair levels of pedagogic clarity. They
are: the bifurcation of psychology and the place of behavior; the nerves and the coördinating systems; the
wholeness of behavior and the abolition of psychic
parallels; the nature of stimulus, response, learning, emotion; Freud; the nature of words, thinking, intelligence.
The amphibious nature of psychology has caused it much
confusion, and the croaks that it gives forth are not always enlightening. The more conservative psychologists
from Titchener to Delton Howard have got it by the hind
legs and are trying to pull it back into the water of in-
trospectionist philosophy. The more radical psychologists
such as Watson and the behaviorists have it by the jaw
and, left to themselves, will pull it up on the dry land of
purely scientific method.

Man, says Dorsey,[40] is "something happening all of the
time, a going concern." He is best expressed dynamically, and that after all is about what behavior means.

BOOK TWO

Studies in Social Policy

The World of Human Conduct and Practical Action

Man is a measure of all things.
— PROTAGORAS

CHAPTER SIX

Early Man

IN SEVERAL ways man is unique on this earth. He invented hair dye for example, and he scrubs his teeth. He discovered doughnuts and the derby hat, and he beautifies himself by cutting off his whiskers. No other animal does these things. The elephant, wise as he is, has never brushed his teeth. The monkey and the horse, products of a thousand evolutions, cannot make doughnuts or dye their hair; the goat cannot cut off his whiskers. These actions are unique in man, and they equip his high dignity among created things with an unassailable prestige.

And in ways perhaps more important, man is unique. He has made the conquest of the word; he builds fires; he uses tools; he enslaves animals and plants; he captures raw energies from the hills and streams; and in other ways learns the art of substitution and the replacement of his own effort by others that do just as well. He is more adaptable than other animals and more capable of learning. He changes more than other animals; his life is more a flux and movement across time. Beside the ponderous simplicity of their experience his is wild and complicated.

Even the dumbest of men is a sparkling conversationalist beside the elephant who can only grunt and trumpet, and the social solidarity of the canine world established by barks and smells and much running about is as nothing compared with the simplest of man's communities. The earliest man was a more social being than any of the beasts, and his successors have built a social structure that is unusual, to say the least, in this world of ours. It is unique, and he has raised up institutions, like articulate buttresses, to support it. In this world there is nothing just like man and his works. There is nothing just like a safety razor or Bishop Manning or any other human being. There is nothing just like the Democratic party or Sloan's liniment. They are man's contribution to this universe, and they are unique.

But man is our kind of animal, and in that lies his main distinction. He is ourselves, the nucleus of our interests, and being ourselves is very different from being something else. He bears a light, called our personal point of view, that illuminates the world and casts the shadows all in one direction. In him we find a local interest that outweighs all the claims of other things. There is warmth in it and an intimacy with being that nothing else (for us) possesses. Because he is ourselves, whatever that may mean, he is unique. We see things in his terms and we build up relativities and values with his welfare as the point of reference. There we abandon science and its categories to some extent and raise a new world of human values. We establish new anthropomorphisms, and we see things colored good or bad and their realities accepted or denied according to their bearing on his life.

Man stakes out a world around his central self and accepts its bearings on him as fundamental. He could not well do otherwise. He finds all things soaked in the human idiom and founds therein his sundry systems of value. Though science may come at last squeezed dry of human prejudice, more or less, the worlds of value are the more antique and in some ways the more natural. Man began with prejudice as his only pathway to the world and he retains it still as a prime desideratum. It is an organizing factor of his world. It is the monism of the ego.

At the core of that world is the human society and the individual. They are jointly the point of reference, and though they are distinguished from each other for reasons of convenience they are more accurately one in most important ways. For if society is composed of individuals it is also true that the nature of the individual is in great part social. They are but different aspects of the same human reality that resides deep in the heart of any world that human beings build. Biologically the origins of society and of the individual are closely related. Speech, for example, sex, religion and play in man are set to a social theme. Apart from society, the individual as we know him could not well be. And "it goes without saying," says Goldenweiser,[1] "that the individual as a discrete unit, as a self-conscious individual juxtaposed to society, is a later product of social evolution."

In the beginning man created his own heaven and earth. He saw what he had eyes to see; he used what he had hands to handle; and reality to him was what his faculties could appreciate. It was a simple world that he entered, not altogether lovely, and it was swollen with his seekings, colored with his emotions and subject to every shift and growth of his facility for experience. It was a world, externally, rather late in evolutionary development. The reptiles had long since declined and mammals and the modern plants were dominant. The anthropoid apes had come and found life, presumably, like a green country ready for tillage. There was an opening, as the business man would say, for a new species; there was room at the top, and man came to take it.

That was half a million years or so ago. The age of ice was gathering momentum for its first attack. The Tertiary, according to geologists, was about over, and the Quaternary period, which includes today, was moving down with its squadrons of great glaciers upon the northern temperate zones. From Britain clear to Java the eastern land mass of the world was more or less continuous. In North America the true horse had come to its first home and in Asia the true elephants and cattle had found nativity.[2] And in the forests and flood plains of southern Asia an apelike creature with long arms and

a bulging belly stood on his hind legs, gave his chest a
mighty thump, and said, "Well, Leonora, let's found the
human race."

In Java the souvenirs of early man are few but most
important, for it is there beside the tropic Bengawan that
man's earliest relics were uncovered. A skull top, two
molar teeth and a left thigh bone are all this "Trinil"
race has left for modern observation but they are enough
to tell the story of a shambling, ape-like man among the
shadows of an ancient forest. His thigh bone says that
he walked erect and was five feet seven inches tall. The
teeth say that he was well beyond the ape but not yet
man. The skull cap says a multitude of things, for a man's
bones are his first biographers, and his skull bones are
always talkative. Bones, flints, bronzes, gold, silver,
pottery and architectural works [3] tell stories of the prehistoric men. But of all these the Java man had only his
bones to leave for record.

His skull is larger than an ape's but smaller than a
man's. Its 900 in cubic centimetre content compares
favorably with the 600 of the highest simians but not so
well with the 930 of the lowest kind of man.[4] His areas
of touch, taste, and vision were well developed; his
memories of actions and of feelings no doubt were good,
but his prefrontal areas were weak. His profit from experience and his memory of the consequences of experience were none too great. He was a low-brow and
compared with modern man unintelligent.

Over his eyes were bony ridges, and the skull above his
ears was low. His nose was flat and his jaw lurched forward from his face in an ungainly muzzle without a
chin. Unlovely as he was by modern standards [5] he
found life somewhat sweet, for his race no doubt endured
a hundred thousand years or so. He was no quitter.

Back in the middle Tertiary, the Oligocene to be exact,
his forefathers (and ours) probably descended from the
trees. They had learned there, a million years or more

ago, to use instead of smell their powers of vision, touch and hearing. They became accustomed to erect postures and to grasping things with hand or foot. Quickness and agility in diversified responses were necessary and head movements, eye movements, hand movements, and their corresponding nervous centers were delicately adjusted and developed. Our prehistoric life in trees — it is of course conjectural — was a fit preparatory school for civilization. And small boys now will recapitulate if given chance.

For man came back to earth able to stand erect and with his hands released from walking duty. His brain was growing. His thumb, unlike the ape's, could oppose all four fingers. And he had some instruments for speech. These four distinctive human powers coincidentally developed, says Osborn,[6] are the secret of prehuman evolution from the tree life of middle Tertiary, or Cenozoic, period to the Java man.

Neighbors to this Java man with a name, Pithecanthropus erectus, that any Doctor of Philosophy might envy, were the elephants and boars,[7] tapirs, hippopotami, buffalo, rhinoceroses, deer, felines, hyenas, porcupines and macaques; but for all his savage need of tools and weapons, fire and protection, it is probable that he possessed none but those that nature gave him. Rude flints, picked up and dropped again may have served him in emergency, but they were few. He was toolless, fireless, unclothed and shaggy. Of property he knew nothing except the right, perhaps, to carrion left from a fiercer kill; and of shelters he had small choice against the sharper teeth of other animals. For ages man must have been a skulker, ungainly, weak, without the power of the gorilla, the agility of the chimpanzee, and the wit of modern man. He was no conqueror then. He lived by hanging on.

For with generalized abilities man had not the neat and ready made adjustments to a routine situation that the great cats, for example, had. Without tools man could only stumble immaturely like a child across his field of living and the wonder is not that he did not conquer when he came down from the trees but that he lived at all. Presumably he did not leave the forest regions or the rocks [8] before he had found tools.

The ice age, it may be, was man's opportunity and test. It thrust now its giant plows of ice into the northern soil and drove its furrows southward. It turned the top of continents and shattered life routines far beyond its southern limits. Four times or more the ice came down over northern Europe and America and as many times retreated; and four times the waves of life ebbed and flowed and eddied distantly along its borders. The musk-ox was in London, the reindeer in North Germany; the woolly mammoth wandered over France. There was tundra and the arctic steppe where Bordeaux is; and the Greenland that grew magnolias and figs in Tertiary times and was perhaps the fatherland of mammals [9] became a frozen silence. One after another the ice thrusts came in intervals of a hundred thousand years or so, and between them warmer, interglacial climates opened the gates to resurging life.[10] They bent and warped the environment in slow distortions, and man with his generalized abilities, his capacity for learning, his facility for living in a flux and diversity of conditions could take advantage of the change. He is the child of the ice age, and his development has followed the shift and upsetting of the old routines. In a world of new problems he was fitted to flourish.

Along the way to modern times a few old fragments lie. A shattered bit of bone is all that there is left to tell the story of a race of men. A flint or so bearing the rude workmanship of a prehistoric hand tells of a people's labor. Near Heidelberg a massive jaw was found,[11] human as to teeth but with an apelike chinlessness and forward thrust, and here we read the history of another

race somewhat more developed than the man of Java.
In Piltdown, England,[12] some fragments of a skull and
jaw, a tooth and nasal bones were found to indicate
another race of man still a step higher. In Africa at
Taungs and Broken Hill other finds have rocked the
scientific world with controversy. They straggle in one
by one in shattered bits, mere refugees from the floods of
time. They were men once, low skulled and rather
dumb, long armed and dirty, but they, or their cousins,
are our fathers.

The eastern hemisphere was the seat of earliest man,
no doubt, and it is more than likely, in spite of arguments
for plural origin,[13] that he descended from a single line of
anthropoid stock. Somewhere northeast, east, southeast
or south of the Mediterranean man found the long and
dangerous trail that leads to modern civilization. It was
a mere thread then coiling through the forest. Only the
blaze marks at long intervals — a word stumbling
from ungainly lips, a ragged flint picked up, a club,
a firmer step, a new trick with the hands — had
saved it from relentless overgrowth. The Java man
walked 500,000 years ago upon that trail with neither
club nor tool to aid him.[14] The Piltdown man was shuffling
down the trail 100,000 years ago, with rough flints of the
type called Chellean or pre-Chellean in his hands; for the
ice had come and gone and the sun of the third interglacial period was sweetening the earth. Then came the
ice again and a new man, called the Neanderthal, appeared. That was 50,000 years ago, and we know him
fairly well.

Homo Neanderthalensis is a graceful name more like
the sound of Algernon or Percy than the black browed
men of glacial times who bear it. For though they used
a toothpick and suffered from pyorrhea[15] they were not

coddled darlings who bore the desert cold and wastes of
Europe for twenty thousand years or more. Their relics
and their bones are scattered over Europe. Their flints
are there, made into rough tools for killing. And their
scrapers and their drillers and other tools of stone lie in
the caves where they left them. They learned the use of
fire. They wore skins.[16] They liked fresh meat, perhaps
of their own species. And they were fighters, for the age
of skulks and scavengers was passing. Man fought now
for his shelters and his food, and a giant cave bear's
skull in Europe carries to this day a hand ax buried in its
temple as a souvenir of war to death between the race of
bears there and of men.[17] Though this bear lived, for the
bone around the ax had overgrown, his race — unless it be
the grizzly — did not survive that prehistoric struggle.

Thus comes cave man onto the testing ground of
Europe to make his bid for life, to struggle for a while
and finally to disappear without descendants. He was
built for the dumb threat of cold and barren tundras,
and when those hardships passed a handsomer race came
and destroyed him with genial power. He was a shambling
figure, on slow, flat feet, with thigh curved and a knee
never quite straightened.[18] He was a squatty man, some
five feet four in height, with chest and shoulders power-
fully developed, and with huge hands and a thumb that
was awkward. His head lurched forward on a spine lacking the final curve of neck in modern man's proud carriage.
He was chinless but his jaw was large and with a forward
thrust. His face was uncompressed and open like an
ape's; his nose was rather prominent. Over his eyes the
heavy ridges met; his skull was low and long from front
to rear and its size was 1400 as compared with maxima
in modern man of 2000 cubic centimetres. He was no
morning star; he was not rosy fingered Eos telling of the
dawn. He was the dusk and fog of morning and the vital
stench of earth.

His culture, called Mousterian, was arid. His stone

tools were few and made for hunting or the fireside. He lived in grottoes whence he drove the bear and the yellow skinned hyena, and in bad weather he stayed there eating odds and ends of meat stored in the corners. Fire he had, glorious as always, that must have been a precious thing to him, carefully preserved. It was woman's work, no doubt, along with making clothes of skins, preparing meals and nursing children. It was a division of labor, and while man chased the beasts and killed and loafed, women founded industry and preserved the fires of the home. It is a male and female motive destined to persist.

The cave man had few sentiments. He was red blooded; and he threw the old folks and the dead out to the hyenas, if they weren't worth eating. Later his habits were ameliorated somewhat, but they were never gentlemanly. His talk was crude at best. His jaw bone had no button at the end for fastening labial muscles. He was burdened only with raw life, for church and state and taxes had not come. It was direct life, hardly conscious of itself, and though in flints, or women or pieces of good meat he probably had a sense of property, the institutional developments among Neanderthals were not complicated.

His colleagues and competitors in Europe forty thousand years ago were the woolly mammoth and rhinoceros, the bears, reindeer, the arctic musk-ox, lemming, fox, the arctic hare, horse, the eastern bison, cattle, even the cave lion, hyena, leopard, and he more than held his own. He hunted them with spears and "throwing stones" and the stone ax. He may have used the pitfall, but his way of killing mighty beasts is still something of a mystery.[19] It was an age when man finally won security for himself against the animal. It was the turning of the worm. With three inseparable factors, "the hand, a brain that is fairly well balanced on a spinal column normally approximately erect, and stereoscopic vision," says MacCurdy,[20] "a culture that we may call human would as surely follow as does the day the night." Tools without a hand are hard to imagine, and a hand without tools is hardly less so. That hand with tools made man master of the beasts in battle.

Man has incorporated various materials into his life system as no other animal has done, and his physical equipment is well adapted to the purpose. The cat's paw is fitted with a scraper and a scratcher by heredity, but a man's hand is incomplete without a tool of stone or steel or other outside thing used to his need. A beaver carries his paddle or his trowel upon his body, but man takes a shovel, which fortunately is not a part of his anatomy. The fish wags his tail and travels through the water, but man can use a screw propeller to be discarded when he pleases. If man were forced to carry all his in-instruments as part of his anatomy he would be as complicated as a sixteen bladed jackknife and even less efficient. But he has a better method. The tool — and corresponding use or value in external things — is the theme of human evolution. With a "general purpose" hand and brain man extends the practical organization of his life beyond his own physique to other things. Tools he used as long ago, perhaps, as 125,000 years. He used tools, and later organized societies of men, beasts and machines. It is the vital imperialism. He assimilates the energies of the environment to his own uses.

With tools man makes minute specializations without the burden of new and complicated anatomical appendages. He divides his labor. He distributes energies in new and more effective patterns. With tools and hands and brain and words he does what nature has always done in evolutionary process, but with a new economy and speed. He finds a new route to natural results.

But the tools of Homo neanderthalensis were few and very crude. His was a world without a pot or pan or any vessel. There was no cloth or basketry. There was no farming or domesticated plants or animals. If he knew that he was mortal he left at least no mortuary implements or relics. There were no fountain pens or six tube radios. A raw "point" or so of flint four inches long, roughly triangular and with two sharpened edges was his proudest implement, his high power rifle, hunting knife and skin scraper all in one, and with that he was 400,000 years beyond the Java man. Time and events condense as the world's process moves on: It took ten times more time to move from the bare hands of earliest man to the Neanderthaler's two edged flint than from that flint to modern guns and factories. Life is an accelerating tempo. It is a change of rate, and what its absolute velocity may be we cannot know. Perhaps there is no absolute velocity of life.

The grotto life of man was not without its satisfactions. He found there in the warmth and twilight of the smoke a new security, and before the hearth there rose a new era in human living. There was reindeer meat to eat while women worked on pelts for clothes, and the smell of the broiling flesh of the wild horse and of the ox welcomed his new hungers. There were long bones to split for marrow and there were warm spots on the floor where sleep was good.

Some dominant male controlled the little grotto group, and the women no doubt were his.[21] Children were there and perhaps a skulking dog or two, and young men were tolerated to help the hunt only so long as they were harmless. There was a fight then and low slung, shaggy men swung hugely with their clubs, and breathed and grunted, and wrestled with their great arms. For it was a hearth society — some say the tribe and some, the family started first — and what one hearth would accommodate was enough. It was a social group compressed there by outer danger, but cohesive factors were not lacking in sex instinct and in domestic blisses such as broiled horse steak, warm pelts, fire and a sheltered sleep. Life ranged from hunt to hearth day after day and there was no great spread of interests.

That the cave life of the Neanderthalers, however, was wholly unprogressive is hardly true. They had no civic opera or Kiwanis clubs, but they painted their skins, perhaps, by way of ornament. They had no grey Westminsters or Roseland cemeteries, but they may have buried their dead at times.[22] Their clothes were fashionably one piece things made of one pelt, and their love affairs entailed less fighting, no doubt, than those of their predecessors. There are faint signs of social system, of tribes, families, clans [23] and a fireside code of conduct.

Three primary hungers in mankind found some satisfaction in the cave smoke and the lounging by the primeval hearth. Hunger for food, hunger for sex and the desire for shelter here met some crude measure of institutionalized response and the hearthside group that was family, city, tribe and state in one was no doubt the primary ancestor of all our social forms. Around fires society has developed. Ours is an igneous civilization, scented with smoke and burning.

But the last great ice was leaving and with the muskox and the lemming and some other ice age mammals went the race of Neanderthal forever from Europe. That was some 25,000 years ago and the squatty, shambling men with heavy brows and ungainly heads, who had fought through 20,000 years of Europe's cold and hardness, plodded on down to the continent of death. For Europe was sweetening. The sun was rather warmer. The forests were returning slowly and the kind warmth of the post-glacial periods approached. It became a pleasanter place in Europe and a tall people, lovers of beauty and pleasantness, came to take it.

Before these Cro-Magnons the race of Neanderthal melted away like the grime of ice and dust after a winter. They disappeared abruptly, and except perhaps for some morainal remnants of them and detritus along the Danube, only their bones and flints remain.[23] Handsomer men came in, tall and commanding, with bow and ar-

row, it may be, already in their hands, and no doubt
exterminated the Neanderthals. At any rate, the ice
age man is gone. His species is extinct. *Homo sapiens*
henceforward has the earth.

From Asia's breeding place of man came a new race
and species into Europe. It sifted through Phoenicia and
across Tunis and Morocco into Spain. It crossed the
Bosphorus perhaps and thrust a northern branch over the
Balkan hills and Italy into southern France [24] or along
the Danube and Rhine basins. It was a race of modern
type irrupting with some suddenness into the raw country
of the Neanderthals, and it dispossessed the old inhabi-
tants of their stations across Europe, and exterminated
the antique race, it would seem, with suave ferocity.
They were a tall and powerful stock with great brains and
subtle hands and a wild love of beauty, and they mated
not at all, from all evidence at hand, with the conquered
race. They killed them; and of that hard bitten, low
skulled, squatty race that had withstood there the last
thrust of the great ice, not a living trace remains.

It was a new people bringing their own culture, and
an outline of the ages shows no race their betters. They
are the characteristic stock of the upper Paleolithic (or
old stone) [25] as the Neanderthalers were characteristic of
the middle Paleolithic age.[26] Beyond the Neanderthalers
are the Neanderthaloid and other races of the lower
Paleolithic age extending deeply into the warm period
preceding the last ice advance. These may include the
Piltdown man. Further back than these and earlier
perhaps than the next to the last glacial period is the
Heidelberg race. And still further, and beyond one or
perhaps two even earlier ice advances, is the Java man.
Four great ice advances conquered Europe, and between
each one or through them lived a race of men. The new

people, called the Cro-Magnons, stood on the broken skulls and bones of many predecessors.

It was a new land, too, cold but not so cold as it once had been, with prairies and some forests and great winds. England was joined to the continent [27] and the Baltic was a lake of fresh water, for Europe had been rising and subsiding more or less in correlation with the ice advances, and a high Europe was now in being. There was still tundra life in Europe, however, and the reindeer, woolly mammoth, woolly rhinoceros, arctic fox, hare and wolverine [28] still lived in the valleys of the fluctuating continent. There was alpine life with the sheep, ibex and ptarmigan as representatives. There was the steppe horse and the kiang and the central Asiatic ass. Forest life was building up its numbers in the giant deer and the red and roe deer, the brown bear and the cave bear, the wildcat, wolf, fox, lynx, otter and weasel. There were bison and wild cattle in the meadows and the Asiatic cave hyena, cave lion and leopard had not yet retired. Old bones of mammoth and rhinoceros still come up in the nets of fishermen over the Dogger Bank that today is eight fathoms below the level of the sea. Europe is half sunk.

A prehistoric renaissance came to Europe after the dark ages of the last great ice, and the new man, the Cro-Magnon, who fought for place among the other fauna of the region, is no mean specimen of animal physique. He was taller than his predecessor the Neanderthaler by eight inches or nine. He averaged beyond six feet in height — three or four inches more than modern man — and six feet four or more was not uncommon.[29] Great men are found from time to time lying in the ancient dust and fill of caves and grottoes and open camps of Spain, France, Syria, North Wales and Italy and their bones are testaments of a race greater in many ways than any that the earth has borne. Their chests were broad and deep and their shoulders powerful. Their arms were short in ratio to their legs; they were fast of foot and their

hips were trim and muscular. A high domed skull with
an average capacity a little greater than that of modern
man tells of a race symmetrically developed both in
brain and brawn. Their heads were long from front to
rear (dolichocephalic) their foreheads high but their
faces broad and strong. Broad face, long skull — called
a disharmonic type — aquiline nose and powerful
but pointed jaw, high cheek bones and with a skull
capacity of 1800 cubic centimetres more or less, no race
today is like them, even if it be their equal.

These were the nomads, fast footed and alert, who
came on Europe 25,000 years ago, and swept away that
continent's previous experiments in humanity. They
were in origin and type quite Asiatic,[30] and though other
races such as the Grimaldi [31] with negroid characters and
the Brünn race and that of Galley Hill left signs of resi-
dence, the great Cro-Magnon dominates them all.

And with him came new implements and new ideas to
Europe, new thoughts and new desires. It was a new
world set to new themes and values. There were new
ways of living and of dying, and down the narrow track
of life that all animals alike must travel came new and
high powered vehicles bearing the old burden with a
novel ease.

Flint was still the mineral closest to man's uses, and
chipping it was his basic industry much as steel making
is today. He had drills and knives of it [32] and five kinds
of skin scrapers, as well as gravers and sharp edged
microliths for carving bone. He had planing tools and
beautifully proportioned lance heads, and the diversity and skill of his flint technique increased as time
went on. He learned to retouch the edges of his tools by
little chippings, and that was one age. He learned to
retouch the edges on both sides with more delicate chippings, and that was another age as much beyond the last
as the steamship is beyond the sailing vessel. It took
man 10,000 years to learn to barb his hooks and spears,

and almost as much again to drill a hole and to make needles with eyes in them. In the so-called upper Paleolithic age to which Cro-Magnon man belongs there are five sub-ages [33] distinguished largely by their flint work. And though bone and ivory gains an increasing place, stone is still the basic stuff for tools.

With bone, too, man was establishing more control over his environment and reaching for new enrichments and complexities in the experience of living. He had bone blades and daggers, harpoons and spear throwers. He had pins and needles, or rather she, as always, had them, and smoothers, anvils, spatulas and bone awls. And he had bone wands and a great staff for ceremonies that he made of reindeer horn. He made new tools and they in turn made him, in mutual stimulations to advancement. The effect is cumulative.

He could build a house. It was of logs no doubt made weather tight with hides, and with that artificial habitation a new motive entered to urge on man's constructive genius. Simpler forms of houses have been built, such as the woven, brushlike windbreaks of the Philippine Negritos, but in Europe human shelters changed from caves and natural camps to houses rather suddenly. At the great open station of Solutré where the bones of 100,000 wild horses lie in a vast magma of prehistoric slaughter,[34] there were houses no doubt of logs and horsehide where the families of the old stone age found warmth and shelter and some measure of domestic privacy. The house even more than the cave is no doubt a source of human privacy. There are profound influences on our institutional development in that privacy of man, and modern moral codes are in no small way its consequence.

But caves were still man's safest refuge, and he used them for tombs, cathedrals and for homes all through the old stone age. Here he brought his horse meat and his fish for women to prepare. Here magic charms were worked and games played perhaps with painted pebbles.

There was time here for play and mimicry, for pigments
to be ground and the slow growth of words. There was
time to think of the strange stillness that came over
men struck by a foreign spear or mangled under the rush
of wild horses; and thinking could be play where a world
of words like new toys could be built and rebuilt in diverse forms.

For those still, silent men they learned to build small
caves or niches in the earth to shelter them until the sleep
was over. They decorated the dead and laid away with
them precious ornaments and tools. They prepared burial
ceremonies for the dead, no doubt, and discovered reverently strange powers and personalities surviving. There
were priests, very likely, with occult powers; and bards
and painters, who could build the absent worlds, had
favored place.

These early men had never made the separations that
we have made today between death and living, between
man and animals, between matter and spirit, between
thought and mechanism, between the ego and external
things. Theirs was collective thinking, it may be, or,
as Lévy-Bruhl [35] suggests, pre-logical. They had not
made abstractions as to fact and value, things and feelings, animate and inanimate, and philosophically no
doubt they were as right as we. But our categories
and analyses, that they neglected, have made a different
world for us. They accepted supernaturalism as naïvely
as a father's love. To them it was all natural.

An animistic faith, says Goldenweiser, [35] is the first
tenet of that world view and in it things have spirits as
well as forms and matter. Magical faith, or power to
influence things and spirits by manipulations, rituals or
incantations is second. Faith in power is third, for spirits
are powers or at least they count as such, and magics
are systems of powers and coercions over this world.
And "the concrete living participation of the individual
in this world of supernaturalism is through the experience

of *the religious thrill*." He lived with God as none of us can live today. He played solemnly with spirits while he worked with flints.

Deep in the caves where light never was these Cro-Magnon men have left a record of their loves and superstitions and that strange *élan* of life that does most splendidly what is not needed. With torches or the lights of shallow lamps of stone they painted there over the ceilings at Altamira, Spain, [36] or deep in Dordogne caves in France, and elsewhere on walls of stone, long marchings of the animals. The hairy mammoth and the wolf, the reindeer and the European bison, the ibex, the horse, [37] the bear and the wild cow, the red deer, fish, the boar, the lion, rhinoceros, and the saiga antelope are there marching through the damp and trickle of the centuries. They are captured there in an abstraction as it were, for the cave artist had learned to separate the form of things from their residual realities and to love that form and take it reverently. It was profoundly there in the heart of the earth, eternal in the darkness, and though the flesh of animals, like the flesh of tribes of men, might wither and be lost the form lived and somehow was one with being. No men before nor since have surpassed their hard cleanliness of line. There is no work of greater spiritual precision.

Five ways were used to capture things in an artistic form. They were, to quote Osborn [38]: Drawing, engraving, and etching with fine flint points on stone, bone, ivory and the limestone walls of caves; sculpture in low or high relief in stone, bone or clay; sculpture in the round in stone, ivory, reindeer and stag horn; painting in line, in monochrome tone, and in polychromes of three or four colors, usually with line engraving or low contour reliefs; and last, conventional ornaments with geometric or realistic lines; but animals are the greater interest.

There are bison modelled in huge urgencies in the clay

of a cave floor. There are red painted bison that stand taut with life on the dark walls. There are mammoths charging, and Diomedan horses carved of bone and ivory that the Greek could not improve. There are antlered herds of reindeer flowing like smoke across the walls of caves, and there are squadrons of horses with noses horizontal as they run. Before farming was invented; before plants or animals had been domesticated; before the work of weaving and of pottery and metals had been undertaken, before money was thought of, there were great artists.

And from ivory and soapstone and talc [39] they carved human figurines sometimes, strange creatures, usually women, with neither arms nor eyes, with egg-like heads and bodies that were bearers mainly of great breasts and reproductive organs, bulging hips or pregnant wombs. They were symbols of fecundity, as MacCurdy says, rather than ideals of woman's beauty, and they no doubt were kept as idols. These ancient carvers abstracted to their art, no doubt, what seemed to them most real in women and let the other perish. They found a form that was more real to them than what their eyes could see and carved it from dark soapstone. They were artists and did what artists always do.

But the great race declined. The men of Cro-Magnon flamed high and sank again, and finally ten thousand years or so ago, died out. Some ill adjustment favored them for death, and death delayed only a few centuries before it took them. Some feature was not right in these artistic people; perhaps it was an instinct, such as sex, out of running with the needs of life; perhaps it was a sedentary life of fishing for which these hunters were not built; perhaps it was climatic burdens of increasing damp-ness [40] and encroachments of the forests on their semi-arid steppes. The race declined in stature and its drive slowed down and stopped. Though a few Cro-Magnons may remain in Dordogne, in Brittany, among the Ber-

bers, on the Canary islands and in Scandinavia or transplanted to America, they are at best a lost and scattered people whose day is long since gone. They have gone into the great speechlessness of a race that could not write. Only bones and flints and the long marching of painted animals on the inner walls of caves are left to tell of them.

There was a change in the human texture of Europe. Art was forgotten. New races filtered in, and strains of humanity that were to mix in the composite structures of today gradually found their places. It was the end of the old stone age, and the new stone age came in. It was the testing of new peoples.

For the Java man died deep in the past of eolithic or preglacial times, and the Heidelberg man died some hundreds of thousands of years thereafter. The Piltdown man finished his course in the lower paleolithic age, and the Neanderthal species of man came to an end still later in that age. [41] The Brünn man, the Grimaldi and others of the narrow heads died in the upper Paleolithic age and the great Cro-Magnons died only in recent times. This was the procession of races down to their extinction. They have left no descendants. They have gone forever from the earth. Of the great modern stocks, the negroid, the mongoloid and the Caucasic, the latter is most interesting to most English speaking peoples. It has three strains, [42] the broad headed Alpines, the narrow headed Mediterraneans, and the narrow headed Teutons.

Into the old stone age man came with nothing but his power to walk on two legs, to use rough stones and perhaps to fashion flints a little. He left the old stone age with fire, clothing and the fine arts. [43] It was 150,000 years or more of growth that constantly accelerated, and on that three-form base the new races of the new stone, or neolithic, age took up the work and play of living.

Compared with the Cro-Magnon those new races differ variously: The head of the Cro-Magnon is long, [44] while the head of the Alpine is round; that of the Mediterranean, long and narrow; and that of the Teuton also long and narrow. The face of the Cro-Magnon is low and broad, while the face of the Alpine is broad; that of the Mediterranean high and narrow; and that of the Teuton also high and narrow. The stature of the Cro-Magnon is tall to medium, while the stature of the Alpine (or Celtic) is medium, stocky; that of the Mediterranean is medium, slender; and that of the Teuton tall. The nose of the Cro-Magnon is narrow, aquiline, while the nose of the Alpine is rather broad, heavy; that of the Mediterranean is rather broad; and that of the Teuton, narrow, acquiline. The Cro-Magnon's skull capacity was 1700 cubic centimetres or more and his height six feet one or two, while modern European stock [45] has a skull less than 1500 cubic centimetres and a height of five feet seven. It was a rather scrubby people that replaced the great Cro-Magnon race.

They came with bows and arrows, one from the south, one from the east, one from the north, and from these mixings of Mediterranean, Alpine and Teutonic stocks the Europe of today, and America as well, is made. Some of them brought domesticated horses. Some knew agriculture. There was pottery and weaving, much fishing and domesticated pigs and dogs, and there were — which names this neolithic period — tools of *polished* stone. [46] They brought with them ten thousand years or so ago lessons from an Asia somewhat more advanced than Europe. They brought new languages and a love for horses, not as meat but animals whose living energy could be utilized.

New fires were burning; new songs were sung over the continent of Europe; it was a warmer, sweeter place with great lakes and fragrant forests, and the men who wandered into that land of many horses were our ancestors. Among them came the Nordic, Aryan stocks who bred their language on the Danube [47] or in south Russia and emigrated thence in slow tides to Persia, northern India, down into Greece and Italy, northward to the plains of Germany and the lakes and estuaries of Scandinavia. Old relics of them are scattered across Europe as if a restless child had tossed them there. They were wanderers, and even before the neolithic age vestiges are found of them, or other Teutonic forbears, at Maglemose in Denmark. [48] They were lake dwellers then and lived no doubt on rafts close to the shore.

Later the shellfish eaters raised vast piles called kitchen middens along the Baltic coast,[49] and later still, well immersed now in neolithic time, come lake dwellers of a maturer stage.[50] They built their huts of logs and thatch high on piles and platforms over the mountain lakes of Switzerland or in Germany. And there they kept their flocks of strange Asiatic animals, called sheep and goats and Asiatic cattle during the winter. For that a forage crop was necessary and, it may be, the beginnings of an agriculture. Dogs, pigs, oxen, sheep and goats were kept there for domestic purposes; and elsewhere horses were in use. In Indo-China the chicken, elephant, the peacock, buffalo and zebu were reduced to gentleness. In America the alpaca, guinea pig, llama and turkey were tamed, and in Africa the cat and the ass were made members of man's domestic group.[51] Man has acquired serfs, allies, friends and food stuffs among the animals in return for racial preservation, some shelter and free food.

Plants, too, were captured in neolithic times and organized into the human economic system. There was wheat cultivated, and barley and millet around the villages. Mill stones are found, and a loaf or so of bread ten thousand years old remains to shame some neolithic housewife. There were flax and lentils and peas, and perhaps the parsnip and the carrot. There were poppies

raised for opiate; there were apples and perhaps there
were grapes. Men became herbivorous in part, and they
learned to organize plant production to that end. They
imposed upon nature a new order and utility. They reg-
ulated natural competition or abolished it in favor of a
useful species. Where men had hunted once women now
were cultivating the soil favorable to some selected plant.
They became a selective factor of huge importance in the
environments of certain animals and plants.

It was a woman's age, indeed, of constructive care and
discipline, of thrift and industry, for the wilder days of
hunting, loafing and of art were on the wane. The days of
joyous killing, of violence and sweet singing that suit
man's nature were rather less appropriate than they had
been five thousand years before. The crafts and industries
were hers and the slow taming of the soil that made cities
and civilization a possibility were woman's contribution
to our progress. She was the tender of fire, the dresser
of skins, the cook, the weaver, the potter, the first beast of
burden, the farmer, the nurse, the teacher, the founder
of society, the patron of religion and the arts, the jack-
of-all-trades.[52] The Moki women have fifty ways of
making maize for food, and there is succotash, four
millennia of age, from maize and squash and beans.
Always women are conservators of social solidarity and
good cooking. They are cohesive factors of an
increasingly organic group, and though a price is paid
in male liberty [53] and inventiveness, it is worth the price.
They are centripetal, and without them male centrifugal-
ism would shatter and wreck mankind.

Basketry, weaving, pottery, the taming of animals and
plants, the tilling of the soil are the features of advance
over the old stone age, and all are mainly woman's work.
It was an age when her unique abilities were utilized and
her conception of the universe impressed on human
evolution, and though still man's servant she was dominant. It was an age of mammalian nourishment and

rather less of killing, and it is no accident that some human beings learned to milk their cows and goats and to feed oddly on dairy goods in Neolithic times.

The world over, this is true, for neolithic times were not limited to Europe. It is a necessary stage perhaps in human progress and in some parts of the earth it arrived early, in some parts late. Some of Asia reached it first and passed on. Then came Europe lagging perhaps three thousand years. Most of the savage tribes today are neolithic, for they, as someone says, are our contemporary ancestors. Most of the Indians of North and South America, with exceptions in Mexico and Peru, were neolithic when Columbus came, and it is doubtful if there was another race preceding the invasion through Alaska of those neolithic mongoloids. Africa has its neolithic cultures; south Asia and the great isles of the Pacific foster them.

For neolithism is a point of view; it is a system of responses to this world; and the polished pole axes of stone, the flint daggers done with a fine hand, the domestic plants and animals, the working women, the huge fights and wanderings and the tribal restlessness are but details of it irregularly exposed in time. Man had a different outlook. To him it was a different world from ours.

It was different, says Franz Boas,[54] because he had a way of putting things together that to us seems heterogeneous. He classified experience in ways that modern men do not accept. He was a learning animal like modern man, but his schedule of traditions was far different. He was intelligent and rational but his outlook on the world, like ours today,[55] was an association of phenomena and a synthesis that was on the whole unreasoned. The pattern of his world was based on lost or long forgotten factors, and that pattern was not like ours.

To us the heavens and the weather and the streams are all inanimate, but to early man they are alive. To us the attributes of objects are parts of the thing in question, but to him health is a separate thing from what is healthy; disease may be removed like a bullet from the flesh; hunger, exhaustion, even life itself, are objects separable from the body. And the luminosity of the sun is donned or laid aside like a gold brocaded robe.

Most outer things, especially those that move, are included in his living group, and blood relationship in some degree establishes an identity to be preserved against incestuous violation. Thus arise exogamy and clans, gentes, and the like; tribes may start here and nations, around the ritual of a sex impulse.

We have built up in some measure a sum of knowledge by logical interpretation, but early man had no such *Weltanschauung*. To him each new perception came in a smoke of uncritical tradition, of superstitions and taboos that differ in intensity and in kind from those of modern life; and the result was a different world. For "the difference in the mode of thought of primitive man and that of civilized man," says Boas,[56] "seems to consist largely in the difference of character of the traditional material with which the new perception associates itself."

When we realize, says Boas, "that neither among civilized men nor among primitive men the average individual carries to completion the attempt at causal explanation of phenomena, but carries it only so far as to amalgamate it with other previously known facts, we recognize that the result of the whole process depends entirely upon the character of the traditional material. Herein lies the immense importance of folk-lore in determining the mode of thought. Herein lies particularly the enormous influence of current philosophic opinion upon the masses of the people, and herein lies the influence of the dominant scientific theory upon the character of scientific work."

It would be vain, he says, "to try to understand the

development of modern science without an intelligent understanding of modern philosophy; it would be vain to try to understand the history of medieval science without a knowledge of medieval theology; and so it is vain to try to understand primitive science without an intelligent knowledge of primitive mythology. Mythology, theology, and philosophy are different terms for the same influences which shape the current of human thought, and which determine the character of the attempts of man to explain the phenomena of nature.''

But modern man can criticize tradition, where the child and primitive are bound by their conventions. They will put together — sometimes rightly, sometimes not — things that seem heterogeneous to us, and science and religion, music and the dance and poetry, myth and history, fashion and ethics are for them inseparable. They build taboos from chance associations of actions and ideas that to us seem of no consequence; and in their art, symbols abound. There is a fusion and primeval synthesis of things that we have learned to analyze. There is a beauty and a mysticism, but it has risks to modern human conduct. It controls man's life in odd dogmatic ways. An implacable conservatism controlled man's early years.

In this mental magma society arose like bubbles slowly frozen in the flux and fusion of primitive ideas; and institutions that survive today first took their form and crystalline arrangement. There were small villages grouped for protection, and there were family homesteads made of staves.[57] A house was often twelve by fifteen feet or so built of upright staves and strengthened by a weft of withes. It was plastered out and in, and a piazza was across one end. There was a hearth within, five or six feet long, built in the middle of the floor. A sleeping platform across one end was made of leveled earth, and a refuse pit was dug in a distant corner of the house. In plastered baskets such as these, in pots as it were, smoke-filled and gloomy, the system that we call organized society became articulate. It was largely woman's brewing.

Here she fashioned clothes and formulated a routine of home that lasts in some measure down to today. Here a woman, man and children lived together in a prime unit of all society, called the family. Here modesties developed and prerogatives, and the naïve divisions of their labor were laid down. It was a house that was at once a home, a place of business, a factory and a seat of government, and the mark of that house remains on all the human interests that developed from it. The textile trades and London tailoring no doubt started here. Linen and wool were made up into fabrics. A shirt was worn by women, without sleeves, and coming to the knees or lower.[58] Over it a heavy apron hung in front, and sometimes one behind. Skirts came next, made by sewing up the edges of the aprons. For a man there was a shirt made a little tighter, and this, except the breech cloth, was often his sole garment. Over the shirt, however, he sometimes wore a robe, or toga, hung from the shoulders. Shoes he had more often than the women because he travelled more. Clothes and society, as Carlyle has greatly said, have an intimate relation to each other.

For society but elaborates the relations of mankind to man and nature. It concatenates some diverse human functions. It is a matrix and a contiguity of man's space and time and organism and his blithe urgencies and instincts. For the factors in his early life that were used for social organization, says Goldenweiser [59] are four: space or locality, blood relationship, sex, and time or generation; and the social units based on these "all perform multifarious functions in society." On these four principles rest divisions of society, and the sum total of their social functions is their status in regard to civilization. A social unit is what it does.

On the territory held by a human aggregation are

based the local groups and villages, towns, tribal terri-
tories and states. On the organic relation between men is
based the tie of children to their parents in a family, the
maternal family and loose groups of blood "relatives,"
the clan and gens (often with fictitious consanguinity)
and other groups. On the sex relation — which is functional and instinctive — is based in part the family and a
host of specializations in government and labor and in
war. On the temporal or age relation are based political
and social classifications such as minors, majors and the
elder statesmen.

Society is an explication of tendencies deep in the
biology of the race, and though it may have new perspec-
tives and values that are profound and real, it must satisfy
the biologic urgencies of living protoplasm if it would
survive. The family, for example, as the transfer point
of civilization,[60] the welded joint of passed on learning and
tradition, has a significance not solely social, psychological and cultural but biological.[60] It is an evolutionary
conception in which society is a great continuum. Society
is one living thing from prehistoric pasts to now.

For civilization, as MacCurdy says,[61] is measured by
the radius of man's requirements, and though the materialism of this is rather rigorous for the whole truth of
society, it is accurate biologically. Man of all living things
makes the most demands on nature. He is the hottest
fire. He consumes more energy and releases more than
any other engine yet produced in nature's workshop.
In neolithic times he was mining deep for fresher flints
and trading them to distant barterers in a primeval
commerce. He was building rafts, dugout boats and
fuller fashioned skiffs for crossing narrow waters. He
was making wheels, the key invention along with fire, of
man's progress in the industry and commerce of this
earth. His mobility increased. He reached farther, and
with wheels and domesticated animals coming in together
man was still more moveable.   They were of enormous

consequence to this restless creature. For with each invention man became for all biologic purposes a new and better species.

His society, too, had a functional evolution; and social units hardly based on space, time, blood and sex relations became important. Industrial groups,[62] the boat makers of Polynesia, flint miners, salt diggers, herdsmen and the specializations of women were functional in these times. There were religious, military and medicinal clubs and juntos. There were groups based on birth, privilege and hereditary occupations as the slaves, nobles, castes and modern plumbers. There were the rich — whom we have always with us — the herd owning Bantus of Africa, the reindeer breeding Chukchi, the Astors and the Vanderbilts of New York. With property rights and political power largely a male prerogative this phase of neolithic life advancing towards the age of metals became more sternly masculine.

But society, as Cole suggests,[62] has many factors in its origin, and no one of them, such as evolutionary necessity, no one order of inventions, no one spiritual base, will explain its many forms. Mental evolution, group psychology, environmental influences, diffusions from one center of discovery, convergence from diverse origins and social contact all bear on them. They are all formulative factors. Man's growth of power and complication spread in many ways.

The men who left stone tools and temples strewn over Europe had found the secret of a greater power. They had raised ungainly megaliths and dolmens. They had built the huge Stonehenge of England, the fortresses and tombs of France and Africa, the mounds of North America and the tumuli, the crannogs and the scharrachs of Scotland. They had set the columned menhirs of Carnac. Now they left them on bleak plains and hillsides and turned in Europe and in Asia to a new interest and material. They had found metals. That was six or seven thousand years or so ago. The age of stone was done.

To the bronze age man came with his fermented liquors and his gods, his languages and labor fairly well articulated. It was an age of war and wandering, for the bronzes gave delight to fighting, and wheels and horses now operating together, the ox drawn wains of Aryans, the rude boats stimulated man's endemic wanderlust. He was shaving now, before writing was invented, with an obsidian blade or one of hard bronze.[63] He manufactured money, symbol of economic power and a responsible society; he used combs, and so did she, no doubt, as well as metal mirrors; and he made saws and trumpets, and blew huge tunes through suave and stately tubes of bronze to call the hunters in. Armor had come for horse and man, of bronze sometimes laid on with gold; and there were recurved hooks of bronze with barbs for bronze age Izaak Waltons. The horses champed on great bronze bits, and there were fine two edged swords and shields of dusky bronze. The times were picturesque, so full of clang and drama, and the men folks must have loved them.

Some prehistoric accident gave man the use of metals. The metallurgy on which the age of bronze is based was founded on some hearth by chance when copper melted down from some crude ore. Man learned to melt and hammer it in molds and to mix tin or antimony with copper to make bronze.[64] Copper was used no doubt in Egypt 5000 years B.C., and mines in Sinai, Cyprus and Soudan go back almost as far. There was gold too and Cornwall tin was known long ago. In these began the age of metals that comes down to this day.

Hector and Moses, Achilles, Roland, Siegfried, Beowulf and Ulysses are bronze age heroes, more or less, in fact or character. They are the fringe of history and an age of heroes held them over for the first literature. Out of the fog and darkness of man's anonymous past heroes such as these appear. They lead a long procession of men and gods. They are articulations in man's past. They are syllables, as it were, in nature's discourse, and a race that more and more became aware of its own forces, elements and divisions held them in verbal and literary memory.

Without their brawls for gold and women the world would be a duller place. Their blinded bards and the long roll of epic rhythms, their golden deeds, the wrought beauty of their swords, their halls and sacrifices and the brave burning of their dead, their joy in carnage and their floors strewn with hides and horns and the stench of butchering; [65] it was barbaric gold; man's life was luxury and squalor and the rough joy of deeds.

Commerce came in and boats propelled by oars and, later, sails left Crete and the eastern shores of the Mediterranean on argosies to Italy, Greece and up the European rivers. Then iron came, perhaps 1000 years B.C., and the iron age down to the Christian era gradually settled on society. At first a decorative luxury, the new grey metal came in time to rule the world. Man's blood has iron in its texture, and the red flow of life is somehow taut and tough like tempered steel.

To iron was a road 500,000 years long, for the paleolithic period began, say, 500,000 years B.C. and ended 20,000 years B.C. Then came the neolithic period ending 5,000 years B.C. Then copper came and, shortly after, bronze and the bronze age ended, say, 1000 years B.C. The iron age followed for about 1000 years. But the bronze and iron ages vary with the place and tribe, and many savages today are neolithic or even lower. In general, though, a million years of human life upon this earth has brought in many changes. They are significant and timely and a written language is not the least of them. For writing and iron, fire and horses, pots and industrial discipline, weaving and gods, wheat and marriage, swords and frescoes, families, wheels, baskets, boats and the slow will to social order are but groping steps in man's progression. And of all these the invention of writing best begins this era of man's historical development. Writing is the portal of history.

In this chapter the social point of view was first contrasted with the scientific point of view. The Java man and his group was next noted, followed by the Neanderthal man, the Cro-Magnon man, the neolithic man, and the bronze and iron ages of men in their respective order as they file into the dungeons of the past. It is a field indefinitely rich in material, psychological and physiological, individual and social, mythical and actual. Man is all of that and more.

Modern Man

MAN is a verbal animal. He likes the thrill of syllables, and the bright experience of new words or of
old ones with new meanings is always worth his while.
His rotund cursing, his rituals, his howls, yodels, rah-ing
at a football game, his songs and poetries carry life upon
their backs. They give literary utterance to his needs and
the dumb pressures of his reality. They are ways of living.

Of these verbalities writing is a record. It is a trick
of catching sounds with symbols and of storing up in
books and papers or on temple walls huge potentialities
of experience to be revived at will. It is a way to hoard
experience from generation to generation, and with it
man can build enormous memories in books and increase
his choice of action in any given situation a thousandfold.
He can expand his life to distant ranges of an ancient
day; he can bind time; he brings to bear upon a present
instance all the workings of the past. In the solvent of
today's experience man can dissolve the centuries gone
by, and life that was a thin and trickling stream becomes
a thick solution. All that writing does for him. It is the
key to history, for history is the written record of man's
past. It is the beginning, six or eight thousand years ago,
of a new epoch and of modern man.

For history is a map of time. It is a man's chronom-
etry; and the measured actions of the past may well
apply upon the future. Man looks forward when he
writes the past or it would not be worth the writing. He
organizes futures and the past into his scope of living;
he extends his vital area; and the instrument for doing it
is writing. Since writing came man has compounded his
experiences in huge increasing ratios. He has made geog-

raphies of time, and with writing finds his way about among the ages with skill and speed.

The need for this new instrument of early man was threefold: to recall something, to tell a distant person something, to establish rights of property and otherwise on tools, cattle, women, pottery and the like.[1] Of the last needs we find examples now in trade-marks, marriage licenses and brands. Of the second, telegrams and newspapers are instances. Of the first, histories and "ponies," knotted handkerchiefs and daily memoranda are examples. One binds time, another space and a third property; and in early human life all three demands for writing probably arose. Writing met these needs, but modern man's ideas of time, space and property were reciprocally developed by his power to write. History is the written record of events, but their character in turn and man's perception of them were no doubt greatly influenced by his scribbling and his books.

But writing has a deeper right to being than these occasions in the early course of man. It is an organic factor in the history of the species. It is a primal tool of civilized existence, and though the radio and movies and other methods more direct may displace it in the future its significance in our past cannot be overestimated. Man can respond to symbols in some measure as if they were the things themselves and in that is a main factor of his letters and his gods and of his human organizations. His society depends on it. His institutions are its products. His civilization in no small way is the technique of his symbols.

When writing came man had begun to reorganize the world. He had pottery and baskets, metal implements and blankets; he had domesticated plants and animals; he had wheels and boats and a rude money; he had legal wives and property, inheritance and home fires, chiefs and medicine, gods, gold, souls and tribal prophets. He had in his primitive life all the aspects of modern civiliza-

tion.[2] His institutions had emerged from the dusk and
inarticulation of an ancient past. They had found maturity of a kind that without writing might well have sat
ten thousand years without a further forward step. Man
browsed on low plateaux and the modern fruits of science
and of highly organized society were far beyond him.
Until he could extend his grasp of nature beyond the
personal limits of his place and time there he must stay.
Until he could organize his life in units greater than his
single self or family the new science and society was impossible. In that organism writing, gradually discovered,
is of critical importance.

If religion, politics and economics, as Wallace says,[3]
"are the three great regulative factors of human intercourse subsumed under the term — society," writing is
a cohesive factor in their institutions on which they all
depend. Modern, large scale societies would disintegrate
without it and settled civilizations would decay. The age
of history is no doubt the development of modern institutions. It is the age of writing.

Settlement is civilization. The little aggregates of huts
in neolithic times, the larger villages of the metal age and
the great towns and cities later all were primeval gardens
of man's growth. Here society was founded in its more
organic forms and men learned to deal with men imper-
sonally in great coöperative abstractions. For settlements
are built on human uniformities. They are living systems
set to the common elements of man's nature, and they
survive alone in their conformity to his common taste.
Without settlements and human aggregation the divisions
of man's labor,[4] the special arts and crafts and businesses,
could not so well develop. Without towns and cities his
writing and his science would be less needed.

There are indeed prerequisites to settlements of any

major kind. They are factors, like all factors influencing human settlement, deeply bedded in the evolutionary order, for cities and societies appear not by caprice but for good reasons in the urgent march of human power and living over the earth.

Settlements come when men have found environments that give continuous support, when animals and plants may be made domestic, when men organize their labor into large wholes of accomplishment in which each human being has his special part, when symbols, such as written codes and constitutions, stand for order and are obeyed. Settlement is discipline. It is the rule of general orders over all particulars. It is extended organism and control, and that is civilization.

But settlements have a dynamic function lying under all of this. They focus human energies upon one place. They organize man's mobilities, and as he grows more mobile a teaming of his actions ever becomes more necessary. Unregulated movements counteract each other. Individual discursiveness becomes a waste and trouble. Settlements are, paradoxically, ways of increasing man's mobility. They increase his power to release and to consume more energy. That biologically is their primal purpose.

Nine steps are found in prehistoric and historic times, says Williams quoting in part Morgan,[5] in man's successive conquests of his world: First there was speech; then there was fire; then came the bow and arrow; these were the savage stages. Then came pottery; then domestic animals; and then iron; these were barbaric stages. Then came writing; then gunpowder; then the steam engine; these are the ages of civilization. Though this no doubt is an imaginative abstraction of man's prime discoveries that in concrete cases may not be true in order, number or significance, it serves well no less as a rough estimate of his inventions to which variations may be hung. They all, and many others, are no doubt cumulatively necessary to the growth of settlements as we know them, and of great societies. They are epochal discoveries by the human race but their findings were not capricious. They are implacably built into the evolutionary order and though that order is always retrospective, it is no less true that what our settlements are now could not be except for those inventions. They are as necessary and impersonal as settlement itself or the rise of the human species.

Thus man built his littered world of settlements and failures, of slow aggregations of the decencies that we call civilized, of urban customs and gallantries and pungent hates, of steel towers and divorces and irrigation projects in one shambling organism too natural to be neat. It is a world that grew before the thrusts of nature's dogged impulse like the rank forestation of new cut over land. Waste and disaster and a ragged power and pertinacity follow it through.

Along the bottom lands of four great rivers man first made extensive settlements. The Nile and the Hoang Ho, the Ganges and the Tigris-Euphrates bear ancient messages on their banks from his plurality of pasts. Cities and temples and the ruined stones of tombs, old palaces and hovels and the eternal dead lie where life left them. They are only mounds of sacred rubbish now but they tell from many provinces of time one human tale. Here sessile herds of human animals first learned to live in orderly coöperation, and the river bottoms that they farmed were taught to yield a regular supply.

Eight thousand years ago, or maybe ten or twelve — the dates are in dispute [6] — the valley of the Tigris and Euphrates was bearing cities and their strange progeny of sun baked brick and monuments. Seven thousand years or so ago the first kings came in Egypt.[7] Five thousand years ago, perhaps, China's first emperors strutted and puffed as rulers always must. Four thousand years ago Aryan invaders from the north were founding settlements on the Ganges. Crete and the sea kings after Minos thrived about this time. A Semite sheik named Abraham [8] was sacrificing Isaac to his nomad god. Aryan tribes were shifting restlessly across a Europe deep in neolithic and post-neolithic barbarism, and mongoloid savages were first wandering southward into the unpeopled continents of America.

They were valley settlements and civilizations up to four thousand years ago, where people herded densely under similar conditions and massive governments appeared built to an outer rule without much inner diversification. They were dense monotonies of power, and whether it be in China with its early city states and its five emperors, or in India with its white castes and its dark outcasts, or in Sumeria or Egypt, huge authority sat upon the settlements and constrained the subject people by an outer force. It was the age of despotism.

For with armies and with gods kings could rule these valley settlements. By capturing man's fears, his dread of punishment physical and spiritual, they could coerce him into orderly routines good for their purpose. Kings and the priests worked in coöperative despotism for an absolute control, and as the dynasties grew older kings became gods.

In Sumeria and Babylon and Egypt, in Assyria and Persia great god-kings marched in long processions down the ages, and even Alexander, the conquering Greek, set god upon his shoulders, and the Roman emperors and their successors claimed divinity. It is a theistic concept of control, says Ferdinand Schevill,[9] that recurs in giant rhythms across the seas of history. It is a way to unity and solidarity after human freedom. It is an alternating shift to security and peace with slavery after free souls and fighting.

For the great valleys so organized for despotism were reasonably secure. Along the Tigris and Euphrates men lived and died without the need of bearing arms, and the soldiers of the armies there fought less, no doubt, and with less danger, than in nomadic, wandering wars and forced migrations. They were despotic governments, but in immature societies they no doubt had their function. They forced peace and slavery on the earth. They conquered war with war.

Millions lived in baked clay settlements upon the Mesopotamian plains, and great towers and cities such as Babylon and Nineveh, Eridu and Ur bulged slowly from the ground. They were a fertile place for human life, and living became easy compared with the wild struggles of independent savagery. Nomadic peoples, now Aryan from the northern mountains, now Semitic from the southern deserts, swept over them in waves of conquest and settled there until refinements, riches and the slow debauch of cities weakened them in turn before invading thrusts. Sumerians, Akkadians, the Amorites with great King Hammurabi, giver of laws, the white Hittites, the Assyrians, the Chaldeans with king Nebuchadnezzar, patron of earliest mathematics and astronomy, the Aryan Persians, the Greeks of Alexander, under whom Mesopotamia first became a province, Parthians, Romans, Arabs, Turks [10] and then the English conquered this land of ancient irrigations and clay cities, of burning suns and despotisms and wild rivers and made it theirs. It is a bitter, desert place without much life remaining.

But another ditch and river people grew to great place and learned to make gods of kings. The Nile, too, built its despotisms. The control of the great river bottoms and the irrigations subject to it was easy for a concentrated power, and a people waiting on the stream as a sole means of livelihood must surely lose their several freedoms. There were dynasties and dynasties over Egypt, like great birds with black wings of death, from 5000 years or more B.C. to Cleopatra.

It was a land of stern conformities, of many gods and death, and of stone tombs and temples which no men since have equalled in size and saturnine repose. For death captured their imaginations; there were souls to care for, and the formulas of resurrection were detailed and most difficult. There were pantheons and priests; the minutiæ of holiness required much attention. Protestants there were, even in those days; the young king, Akhenaten founded vainly a new city of the sun and laid with apostolic zeal upon all Egypt a new monotheism and an universal god.[11] But it was not to last, and the faith that might have liberated Egypt was overwhelmed by vested interests of the priests and an empire crashing down across its path. Death is a great conformist and Egypt was built for death. After five thousand years and more death was her last despotism. Her final dynasty was silence. It was her last god-king.

Meanwhile the Cretan sea kings [12] and the fair haired mountain men of Greece and later Italy, the Balkan states and northern Asia Minor were building more flexible societies than these great river valleys had produced. Theirs was a world of variable conditions, of routines often broken and of constant shift and changing, and a drastic, centralized control of them was hardly possible. Instead of specified traditions to meet life's problems they must have generalized ability to adjust themselves according to the situation. They were freer men, for the old despotic systems failed. They used some measure of intelligence where others used convention. Theirs was a maturity, somewhat beyond the ancient valley life, and man's evolution was that much further on.

Then the sudden flower of Greece flamed across these dark gardens of humanity with a novel loveliness and for three centuries or four human living found a new release and wonder in this tiny segment of the race, that was overgrown again only in the Alexandrian conquests of the fourth century before Christ. It was a momentary founding of the modern west so far as that has been idealized; then it was lost again in the dark mesh of empires, and Alexander came exploiting its fresh energy and power in world old conquest. It was Greek mobility and speed employed in the last extermination of those dinosaurian despotisms of the continental valleys. The west and north and a fair haired, neolithic people trained in freedom and the arts of cities first broke the eastern order and the Afro-Asiatic supremacy of the world. They were restless tribes organized under Alexander, that a thousand years before had beaten down the towns and citadels of a dark skinned Ægean race and assumed control of Greece and coastal Asia Minor.

The young conqueror struck with the skilled punch and foot work of a modern boxer, and gigantic Persia crumpled, kicked convulsively once or twice and died forever.[13] Across Asia, into Egypt, across the river country and the mountains into India the armies of Macedon strayed triumphantly until no more worlds were left to conquer. Western diversity and experiment, western freedom and the tolerance of individuality first reached ascendencies here that were to grow in increasing cycles down to this day.

Rome was Alexander's real, though not immediate, successor, and Rome like Greece — and like America for that matter — drew its imperial energy from a youth given to liberal institutions, and while this strength and character of an earlier Rome persisted she was invincible. From families, clans, tribes and chieftainships to petty monarchies, to aristocracies, thence to republics,[14] or democracies and then to empire and decay was the evolutionary order both of Greece and Rome.[15] It was a rapid shifting, for the despotisms of 5000 years or so duration in the East were not well suited to the broken lands and peoples and the social flexibilities of Europe.

The sea with myriad arms, the diverse hills and forests of the European continent must have been important factors in the growth of western power and character.[16] They were defenses that in Africa and western Asia took the form of massive disciplines and armies. They provided safety in some measure without the crush and swagger of gigantic social conformisms and autocracy. They called out invention and self-reliant characters. The sense of individual rights no doubt was fostered by them.

For in this ragged, northwest promontory of the Afro-Asiatic land mass that is called Europe the energies were brewing that now dominate the world, and though the East and Africa no doubt influenced them through emigrations like the alphabet and Bible, Arabic numerals, cherries, Aristotle — through the Arabs — astronomy and inventions, the line of history in Europe and America is relatively discontinuous with Africa and Asia. It moves back on a red path through Rome and Greece to neolithic tribes in Europe; and western character and impetus today is a complex of the sea lore and discursive barterings of Minoan peoples and others on the Mediterranean, of restless mountain men and of little milk fed, valley settlements, of federated clans and tribes and quarreling city builders. It is a shifting field of many energies, restless, uneasy, with great diversification within, with many factors working and with a freedom unknown before in continental aggregations.

In Alexandrian Greece, in the empire of Rome and again in the industrial coördinations of today these quarreling energies of the west slipped for a moment into a single rhythm and moved across the world in conquest. The free spirit and self-reliance, the initiative and experimental interest, the ready handling of material and the engineering instinct developed in the liberal institutions and the quarrelings of the west gave energy to those conquests. Empires exploited what they themselves could not produce and in time destroyed them.

And Rome, after four hundred years or so, began to move in the first and second centuries before Christ, down an ancient path of universal empire and decay. For with the utter fall of Carthage the blessing of great enemies was denied her; the controls on human avarice and the greed for power were loosed by new conditions; money was developed to a use and scope not known before; [17] wealth became fluid; and the slaves from foreign conquests came in huge numbers to depress the labor market and to make small businesses and farming more and more unprofitable.

Capture by conquest of a batch of 10,000 slaves compared no doubt with the discovery of an oil field or a coal mine of today, for it added to a few hands in Rome a net sum of new energy. And combined with more mobile economic methods, livelier money systems, and the like, it made for huge estates, large scale operations, a reduced overhead, fewer landed farmers and more employees without a stake in Rome except their job and the good nature of their boss. The rich grew richer and the less rich were more and more dependent on the prosperity of those with power and wealth at hand.

Cæsar and Augustus came, and the emperors of Rome began their march through five centuries of massive circumstance and power to final degradation. It was an empire that imposed on western European tribes a language and a set of institutions that endure in large measure to this day. From Spain and Britain to the Rhine — the Germans were not conquered — from Gibraltar clear to Egypt, from the Balkans [18] across Asia to the east of Mesopotamia the Roman empire reached in one administrative unit. There was order there and, in spite of slow communications, obedience and peace while the god-emperor ruled in Rome. There were teeming populations and the cities grew in disproportion to the rural districts. Rome alone had a million or two in her greatest days.

But there was inner restlessness and misery. The Roman plutocrats increased in scope and power and the stern loyalties of Roman citizens and their devotion to the city state declined. Mercenary soldiers kept the peace and fought the foreign wars while landless mobs at home shifted from place to place and from job to job. A senile nomadry, like a second childhood, came to this huge settlement; and the lands and stable properties and the sound attachments that give settlement a value and responsibility to citizens were gradually withdrawn into a few hands. The Roman government, says Seignobos,[19] "existed for the sake of the governing class and not for the sake of the governed."

And without there was more restlessness, for China was about to break the Roman empire.[20] In the far east China had made an empire that in power and integrity, in civilization and endurance equalled, if it did not exceed, any that Rome or Greece had built. It checked the incursions southward of Hun and Mongol tribes from Mongolian plains, and it appropriated their pastures. It turned the course of these nomadic horsemen westward and they invaded eastern Europe. Here Aryan tribes were living and they in turn were set in motion, wave on wave westward and southward. Finally they broke the Roman empire. One more unity of empire and a god-king was down under the trample of freedom and the wandering tribes of our Germanic ancestors. To the Roman of the great average the crash was no disaster. He had no stake in Rome.

Modernity sits on three layers of the past: the Aryan tribal institutions and the culture of the Greek and Roman small republics; the spiritual intrusions of the medieval times; the rise of science and modern industrialism. It is an amalgam of historic metals.[21] It is a new world, suddenly different from the ancient course of empire that ended, perhaps finally, with the fall of Rome. Institutionally, if not in history, they were transitional empires that Greece and Rome produced between the age-long despotism of the past and modern liberal peoples, and they bore within themselves the factors of their own destruction.

And we are still transitional, no doubt, for satisfactory governments have not been found up to this day. Perhaps they never will be found. Man is not wholly a social animal, and his adjustments to large masses of his fellows can hardly have the neat articulations and efficiencies that he has found in family life, sex life, hunting life and dispersed nomadries. The raw freedoms and the love of wanderings and conflicts that assail him are not easily conformable to life *en masse*.

Modern emergence from Europe's early barbarism began no doubt in the desultory conflicts of the sea kings in their brunette towns on Minoan coasts and islands of the Mediterranean with the northern wanderers and tribesmen who became Europe's dominating strain. A simple people, nomadic Aryans, mainly neolithic, with herds and ox drawn wagons, filtered slowly down the valleys of Greece and Italy, and learned the arts and disciplines of the Ægean cities on the hills. They learned of piracy and trade militant on the seas and transferred their joy of exploration and of wandering from the mountains to the creeks and open waters. They learned mechanics and some rudiments of navigation; they learned the measurement of matter and of time and seaside engineering; and their senses were alert with a raw hunger for new things. And they learned to fight and conquer one by one the great Minoan towns. They cleared Greece and Crete of them; they took an early Troy; they took Sidon, and under Alexander Tyre fell tremendously before them. Finally Carthage, last of the Ægean powers, fell to Rome after a bitter century of hatred. Traditions of mobility and mechanical resourcefulness of the western mind were much developed by this inland sea experience. The siege of Tyre, for example, must have been an educative factor of some significance in the forming of the modern world.

Here a tall town was built half a mile from the shore upon an island rimmed by massive walls.[22] Fleets of eighty ships or more along its quays could keep the waters clear of Alexander's navy. From January down to July, 333 B.C., Tyre resisted.

It was a fight of engineers and counter engineering. The siege was won at last over a mole driven by the Grecian king from shore to town. It was easy work at first, says Bury, in the shallow water near the shore. But as it neared the island the channel became deep. The workers were assailed by arrows from the walls. Triremes from the harbors of the town pestered them on either side.

Two towers with leather curtains were put up to shield the men at the mole's advancing end. A fair wind for the Tyrians strewed fire from a fire ship upon the towers. It burned them and their engines down while the Greeks were beaten off by Tyrian triremes.

It was disaster. The resourceful Macedonian made the causeway wider. He built more towers and engines on it, and strengthened by accession of 200 more triremes, drove on the siege. With sea supremacy, as Mahan says,[23] all is transformed. The mole was now completed. Siege engines were brought up on ships and on the mole to crash the gates. But the defense was thick. Its battlements were 150 feet and more above the sea. The engines harmed them little. To find a weaker place the Greek put new machines on older ships and tried to anchor near the town. Tall rocks under water held him off, and he sent ships to drag the boulders out. Covered boats shoved off from Tyre and cut the cables. He stationed other covered boats to guard them, but swimmers came from Tyre silently with knives and cut the anchorings again. Then Alexander found a chain and the work was done.

Seven Tyrian ships now chose the noon siesta for a raid. Behind a screen of sails the boats left port. They caught the Alexandrian squadron unawares and sank and stranded many. Alexander saw the raid by chance from shore. He took a small squadron, rowed around the island, and in turn surprised the Tyrians and dispersed them.

Then the assault began. A breach was made. Two days later a larger hole was pounded through the walls. Ships were placed about the town to veil the point of effort. Two triremes were laid up to the breach and over lowered drawbridges Greek troops with Alexander at their head mounted the walls. Tower by tower the city fell; 6000 Tyrians were killed. All the rest, some 30,000, were sold in slavery. They were boyish fights in early days with all the adventurous furnishings and simplicities of a youthful fiction, but they had savage endings. In Tyre's siege a static notion of defense went down under Aryan mobilities and directed power. In many fights like these the modern west learned to meet mass with movement.

In the Greek town the tree of modern life had its first quickening, and in the Homeric state, says Walker,[24] "we find the germs not only of the oligarchy and democracy of later Greece, but also of all the various forms of constitution known to the Western world." The tribe and clan and phratry are there in common Aryan forms, and the Greek kings are limited already in ways that will abolish them later on. From these naïve beginnings the evolution of Greek character and politics goes in slow cycles on to the Periclean age.

It was enlightenment burning, to be sure, on a slave base that vitiated the culture of the Hellenes and their stock in time by slow interpenetrations. But the free intelligence and scepticism of the greater Greeks, the unbound love of inquiry, the growth of science and the

individual and the splendid blossoming of art was unique
in human evolution, and though not well protected from
corrupting penetrations, the consequence of its few
illumined years was the founding of our modern life.

The Greeks first found the joy of reason and the sur-
pluses of interest beyond the needs of human fear and
hunger. They were released like prisoners from the age
old cage and darkness of old dogma and convention, and
they were drunk with light. All through their lives
shines the love of being and a playfulness. All through
their works there is a sweet profundity and joy.

Under a plane tree beyond the walls of Athens Phædrus
comes to talk with Socrates on love, eternity and true
being.[25] In the house of Cephalus, who sits upon a
cushioned seat crowned for a sacrifice, they talk of states
and justice and the ideal Greek republic. To the prison
where Socrates will die Plato comes with friends to talk
of immortality. And with Philebus and Protarchus
Socrates argues of the good. Thus the dialogues of Plato
one by one explore worlds of reason and of sun-touched
poetries to which no caustic disillusionment as yet has
come.

Plato and the soberer Aristotle, the dramatists and
poets, architects and sculptors, philosophers, historians,
generals and statesmen and young men: in our murky
skies no stars have shone so bright. They were a people
who penetrated being with low laughter. Their hearts
were fire, as Jowett says, with a marble crust.

Like the Greeks the Romans grew from little Aryan
tribes clustered on the hills of Latium, but they were of
different temper. From the Greeks the modern world
would hope to draw its heritage of freedom and of free
inquiry, its resourcefulness and love of beauty, its
humane sweetness and its joy. From Rome comes law
and formal organization, its stern conventions and
stabilities and its military temper.

The ancient Roman, says Seignobos,[26] led a routine

life. He rose early, often earlier than dawn, and after washing, made his prayer to the god of the morning and went to work all day but for a noon hour meal. In the fields he spent that day, while the women stayed at home weaving thread that their servants spun.

There was no dancing and no pleasure trips. There were no vehicles but farm wagons. There were two or three great games a year in Rome, and in a nine day period the country people went to town to sell their grain and fruit and cattle and to buy a little stuff of metal or of pottery. At home the farmer made his flour, bread, farm tools, wagons, baskets, rope, his house, and the women wove his cloth and made his clothing. His food was simple and, before the conquest, eaten for the most part in one meal. Later the joys of Greece came in and the florid Orient, wines and dancing, and the grim Roman type with slaves and wealth and women, declined. Roman republicanism moved toward voluptuous empire. It once had character but had never taste.

The German tribes were less settled at this time, and fair and towering men followed their flocks, says Breasted,[27] over a broken Europe or quarreled with terrible muscularity among their neighbors. They lived in villages, each of a hundred families or so and their larger groups, or nations, were rarely more than forty miles across or of more than forty thousand souls. For village life and small administrative units, that to this day are the Nordic peoples' natural and most efficient forms, suited well their individualism and the adjustment of a situation to the free personalities involved.

There was less wilderness, four hundred years A.D., for the human race was older by 6000 years or so than it was when metals were first used, and writing made its strange and wriggling progress down the page. There was less wilderness, for man had realized on inventions of his savage and barbaric age, and though no new discovery of revolutionary import had been made since then — unless it be the free thought of the Greeks — the human race had grown; it had increased a thousand times perhaps in mass; and the free wandering tribes found their orbits more and more constricted.

And the quality of modern man is much involved in the slow settlement of these restless ancestors of ours. For the roving stock does not make settlements of size with any natural grace. It is not sessile in its nature and forces like the Christian church, the Roman empire, and the concentrated industries of today that tend to settle it in masses of large size, sit with some awkwardness on their preëminence.

Europe was an old and crackled vase in the middle centuries of the first millennium A.D. Constantine had moved the seat of power eastward to Byzantium and become a Christian. The Mongols from the east were driving in; and the Nordic tribes were sifting through crevasses of the empire in resistless storms. New wine was pouring into ancient skins that could not hold it.

For the empire was contractile and defensive. Its thrust and impetus was gone, and another power reached out from a new center of expansion to organize the mobs of Europe and to coördinate men's lives. That was the Christian church, and though it was successor in a measure to the empire of the Romans it was much different.

On haughty Roman decadence and pride came a new levelling of spirit, and the class differences and fear of labor with the hands, the sour snobberies and shows built by centuries of urban artifice that had brought Rome to her fall were cast aside, where the new faith was, like a soiled and tawdry robe. "The cold contempt for a man who works with his hands was changed," says Stawell,[28] ". . . into reverence." It is hard to say "how much our modern belief in the dignity of labor may not owe to the steady example of a rule of life so remote from modern belief on the whole." For Christ was democratic.

And on the restless barbarism of the German tribes new gentleness and a new urgency for peace was laid that had in time wide spread effects. For peace was needed in these years, peace and coördinating power; and this, spiritually and administratively, the Christian church in some measure brought about. It is a tropic influence and a sweetening of the rigors and the violence of the Germanic north.

For religion in some sense has its formal evolution; and the spiritual maturity of the Christian faith was not unique. In China an ethical religion that was meant for all humanity was articulated by Confucius in the sixth century B.C. In Aryan India a profound and beautiful religion was expressed in Vedantic mysticism; and Buddha, most speculative of all the world's messiahs, carried it in the fifth century B.C. to an ethical and intensely spiritual conclusion. There was Mohammed in the sixth century A.D. with his universal god, his dogmas and the driving impetus of faith, building a Semite power and a Mediterranean resurgence, that swept up into Spain as well as eastern Europe, captured Constantinople, broke the Eastern empire left by Rome and threatened to engulf all Christendom and our western life. And there was Jesus, a simple man, founding a world order on his faith in human gentleness and love. From tribal gods and superstitions four faiths arose, and no doubt more, devoted to all men. One in character is mainly ethical, one spiritual, one dynamic and irrational, one humane and sacrificial. They are maturer formulations of an impulse of the spirit common to all men.

For the evolution of religion, Menzies says,[29] may have three phases correlated with human social growth. The religion of the tribe "belongs to that stage in man's existence in which his energies are entirely occupied in

the struggle against nature and against other tribes."
It is a "mass of childish fancies and of fixed traditions
which he cannot explain, but does not venture to criti-
cise or change. His gods are petty and capricious beings,
and his modes of influencing them, though used with
zeal and fervour, have little to do with reason or with
taste or with morality. It is in this kind of religion that
magic of all sorts is at home."

In the religion of the state and nation ideas of a nobler
order are revealed. For the leading classes of the state at
least have gained some measure of security and leisure.
And now it is, Menzies continues, "that great religious
systems arise, so powerful, so highly organized, so splendidly adorned, and surrounded with such venerable
traditions, that they seem destined for eternity." The
priesthood becomes a mighty class, he says, with a
holiness that marks its members off from other men;
there is ritual and sacrifice that have the character of
divine mysteries, there is creed and dogma; every detail,
even the most trivial, has a sacred meaning; and religious
books are written and compiled that come to be regarded
as infallible and inspired.

The third phase is a change from external to internal
authority. And in a society where the individual has
become worth while a new religious scepticism appears.
It questions outer orders and establishments. It seeks an
inner spirit and responsibility for goodness based on love
not fear. From Christ and Plato, from Plotinus and St.
Augustine,[30] from the mystics such as Eckhart and Tauler,
from Luther and John Wesley, from Emerson and Walt
Whitman and from all human yearnings the modern world
has drawn strength and teaching and a slow growth of
religious universalism founded in man's inner life.

Of the disruptions and barbarities of medieval life
Christ was indeed a healer. He brought a type of continuity and order into a torn world that was sorely
needed. He gave humanity new hope; he motivated

anew the poor; and though the appeal to spiritually irrelevant hells and heavens carried great weight no doubt among the raw barbarians, the consequence of Christian teaching on the whole was an amelioration of the darkness and disruptions of the times.

For it was Rome again that this humble subject of the Cæsars taught. It was Rome without the flesh and rottenness and coarse power; Rome transcendent over boundaries, creeds and races in an universal brotherhood held not by war but love. For in the growing class distinctions, serfdom, slavery and contempt for human kind in general the Roman empire fostered the factors of its own destruction. Long before this China had learned the dangers of this human tendency, and the Chinese empire has lived down to this day. And in the universal brotherhood of man the Christian church found the chief principle of its permanence and power. Modern democracies find there spiritual support. It is a coördinating principle in man's societies of huge significance.

From Greek freedom and inventiveness, from Roman continuity and organic sense, from Christ's interjection of the brotherhood of man, from Germanic energy and control of matter may fancifully be woven a web not unlike our modern life. Such analogies no doubt have value, but abstract principles like these are hardly causal factors in the building of our world. We are a pool no doubt, where many streams have flowed, but to disentangle them so definitely is hardly valid, for the terms freedom, brotherhood, order, energy and the like are after all abstractions that never have been isolated and set aside in a concrete case. They are but attributes accented more or less in all human behavior, and to name their sources so specifically in modern life is not sound history.

What we are, we are for a myriad of environmental and hereditary reasons, and among them are no doubt the dominating pasts of our ancestral stocks and institutions. But those are not all. Climate, food, soil and the general aspect of nature are, as Buckle says,[31] important agents; language and its evolutions; fecundity and fears, fevers, pestilence, I.Qs. and fires, earthquakes, floods, geniuses and generals, jazz and great men's love affairs all may contribute to the modern pattern of our lives. Its causes are not simple.

But among them all few have more weight than the development of man's tools. It took Christ and gunpowder to break the feudal barons and establish liberal nations on the earth. It took the Reformation and democracy and power from expanding gases to build the tall industrialisms of today. The causes are complex, but the evolution of the tool is one appropriate key, at least, to the modern situation.

For power and its control is after all the dominating motif of man's relation to the natural world. Be he Napoleon or pacifist, hydraulic engineer or preacher of the gospel, he is first of all a dynamic factor in the world of things and changes. He is the proprietor of energies that increase in scope and number with his evolution and his command of tools. Speech, fire, the bow and arrow, pottery, weaving, domestic animals and iron as well as writing are discoveries and uses that took hold of man's career and gave it new emoluments and powers. Directly or indirectly they are accessions to the energies that are called mankind. They are reorganizations of the world to some extent, in favor of man's system. They are conquests of new energies and new powers.

When man learned to use the energy of expanding gases he first found modernism. With gunpowder discovered — so far as Europe is concerned, in the thirteenth or the fourteenth century — the first of a long series of expanding gas machines, including guns, steam engines and all motor cars, began its mighty work on human institutions. Guns blew up the feudal system, cracked the fear of fixed authority along with castles, armored knights and dukes and counts and helped make way no doubt for Reformation. A mix of charcoal, sulphur and saltpeter found, they say, by a cloistered genius, named Roger Bacon, had no small part in building science, freedom and our modern life. It was a new mobilization of man's power. It was power distributed to many men and it prepared the way in part for more integrated social structures and political cohesiveness that mark the modern state and nation.

But our modern gunpowder civilizations had other factors in their making that are sweeter to the educated taste. For "Greece had crossed the Alps" and a new release of learning and free inquiry sprang from the sullen soil. It was the fifteenth century and Asia under Turkish leadership had blocked the eastern exits of all Europe and turned our continental face about to the Atlantic ocean. Greek exiles came from captured Constantinople [32] to stir Italian towns — as Rome and Florence — with new, exciting thoughts and adventures in new freedom. New schools and colleges were founded over all Europe; old Charlemagnian schools revived, and young men rushed to the new studies and endured "watching, fasting, toil and hunger in the pursuit of them." Printing came in Germany, like a mental gunpowder, distributive and democratic in effect. Explorers searched the seas, and Admiral Columbus in a futile effort to find India by going west raised the new world. Copernicus and Bruno overhauled the universe and swung the earth and other planets in huge cycles round the sun; and later Galileo, Newton and the great line of modern science began their stately march down to this day. Art flamed in joyous gold and spontaneity; dynamic Christs with bulging shoulders and great thighs, madonnas that were women first, and pagan beauties followed the brush and chisels of Michael Angelo, of multipowered Leonardo, of Raphael, Tintoretto, and Titian. Cities rose to power out of agrarian medievalism, and the burghers and new kings joined to break the feudal lords. To the cities came the riches of discovery, for the most part; and there this cultural rebirth of Europe,[33] the Renaissance, took place. England rose like a great sea city, as transatlantic interests developed, and became with time the blond Byzantium of the west.

And deep in the heart of the new learning the hardy bud of Reformation came; a peasant's son, named Luther, contemporary of Columbus and Leonardo, brought the north's rebellion against the church of Rome to a climactic crash. It separated finally the protestant and Platonic strain of Christianity from Rome and Aristotle and scattered divers transcendentalisms over history from John Fox to Emerson. It founded spiritual authority on the life within; and free thought, free speech, free press, assembly, conscience and free scientific inquiry all depend upon that impetus and vision. In this the Nordic characters and institutions still inhere; modern life from science to bobbed hair, from electricity to bath tubs, from literature to individualism, Windsor ties, divorce and Theodore Roosevelt stand deep upon it.

For Germany and England and the new North America were founded here. Great states, democracies and representative governments were protestant experiments in some respects, that have yet to prove a failure or a clear success. And above all America, massive offspring of these modern times, came of the mating of northern freedom of the spirit and inventiveness.

The great enemy of civilization, says Buckle,[34] "is the protective spirit; by which I mean the notion that society cannot prosper unless the affairs of life are watched over and protected at nearly every turn by the state and church: the state teaching men what they are to do, and the church teaching them what they are to believe."

From earliest time the traditions of the human group have been all powerful; they have set like concrete in a mould about all individuals and fixed their lives in rigorous detail. Primitive man, paradoxically, is most traditional in behavior. He is least free to find himself except in social conformation, and as the times advance down through our history he frees himself only by slow effort and much failure.

In western Europe reformation worked its slow and complicated way in England and in Germany and France. Slowly the distributed power of men was built up in governments more popular than before. English parliamentism found firmer footing, and the ancient Roman unity of church and state under the leadership of Spain was thrust back in 1588, with its great armada broken and dispersed by the Elizabethan ships of Drake and Howard, Frobisher and Hawkins.

Shrewd and voluptuous Elizabeth was queen of those sweet isles that sit upon the back of Europe facing the west; and poets and pirates in new liberties bloomed now in rank profusion there. Bacon founded his inductive science; Spenser wrote his Faerie Queen. While the English pirates blasted galleons from the Spanish main by the queen's connivance, Shakespeare rode the skies on flaming dramas of humane imagination.

It was an age of careless power and freedom and the raw sensuality of man was loosed in wild mixtures of love and ugliness, beauty and fiery hate. Later the Puritans and dissenting churchmen wove a gray strand of firmer fiber into this English web. For they were a Nordic stock, these English, with brusque contrasts and diversities and protests, and consciousness of a great nation was growing in them. It formed around trade and conquest, the inductive sciences and freedom and the rough energies of peoples who have found ways to freer action. The idea of government by constitution, written or remembered, the English bill of rights of 1688, to protect the rights of men in perpetuity, was developed in great states and nations. America, France, Germany, Japan and Russia in their turn have founded national states of power and consequence.

In England revolution grew apace up to the eighteenth century. It was an age when politics bore the changing urgencies and hopes of western peoples: and in England government was popularized successively in rough cycles; and democratic forms were born. This in an English stock, largely Puritan and churchly in tradition, became the great American republic after the Revolutionary war,[35] and it realized in its sudden formulation what England had been reaching towards for three hundred years or more.

In France the war remained within. The monarchy, though powerful and brilliant since an earlier Louis broke the nobles' strength, was outgrown; and an un-privileged people governed by absentee lords and court-iers was learning to revolt. It came at last in 1783 and a few years later royal heads were falling into the red baskets of the guillotine. A new French republic rose — liberty, equality, fraternity — from Rousseau's natural-ism — today most unnatural — from the leadership of Mirabeau, Danton and Marat and from the frantic craze and energies of an urban mob that had no stable means of earning bread. And out of the French republic came a man, Napoleon, [36] destined to lead the tramp of armies over all Europe, to discredit old régimes, to free Germany from dynastic yokes, and to fall at last with all of France around him in the crash and hiss of imperial deflations and broken Cæsarian hopes. They were years of hunger, guns and of mighty music, for Beethoven was then alive; Goethe and Schiller lived, and Kant was building still and stately monuments of thought that towered above the ruck and wear of life, a citadel of reassurance.

Germany came in 1870 into the lines of power; Bis-

marck built a German nationalism on the defeat of
France, and his strong and earnest people soon were
moving towards industrial conquest of the world. Japan
won leadership in the east after defeating Russia early
in the twentieth century, and thus the modern nations of
the west upraised themselves and forced imitation elsewhere.

Today there is America, Great Britain; there is western
continental Europe; there is Russia, China and perhaps
India and Japan, five modern concentrates of man's
civilization. They are five characters of living. They
are modes of human organization, and no one knows
which is nearer final. One is continental, industrial,
republican; another is democratic, imperial, commercial;
another is communistic, agricultural; another is par-
ticularistic, or decentralized, or agricultural, and so it
goes; each tries its way to live; each makes its human
project; and whether it be China that is better fitted to
man's needs and real progress, or America or Russia or
any other, depends on man and nature, race and tempera-
ment and a thousand complicated facts and fixities of
man's social evolution. It is his driving impetus towards
he knows not what.

For peoples and their institutions have their form and
mode. They weave their shifting patterns on the wind;
their thrusts and movements have their own peculiar
gaits. In the west, says Spengler [37] three cultures have
come to prominence: the classic culture of Greece and
Rome, where life is finite and Euclidian; the Magian
culture of the Jews, the Arabs and the Christians to
900 A.D., where algebraic symbols replace the geometric
figure, where arabesque supplants the human body in
the arts, and where the dome spiritually supplants the
classic straightness of the Greeks; the Faustian culture
of the modern west, where fixed form is not a deep concern
and variable function is the more important, an analytic
culture. But history, after all, is but a past created as we

will it. It is thick with new potentials. It is turbid with
the sweepings and the soils of all the universe. We will
the past with hardly less authority than we will the future. It is profoundly ours to mould and make out of a
timeless clay.

Human progress, if temporal at all, is no thin stream
of movement through the centuries. It is the centuries
themselves as they grind by with all their glacial mass
and acreage, their aggregated realisms and the disordered
push of stone and ice and torn soil, snow and dark
rumbling waters. It has no lonely line of movement, no
single evolution; it is thick, oppressive, surging, a gain
here or now a loss, and a slow push onward of terminal
moraines.

And man's history in this sense is part of all process
and material evolution. It is biology and can be told
from other aspects of that order only by the evolutionary
speed and new extensions of the human race compared
with other races. Though alien modes and new points
of view inhere in the raw conglomerate of man's progress,
and thinking finds release sometimes from the energies
and matter of the cosmic process, man as a natural
creature fits the biologic form. To reorient himself he
must abandon time.

The biological success of man is notable in history, for
with the conquest of the beasts and the capture of earth's
more kindly places it has become ultimate. By traditions,
tools and a potent nervous system, by machines and the
seizure of great natural powers man broke down old
Nature's equilibrium of species. He upset biology's
balance of old powers, and mankind has spread — like
the rabbit pest in Australia — over all the earth.

In numbers and in control over his surroundings man
now surpasses any other large-sized animal. And though

his firm departure from the normal equilibrium of nature has natural causes it remains uncertain whether it can be stable. Unless he can provide within this conquered field the diversities and mutual tolerations, the balances of powers and interests that were provided in the natural world his station and stability is not assured. For the environment will still resist. He can never wholly break it. It may regain its strength and beat him.

Why has man come so suddenly to preëminence in the last twenty thousand years? Among the reasons are: the economy of human thought in the trial and error method; the physical adjustments in the hands, the voice, the eyes, the posture and the head; the grasp of time; the integration of detail in generalities; the sense for tools and in generalized adjustments without the usual waste of time and life; societies and the division of his labor; and the growth of inner authority to replace external dogmas. They provide a greater chance of variation and selection and a more sure adjustment.

Though the anatomical climax of man's evolution may have come and gone — in the Cro-Magnon races — somewhat before he reached the peak of biological success the decline of human powers and consequence is not in sight. Our rather scrubby races are not the men, perhaps, that once were here potentially in body; but traditions carry on, machines and writing still accumulate and the needs for further anatomical evolution are obviated to some extent by their efficiencies.

Man's evolution will be social, institutional, implemental, in greater part, and the continuities of his history will remain, not solely instinctive and hereditary, but conceptual and traditional. They are large Latin verbalisms but they bear some truth.

New ways to solicit power from his surroundings

usually mean new eras in man's life, new marks; and with
steam engines to bring the power of heated gas to industry
this latest of new ages began. That was in the eighteenth
century, 500 years after the boom and flare of gunpowder
had begun to stir the western peoples. But steam gas was
industrial in effect where the gas of gunpowder had been
political and military, and men learned that steam could
lift and carry and construct better than men's backs or
horses' legs or the sails of ships. Modern industrialism
came, and exploitation of the coal resources of the world,
only when men learned steam's lesson. It was the old
tale of gunpowder reapplied: as usual they could do it
better with gas.

These concentrates of power now brought machines
with increasing complications, and production was more
centralized around them. Cities grew, for the clothes
and shoes, the weaving and the soap, the foods and instruments, that once were made distributively throughout the land withdrew to urban factories for quantity
creation. Machines were housed in massive plants and
laborers came to them. Fifty storied towers went up
for business offices. Exchanges grew and the transfer of
goods for gold became a passion without plebeian taint.
And even distribution, with railroad trains and steam-
ships and gas wagons, became mechanized. Towns that
once had been political or the foci of commercial distribution became centers of production, and dragged under
their dingy skirts the poor and the wage earners to live
in slums and unnatural filth, and to labor in undifferentiated masses under men they never knew. In the first
quarter of the nineteenth century, says Stawell and
Marvin,[37] "the growth of wealth was startling, but so
also to any who looked below the surface was the misery
and poverty among the workmen and the chronic trouble
of unemployment."

In all the course of written history perhaps no era
dawned with such devastating suddenness and change in

the practical lives of men. It was industrial revolution, and it divides significantly all man's history following from what went before. Accommodation to it is still the basis of most modern social problems. It faces us with ruin and enlightenment in its hands: and which one it will give us no one can tell. In America the revolution came when civil war [38] had broken the agrarian and slave-holding south and made capital and the power from burning coal ascendent. Now America is industrialism's favorite child.

These are massive times, but delicate organically. The old distributive civilizations of the west are almost gone; the cities grow and rural life declines. For with machinery, this monstrous growth of tools, life is perforce changed, relationships are laid out anew, and the parts depend for food and living on the organic whole as they, perhaps, have never done before. It is a fragile whole and subject to disasters. It crashed not long ago. A fly-wheel broke. Rods thrashed out wildly in chaos and destructions. There was world war with complicated wrecks of causes, hopes, hates, energies and great nations. For small men and untrained engineers were set to run machineries beyond their comprehension. And nations created in an age of politics rode with enormous powers and potencies unheard of in their youth. It was a war arising largely from the break of antique politics and their competitive imperialism under the burden of industrialism.

There was Jutland where the fleets of Germany and England met in terrible concussion, and ships of fifteen, twenty, thirty thousand tons of bitter steel cracked and blew up like broken bubbles in the rain. There were the trenches along war's coast from the sea to Switzerland, the stench of men and death, the discipline, the sullen years, work and the savage pressure of soldiers and machines on other soldiers and machines. There were tramplings over Russia, Rumania and Italy, bombs from

Britain in Gethsemane, men behind the lines, the frenzied
peoples, air raids, the persecutions, sacrifices and greed.
It was modern capital's great war, and in scope and thunder no war of the pre-industrial age has equalled it. It
was a war measurable mostly by the Versailles peace —
failure, lies, corruption, the wreck of Europe. That peace
America never signed.

But America is left, temporarily perhaps, the world's
dominating power.[39] She commands more energy per
capita for her hundred million people than any other
nation. She is biologically preëminent in all pasts and
presents. Her people thrive in their material concerns
and maintain to some degree the freedom that made
them strong. Her resources are unlimited in some respects; her coal alone will last 4000 years. America has
every factor of endurance, if her character can stand.
That is a question; for character after all is a complex
of many influences parallel and intertwining with the
industrial factors and designs of the new age. Will industry corrupt the only institutions and moralities on which
America can stand, or will it change them to socially
more efficient forms? No one can tell. Human fiber is
always under test. Of the next test there is no telling.

In the course of human history there are notable
perhaps six moods and colors of civilization. There are
the Mongolian types and the Indic types; there are the
ancient types of western Asia and Egypt; there are the
Mohammedan theocracies; there are the Mediterranean
and European types and there is America. They are set
on no one category except emergence from the ruck and
indistinguishable details of time. They are projects in
humanity, and to name the best is quite impossible for
there is no best.

But of them all America in power control at least is

dominant. In that its evolution is continuous and pre-eminent so far as man in history is in common with all the rest of cosmic process, matter, energy, living systems. There is no "marching on" to cosmic purposes, no tele-ology in history or in other systems biological and subject to the scientific mode,[40] but there is continuity of instinct and *élan*, of learning and remembered situations,[41] of institutions and of power.

Modern societies now fight nature less and use her more. They persuade the powers of nature to assist them. They throw her energies and theirs into one rhythm. Man allies himself with nature and finds new powers.

In a long chapter mostly of leaving out the diverse stories of mankind nine points were touched upon: writing, settlement, the older despotisms, the transitional empires, the Greek and Roman freedoms, the medieval intervention, gunpowder civilization, man's anatomical and his biological climaxes, coal civilizations and America. Man's past is marble in the rough from which we carve a history suited to our own design. In this outline the growth of tools and the distributions of man's power control are made significant. On the first hangs food and shelter; on the second, freedom and society.

CHAPTER EIGHT

Man's Alliance with Nature

"CHIMP," the chimpanzee, knows invention when he sees it, and is able in some degree to apply science to the daily needs of anthropoid apes. If food, say a score of ripe bananas, be scattered just outside his cage beyond arm's reach but within reach of a stick, he will use the stick to drag it in. That is use of tools, say Chimp's biographers in their learned fashion, though hardly an invention.

If the stick be jointed, however, with the several parts too short to reach bananas, Chimp will try the parts respectively, fail, forget about it all, says Köhler,[1] and play about his cage among the sticks, trapezes and athletic apparatus that equip his home. He will play casually with the disjointed sticks and eventually will fasten them together, by chance, into the longer one.

Then comes a characteristic grunt. It is the discovery grunt, Chimp's way to say, "Eureka," and in a passion of enthusiasm he takes the stick and starts to drag bananas in. His interest runs wild. He forgets to eat the bananas that he brings up to his cage. He drags in everything in reach, and only when no more worlds are left to conquer does he return to former hungers and eat the fruits of his invention.

By an invention, product of his own synthesis, Chimp gets results, and man from the Greeks to Darwin, from the discoverer of fire to Archimedes and T. Edison, for 50,000 years or more has been doing the same thing. The ability to recognize inventive syntheses and to use them is of critical importance in man's civilized development. He can apply his findings. He can see a pattern. He can see the whole and the bearing upon practice of several separate parts. Civilization sits on its inventions. It is a succession of new syntheses.

Man's chief business, says Slosson,[2] "is in reversing the processes of nature." He undoes iron rust to get the iron out. He releases energy from coal that ancient plants so patiently stored away. He takes motion from the winds and waterfalls and freezes it in storage batteries for later use. Man goes about from job to job attaching to himself the energies of other things. By science he learns the order of the natural world, and by applied science he adjusts that order to his social system; he makes energy available to man. Applied science is a correlation of scientific and of social values. It is dependent to a great degree on what man needs; it undoes nature for a human purpose, and its progress hangs on human freedom to investigate all natural orders and man's motivations. Applied science derives from modern liberalism.

For a Ford car or six tube radio were socially and religiously impossible during the medieval ages of repression. A modern bath tub and its plumbing were unknown for reasons largely theological and dogmatic. The world was fixed by an external fiat, and the man who questioned native orders of the world and sought to find its natural causes and successions was a heretic who presently was simmering at the stake. Despotism, theocratic, political or economic, is death to science and its future applications. Man's freedom to meddle casually in the processes of nature is the first pledge to his creativeness.

On culture and the attitude of men towards their environment depend the growth of science and its applications. In the history of the race, says Freud,[3] three successive attitudes appear: first, animism or the "omnipotence of thought" in which ideas are magically all powerful; second, religion, in which man's power is surrendered to objective supernatural beings; third, science, "in the name of which man accepts as his guiding principle the objectively verifiable realities of the world and learns to know his real power by accepting its limitations." And in terms of the "power culture," at least, this analysis seems fairly valid. Modern technical development, machinery, industry wait on a point of view that before the Greeks was almost non-existent, and since them, had developed only in too few fields. On its creative fringe science is always protestant, and the free scrutiny of events is a postulate of modern life. Modern civilization, says Veblen,[4] "excels in impersonal insight into natural fact and finds its highest material expression in the technology of the machine industry."

Society was practically developed by man's power to organize and use matter; but its future will be given, Soddy says,[5] increasingly to the use of natural energies. And to use these natural energies on great scale demands a highly organized society in which the parts are deeply differentiated and interlocked. To use the coal and oil and winds and water, the great machineries and power lines on continental bases demands a closely knit community of interests and hopes, of work and profits, of services and freedoms, and it is not unlikely that individualism of the old kind and its raw urge to un-poised exploitation will fall down on the job.

"The exploiters of the wealth of the world are not its creators," says Soddy [6] in comparing exploitation with creative science. "If they were they might have a wider view than that it was created for the competitive acquisition of the most rapacious, unscrupulous and already too well-equipped." Science and its applications is a constructive and distortionary factor in society of huge import. In the industrial revolution it has brought perhaps the greatest change in the lives of men since history began.

For man's course, says Slosson,[7] has three industrial periods: the appropriative period; the adaptive period; the creative period. They are steps in his conquest of nature. They are changes from outright conquest to alliance with the natural energies of the world. Even Greece, free and intelligent as it was, never reached to any great degree a creative period in the use of natural energies. For Greece loved the mind alone, and the touch of matter there was left to the crude hands of a lower class.[8] Only in modern times has the scrutiny of nature and the experiment with matter come hand in hand to build modern science and its applications.

All motion on this earth that men can use — or nearly all — is motion of the sun. He is the source of mundane energies; and eventually, if not at once, the bright being of our father Sun inspirits every action. This earth is sun in matter and dynamics, in history and in goings on; and what the sun gave once only the sun can keep on going. We were articulated from the sun by his own energy, and we maintain our powers and definition and our consequence only by his radiance. The light that streams upon us is the sun's breath and body. He is the heart that sends coursing through our human systems all their vitality.

For aside from a piece of work done on the solar system in its beginning, perhaps by a wandering star, all earthly energies step off from the sun;[9] and even those termed by Slosson and others non-solar — the lunar tides, the earth's internal heat, the atom's inner energy — may be found eventually seated in the sun's development. Of solar energies, says Slosson,[10] there are the direct as used in solar engines, and there are the

indirect uses of the sun's power. Of these indirect
energies there are two kinds: physical, as winds, sails,
wind mills; waterfalls, water wheels, solar tides, waves;
and there are chemical energies in the oxidation of
carbon and hydrogen stored by the sun's energy in
plants. Of these chemical energies, those from internal
oxidations refer to food, and the energy from external oxidation refers to fuel. Of these fuels there are natural
gas, liquid petroleum, vegetable oils, alcohol. There
are solid coal, old and limited in amount, and wood,
modern and continuous in supply. Such is an inventory
of energies available to man.

Among man's earliest conquests of energies beyond
himself was domesticated power of animals. Horses and
cattle, dogs, llamas, camels, elephants and slaves were
harnessed to his system and helped do his work, and
except for sails and some crude water powers and fire
they were the constructive agencies of his civilizations
until gunpowder and other gases came in after the
thirteenth century. And even now they do much work
for man where concentrated energy is not required and
a rough terrain or irregular conditions of some other
sort make engine power unsuited. Today some 18
million horses and five million mules add energy to the
going on of this United States, and though their horse
power is not great compared with the higher power of
machine industry and travel it is important.

Animate energy is distributive. Its concentrates are
low, and a society that has no way further to nucleate
its energies also will remain distributed. In America
there's a motor car for every horse, and with travel
standardized on paved highways, men cover wider radii
of living and can congregate in denser centers of
activity without deserting means of sustence. Mechanized transportation, and the power foci of great industries have drawn men together spatially in ways that
were impossible when only animate power was used.

They are too close together without doubt, and the next problem for industrial engineers is a kind of power and its transmission that will permit redistribution.

And even on the farm, last hold-out of distributive activity, where horses still were man's best engines until not long ago, and the gray team pulled the plow and cultivator and mower through the soil's dark rhythm, and the slow silence of a summer's growth waxed in crescendos around their knees, the horse is giving way. In fifty years the horse's power upon our farms has doubled but it is smaller now than the 20 million horse power that the farmers daily find available in engines and machines.[11] Gas and the juice of wires, water power and coal have put old Dobbin on the run. He chugs about the fields in a monstrous iron mail, called a farm tractor, and his oats are liquid fuel.

Fossils drive the modern age in nearly all its great exertions. The fossil fuels, coal, oil and gas, the reservoirs of ancient sunshine, now do the world's main work. Their hydrogens and carbons will combine, if raised to kindling temperature, with oxygen of the air. There is combustion, heat, and the energy tied up for ages by solar photosynthesis in the green of plants is released once more in engines of some sort that turn a wheel for man. More than 500 million horse power [12] is constantly available in America today; no doubt the amount is nearer to a billion; and of this billion (minus) ninety per cent or so derives from fossil fuels. In the year 1919, says the U. S. Geological Survey, petroleum was contributing some 14 hundredths of the nation's energy; natural gas four hundredths, while coal contributed maybe 75 hundredths of this country's go. That means much action and mobility. It is the power of 300 million or perhaps 600 million horses.

Statistics stagger under power estimates and contradict themselves,[13] for no one knows, and least of all America, how strong we are. With fossil fuels we do the work perhaps of a billion horses or perhaps 300 million. We burn coal, says Philbrick,[14] six tons or more per year for every person in the country. We hitch ourselves to fires and we ride tremendous rates.

And in the world are more than 7,000 billion tons of coal (7,307,553,000,000 tons) of which the United States has more than half; while Canada has 16 per cent; Europe has 11 per cent; Asia has 17 per cent and the other regions scatter. Those estimates now are rather old,[15] but anyhow some trillions of the black maned horses will trample from the flues and cylinders of our industry before the coal is gone.

When will the coal be gone? If the United States burns coal at 400 million tons to a billion tons a year for four thousand years, a Swedish expert says,[16] she would barely exhaust her stock. Others are not so fortunate. By limiting her burning to 400 million tons a year, England can keep supplied for 450 years; and Germany for one thousand years. "There is not the slightest doubt," says Arrhenius, "that the United States will hold and further secure its position as industrial leader of the world and this is made even more certain by the fact that North America is very well placed as compared to Europe in the matter of supplies of iron. Ninety per cent of the world's known coal reserve lies in the United States and in China, in the ratio of four to three respectively."

America stands on a stratum of black fire, and that potential fire is her power. It streams through flues and engines and it pounds upon the gates of great events in war and industry. The Saratoga, airplane carrier, is driven by machines of 180,000 horses' power. A Greek trireme had 170 rowers. It would take two million rowers to drive the Saratoga. Xerxes' army could not push it on.[17]

But oil is the blithe delirium that bubbles through the arteries of modern commerce. It is a faster fuel with even higher concentrates of heat than coal. After

refinement it will explode when mixed with air and an
electric spark; and in a sort of gun, called a cylinder,
it will drive a projectile, called the piston head, down
towards the opening with brisk energy. It flows; it has
few ashes; and the engines that it drives, called internal
combustion motors, are more efficient and more flexible than those by coal and steam.[18]

In seventeen million motor vehicles in America in
1919 there was, says De Baufre,[19] at least 345 million
horse power available to our use. Gasoline nomadries
have developed; continents are week-end jaunts, and
seasonal migrations of America's mounted millions
shuttle back and forth a thousand miles and more from
north to south, from east to west following the sun.
Seven passengers were carried by our motor cars in
1921 to the railroads' one; and their mileage in the motor
cars was 71 to the railroads' 37; freight tonnage by truck
was 1,430,000,000 tons [20] to 1,641,000,000 tons by railroad. The expenditure on motor cars and their inciden-
tals was well nigh eight billion dollars; today it would be
more. Gas has remobilized man. He takes the air at
strenuous speeds. He digs into the middle layers of the
sea. His motor ships with heavy oils as fuel can march
their oceanic beats on schedule. Gas has inflated his
domain in space. And time swells like a blue balloon
with its pressure.

When will petroleum be gone? In the United States
some six or seven billion barrels of petroleum are left.[21]
Five or six billion are gone forever and the remaining
six of free petroleum can hold out hardly more than
fifteen years. We waste three barrels for every one we
use. Every year a full half billion barrels of petroleum
is burned; it helps to make this nation go. We are im-
porting, but the world supply is limited; oil from shales
is costly to extract; the end of oil is well in sight. America today consumes 67 hundredths of the world's oil;

NOTE: As the price of crude oil advances, the German process of
deriving liquid fuels from coal treated with hydrogen at high temperatures will be increasingly important.

to replace it with the alcohols and such will take much
growing. For to make alcohol with a fuel value equal
to the oil taken from an Oklahoma acre in five or ten
years would need a crop of corn upon that acre for
300,000 seasons.[22] When will petroleum be gone? As
a cheap fuel hardly a decade will suffice; as a costly fuel
or lubrication for special purposes, a century or so will
cover it. The cars swish by like birds on their migrations. They come up from the oily soils of this great
continent like a sudden storm of locusts. Their wings
whiff and whistle as they pass like the million pigeons
of pioneer days. But the last passenger pigeon died not
long ago old and moth eaten in his captor's cage.

There is water power and the great god Electricity
to turn to when the fossil coal and oil shall fail. The
streams will run so long as rain falls on the hillsides:
why not water power instead of coal and oil? If every
river, stream and brook in the United States were
dammed throughout its course and led from stagnant
pools through pipes to water wheels the power generated
thereby, says Steinmetz,[23] would not more than match
the energy now produced by fossil fuels. Far less than
this, of course, is the practically available supply of
water power. Though among the most efficient of prime
movers the hydraulic power turned to electric current
will never meet America's whole need. Only eight
million horse power was generated by falling water in
America in 1919, or less than two per cent [24] of the
country's power, and the total water power that could
be made is not much more than six times that.[25] Water
power will not replace the fossil fuels.

But water power has distributive advantages that
may force coal upon a new régime and method. "Just
as steam power opened up the coal fields of the world
and freed the employment of power from the geographic
restriction inherent in the use of the pressure of falling
water," say Gilbert and Pogue,[26] "so electricity rein-

states water power on terms of equality with coal, offers
the means for the transmission of energy devoid of bulk,
and affords a readiness of subdivision and ease of application that considerably enlarge its range of service.'

Today not more than two sevenths of the water
power practically possible is used. There is much to do,
for every hour of running water is power gone forever;
and there is much to teach King Coal with the white
power and thunder of the streams. Ten million horse
power of hydro-electricity, 700 billion cubic feet of
natural gas, 500 million barrels of petroleum and six or
seven billion tons of coal are America's energy demands
upon her natural resources.[27] There are horses to be
sure, and men, and one tenth of one per cent of wind
power. But the man power of the nation is less by a
good deal than ten million horse power; and horses,
men and water power together are not conceivably
more than ten per cent of all the nation's power. The
rest derives from fossil fuels. Our annual amounts of
these, says Steinmetz,[28] would make a Chinese wall of
coal all around the U. S. A. It would make four hundred
pyramids like to the largest at Ghizeh. And the energy
potential in that fuel would blow the wall or those many
pyramids more than two hundred miles high.

But there are other powers as yet untapped. A wind
mill in our average ten mile wind produces five horse
power — with the Flettner rotor mills even more no
doubt — and with one wind mill to the acre in the
United States, feeding in its power to trunk lines of
electricity, the winds that cross the land, says Ralph
Bennett,[29] would furnish for conversion 8,700,000,000
horse power. And the tide power on our coasts with an
average five foot tide, he continues, would furnish
106,500,000 horse power in addition. There is the earth's
internal heat, which Parsons says might even now be
used. Though these huge sums of energy are of course
not practically available, parts of them can and must
be used as our other natural resources decline.

And then the sun, father of all our energies, who lifts the rain from tropic oceans high into the gray smoke of the sky, who gives the winds their push and regulates the pathways of the earth and moon and bulging tides, the sun pours down direct upon us more energy than the others put together. The solar energy in the United States, says Steinmetz,[30] is a thousand times the total of our coal annually consumed, and even one tenth of our portion of the solar radiation is thirteen billion kilowatts. Two average counties in the drier part of Texas have sun enough to run all the factories and transportation systems in America.[31] If, when and maybe a solar engine is invented that is practical and cheap and has a storage mechanism for putting energy away in some potential form, a new and faster world will march upon us, as different from this modern world that rides on fossil fuels as that is from the pre-industrial era. Our engineers have yet to write the epic of the sun.

And within the atom lie huge energies that some time may be captured for our uses and made available. That overwhelming energy of our sun, which measures one or two horse power upon a plot sixty square feet in area,[32] is involved no doubt, in part at least, in these transatomic energies. But the direct energies of winds and waves, of atoms, suns, of the earth's inner heat and of tides, though great are not easily available. They may never be available; for "maybe" is a dangerous base to set society upon, and the mightiness of an atom or the sun is no excuse for wasting coal.

For our waste of power and the inefficiency of engines is enormous. Out of 2,000 pounds of soft coal meant to go under a steam boiler [33] only 76 pounds are finally utilized in action: Four hundred pounds go up the stack; 600 pounds are lost in mining; 100 pounds are lost in transportation; 100 pounds are lost by radiation and in the ash pit; 600 pounds are lost in the conversion of heat into mechanical energy. Much of this loss of course is not preventable; there must be waste — see Carnot's law, the irreversibility of process — but fully half our waste of fossil fuels is quite unnecessary. Our average steam plants use eight times the coal that our most efficient steam plants use; [33] and for every horse power that is used, according to another estimate,[33] coal is burned for twenty horse power. In water power, in coal, oil, gas our resources nearly equal all the other nations put together. But waste is a mighty leveler; America may find herself before much time is gone below the rest. For each citizen of this country there are fifty slaves at work in terms of captured natural energies [34] but many of those slaves, as Stuart Chase suggests, are loafing on the job.

Coal and iron are the new builders of this modern world — coal and iron — and the ability of man, chimpanzee-like, to join them in new, inventive forms. For our resources in power have their counterpart in matter; and the raw materials of this age, the minerals and soils, the rains and temperatures, the land's configurations and the seas, and the growing stuff and stock that underlies us all have critical importance in society's development. Coal and the metals and productive soils are three factors always decisive in this modern age. For good or bad the growing sector of mankind has left the ancient valleys and denuded soils to follow them.

In the year 1500, the world used 50 thousand tons of iron; [35] in 1870 it used 12 million tons; in 1913 it used 72 million tons of iron; in 1920 it used 40 million tons and of this two score million tons more than 35 million tons were used by the United States. In 1870 the power available per person in the United States of 38 million population was two tenths of one horse power; [36] in 1920 the power per person in the United States of 100

million population was more than five horse power.
Power and the use of iron have grown concomitantly in
the modern age: Iron and coal and man are in alliance.

For iron is a resource limited like coal in distribution
and amount and the people that possess them have
competitive advantage over others. Of four types of
resources named by Fenneman,[37] namely, (a) "materials and sources of power which exist in superabundance
for all foreseeable time," such as common salt, brick clay,
sunlight and nitrogen; (b) resources permanent in
nature but limited in amount, like soil and water power;
(c) resources reproduced in crops, regularly renewed if
not exterminated, such as fish, forests and various
animals; (d) limited accumulations that when gone are
gone forever, such as many minerals, coal and ore; of
these four types iron, it is obvious, as well as coal
belongs to the last and economically most distressing
group. When gone there will be no replenishment.

When will the iron go? The known stocks contain
about ten billion (10,000,000,000) tons of iron and this
would last, were there no more, perhaps a century.[38]
But reserves of iron now not fully known are said to
raise the world deposits to more than four hundred
billion (425,000,000,000) tons; and these it may be safe
to say will extend the iron age some centuries further.
Lower and lower grades of ore will of course be used;
more coal no doubt and power will be required to reduce
them; and finally the human race will turn to something
else.

For this decline aluminum awaits in amounts almost
inexhaustible in the clays and earths and feldspars of
the world. It takes electric power and money to extract
it, but it is there awaiting entrance of the age of the
light metals.[39] Copper is an ancient friend of man
whose stay is limited. Zinc, lead, gold, tin and other
famous playthings of mankind cannot last forever. The
silicon of clay and sand, of glass, pottery and concrete,

the calcium of limestone and complex minerals, on the other hand, that go to make our soils seem relatively unlimited.

But productive soil itself, a third great factor in our modern age is less secure in permanence. Man is himself a chemistry in the maintenance of soils; he fails miserably to fulfil his function as a part of the soil cycle. For from iron ores — a soil precipitate — and other metals to man and animals and plants all are deposited, as it were, in the ceaseless shift and circulation of the inner waters and the slow building of triumphant soil. Coal and petroleum were formulated in that matrix; it is a laboratory of life and of materials that life must have. It is delicately organized. It has color and a skeleton, muscles and colloidal linings, a digestive system, respiratory and circulatory systems, and functions, say the soil priests and poets such as Whitney,[40] not unlike a living thing.

Into this balanced system man comes with harsh hands. He skins the soil; gullies gouge the slopes. He cuts and burns the natural vegetation, drains the swamps and the water table of the soil declines: The world over probably there are not more than 300 million acres of wheat land, and those who live on bread cannot increase beyond a billion people; and still man does not listen.[41] He breaks the natural diversity of plants and animals and specializes on one crop or two; and like a piece of metal hammered long upon one place, or like a workman's arm tired of doing but one thing, the soil becomes fatigued. Soils may not wear out at all, says Whitney,[42] through chemical depletion; they become toxic with the excreta of one kind of plant grown there repeatedly. They need a crop rotation or the natural diversity of uncultivated lands to retain productiveness.

By science in the west and by the long sweetening of experience in China and the far east, man has learned to some degree to give the soil the kindly care that a

high bred milking cow or a child requires, and new
productivities reward him. In forty years the average
yield of wheat per acre in the United States has increased
from less than twelve bushels to about sixteen.[43] But
Belgium in 1922 was raising 32.8 bushels per acre, and
the United Kingdom in 1914 was averaging 32.4 bushels; Germany, 31.7 bushels; France, 19.1 bushels; and
the Shantung province, China, 42 bushels per acre.[44]
Though America raises more wheat per man than China
does, it is appropriate nevertheless to reconsider the
Chinaman in the light of applied science, and to suggest
perhaps that the United States may have several things,
both scientific and artistic, to learn about the soil from
him.

For China has as great a mileage of canals as
America has railroads, and though her many hands will
do what Americans must do with gaunt machines, she will
use those hands to tend the soil with tender care and
patience.[45] From her canals, 200 thousand miles long,
she draws water for the soil; she digs the silt from river
and canal bottoms to spread upon it; she returns all
human sewage to the soil; she allies herself with nature.

China's soils will not wear out, for man there does his
part in the soil system. With an agricultural continuity
of many thousand years, with her watering and transport systems still intact, China lives in her soil in a
settled cycle. Men after all, as well as animals, are but
one step from soil. They are but moveable colloidal
masses detached, as it were, temporarily from the soil
where they were made. They are flying fish emergent
for a moment above the surface of the land, with much
spluttering and motion, but they dive down again into
their native element and system before long.

There are other soils less fortunate than these of
friendly China. There are wrecked and blasted soils,
skinned, eroded and sliding down uncared for to the sea.
Syria and Spain, Mesopotamia and parts of North

America and the treeless mountain tops of China are
such. The gardens of the two rivers, of western Asia
and of Moorish Spain, once raised by ancient irrigations
to a place of green and sweetness, have cracked and
seared under the sun; their canals are torn like twisted
yarns by conquest and invasion of men who never
loved the soil, and today the desert lies like harsh scar
tissue over the earth's flesh.[46]

When will the soil be gone? In America it is going
down the Mississippi to the sea at the rate of nine billion cubic feet a year. We have reaped our forests, and
our soils without the cover and the sponge of vegetation
slip from under our feet with every rain. We have
plowed our river banks, torn the tough sod from the
prairie, and the soil guts and avalanches to the streams
and sea without restraint. The rains spring into floods
across the raw, uncovered lands and the water table
sinks to lower levels.

But there is soil still in America, rich and powerful,
ready to build new forests and new civilizations. The
cereals and tobacco, cotton, grapes and potatoes grown
in our soils in 1919 alone weighed more than 155 million
tons.[47] That is four times and more the 35 million tons
of iron used annually in America; and more than one
fourth the weight of the 500 million tons of our coal
burned every year. It would build a tower, twelve city
blocks in area, more than one mile high. For the soil is
not a piker. It produces massively. With water and the
air and above all sunlight its manufactures are tremendous. Ninety-five per cent of its great produce comes
from the air; five per cent are minerals from the soil.
For every hundred pounds of the vegetation of the earth
(in terms of dry matter) 82 pounds are carbohydrates;
ten pounds are protein; three pounds are fats; and soil
minerals — potassium, phosphorus, calcium, sodium,
silicon, sulphur, magnesium, iron, chlorine — are five
pounds.[48] What the soil produces annually in terms of

vegetation, and that secondary vegetation called animals and men, is almost beyond estimate. It is the mass measurement of life.

Our soil will last forever with care and a regard for the decencies and needs of vegetable production. The Japanese regard their older soil the best, for they return in fair exchange for what they must take out. They pay the soil its honest wage, we rob it of its goods. But the soils of this new occidental land are rich and various. If soil-wrecked Greece or Italy had but a corner of our domain spread beside Olympus or on the Tiber, revival might ride again upon the Mediterranean, and Mussolini's empire might be an urgent fact rather than a third Napoleon's regurgitation. We have forest lands and mountains, swamps and coastal soils, plains, deserts, tundras, boulder hills and lava soils, but the heart of America is the great valley of the Mississippi. Here is a valley competent to feed more people than any valley in the world, a valley like the Nile, the Tigris and Euphrates, the Ganges, the Hoang Ho, designed as it were for a great civilization, and left raw and unexploited until a mature race came in. Here in this great valley, focused more or less upon Chicago, is the productive impetus of this modern age. For its metropolis the middle westerner has an enthusiasm in great part justified:

"Thousands of years ago nature planned this place for a great town," says a middle western voice.[49] "The winds and rivers and the great ice convened upon this spot and left a trampled place with wide gates for a city. The lakes were gouged out and the upper valley of the Mississippi covered with fertile fathoms of Canadian soil. Two great river systems meet in the streets and canals of Chicago. One flows 1,700 miles to the Atlantic. The other flows 1,600 miles to the gulf of Mexico.

"It is no accident that the metropolis of a region

capable of supporting one third of the population of the globe will grow. Ninety-five per cent of the country's iron is easily available to Chicago by water. The Lake Superior region has uncounted million tons of it. It is close to copper, lead, zinc, petroleum. It is the lumber market of the world. Two thirds of Illinois is underlaid by coal.

"Chicago is the grain center of America. It is the live stock center. Fifteen million head of cattle, sheep, and hogs come to Chicago annually. It is the milk center.

"Chicago is the focus of the greatest producing region of the world. Its growth is an inevitable natural phenomenon. But the direction and rate of that growth depends on the character of her people. What have Chicagoans done to make this city great?

"Thirty-nine railways, 40 per cent of the mileage of the United States, end in Chicago. It is the railroad center of the world. That represents in the past human energy and initiative. Every year Chicago freight houses handle more than 10,000,000 tons of freight. Twenty million freight cars are received and forwarded by Chicago every year. More than 60,000,000 passengers come to the passenger terminals annually. Almost 1,500 passenger trains arrive and depart every day. . . ."

And so it goes in one town or another of this broad middle west and in magnificent domains of the far west, south, east, north: the boost, the urge, the vulgar energy and pressure, the rank growing of these peoples in a fresh soil, is after all but a new release of human energy under most favorable conditions. It is a rich soil, with coal and iron at its roots, caught up in a living transformation into deeds, humanity and massive power. America is that.

Though America, as most Americans might well be told, is not the only nation that rides eagerly into the new age, the wealth of its raw resources and natural power, the energy and inventiveness of its people, is

a phenomenon of these times that sets the key to the
entire modern period.

Upon America sits wealth surpassing any other nation. Her coal, spread upon the middle west and the
eastern mountains, is more than that of all the remaining world. Canada, China, Germany, Great Britain
follow at remote distances.[50] Her water power, for the
most part in the farther west, is more than that of
any other nation. Canada comes next, then Norway,
Sweden, France and Switzerland. As a continent Africa
outranks her, also Asia, but their water power is less
available for development. Her iron ore production and
probably her reserves are far beyond those of any other
people. She leads in copper and in oil. Her soils produce
more wheat, corn, barley, oats, apples, pears, citrus
and prunus fruits, cotton, tobacco and more timber
(before the murder of our forests) than those of any
other country. In the pockets of America these are
bright gold pieces put there by Nature as the youth
went out to meet the world. They are our fortune,
hardly our accomplishment. How we shall use them —
as a coarse spendthrift or a miser — is another question.

If materials and resources were put in terms of the
stock market, the stocks "most active" among them in
America would perhaps be lumber and paper, rubber,
gasoline, mineral fertilizers, nitrogen, chemical synthetics, cement, electric power. Problems sit in their
vicinity, and for one reason or another, their status is
more like to change than others. Lumber and paper,
rubber, gasoline and mineral fertilizers are threatened
with declines, not in price, but in quantity and economic
function. Nitrogen, chemical creations, cement and electric power promise huge advances in availability and in
use. The first are problems in descent; the second are

problems in ascent. The first ask how to get along with
less; the second, how to make use of more. In problems
of replacement and of thrift, in spite of Roosevelt and
Pinchot and other conservationists, America is neither
apt nor trained. Hers is an expansion economics.

Once our forests covered more than 800 million
acres. When Roosevelt began his drive for conservation
they covered 550 million acres. Now they cover 470
million acres.[51] In Teddy's day the wood taken from
our forests every year was 23 billion cubic feet, and the
annual growth was seven billion. Today more than 23
billion cubic feet are dragged away, and the annual
regrowth is six billion. Waste in cutting methods in
order to get quick profits, waste in preparation, waste
in construction, waste in consumption mark the trail
through America's big woods. Out of our 110 billion
board feet of lumber cut every year fully 70 billion, it
is estimated,[52] are wasted. There is land enough, now
wasted, to regrow our vanished forests. "Mere care
along old lines" would double annual regrowth. Scientific forestry, a century old in Europe, would quadruple
it. If America wants lumber in the future that must be
done now. Under the present murderous methods our
forests can endure not more than forty years and
probably much less.

Gasoline is more desperate, for it will not regrow;
like youth once gone, it is gone for good. Though
chemists came with a cracked molecule into the oil
business and doubled gasoline's possible production
by a new refining process,[53] even their efforts cannot
save America from oil exhaustion in a score of years or
less. Before the oil is piped three out of four barrels are
wasted, and an individualistic economic system prevents
our saving oil below the ground for fear the other man
will draw it off ahead. More than half of our supply is
gone forever. Oil is America's flaming youth; it is burning fast.

Rubber is difficult but not so desperate as gasoline. Soils produce the rubber of the world, and cultivated rubber now exceeds the wild production eighteen to one. But soils and climate in the United States will grow but little rubber. With imports of 300 thousand tons a year,[54] three times as much as all the other countries put together, and with a rubber market indefinitely expansible, America is subject to the whims and taxes of Britain and the Dutch and others who control the growing. Rubber climbs high. A demand that cannot be saturated receives slight satisfaction. America pays in shortage and high prices for lack of business skill and foresight in building rubber areas under American control somewhere in the Philippines; in Central or South America or elsewhere. Recent rubber projects in Liberia, our African, small, black offshoot, and in Brazil, may help the American supply. Synthetic chemistry may help by producing artificial rubber cheaply, but this is hardly probable.[55] A hardy form of rubber plant that will survive in the south part of the United States, and can be raised in seasonal crops, may come sooner to our rescue. By chemistry, biology or business energy the problem can be solved in time.

And potash is a problem. For America can take nitrogen at will from the world's atmosphere. Phosphates we have from Florida to Idaho. But potash, third of the fertilizer triumvirate, is hard to get in solvent form. Though the German grip on potash was broken by the war, our endemic potash famine is not much bettered. With requirements, as a minimum, of 250 thousand tons of potash every year America was able to produce under the lash of war and high prices only 33 thousand tons in 1917; and in 1918, chiefly through the use of natural brines, 52 thousand tons.[56] Our own resources in potash, says Slosson, are natural brines and lakes, limited but producing three fourths or more of homemade potash, kelp pickled and reduced, molasses residues, alumite rock from Utah, dust from cement mills, wood ashes, waste from sugar beets, other industrial wastes and dust from blast furnaces. But there are not enough. Potash is a problem for the soils and man somehow to work out together.

When limited resources and materials are in mind men think nationally and for their own advantage, and though the oil problem, the coal, iron, copper problems, the forest, the soil, the rubber and the potash problems are world problems, their solutions are, and no doubt will remain, in some sense national. Limited resources are unlikely to be thrown open to the world.

Around the resources and their uses that remain unlimited will develop international estates and institutions so sought by certain factors of our populations. Around nitrogen and chemical synthetics, concrete, and lines of superpower, sun energies and the like will aggregate the elements, such as they are, of that hoped-for human synthesis. Their development is important. As substitutes they economize in limited materials. By giving all men powers and new facilities for living they reduce the drive for war.

Nitrogen is one of them. Food for guns and violets, builders of dark green crops, prosperity of farmers, pusher of projectiles into steel bellies of great ships, driver of the proteins and men's energies everywhere, nitrogen is as free as it is necessary. It is too free, and though the energy of its compounds comes of the ease with which nitrogen lets go and hastens back to former single bliss, it is hard correspondingly to arrange liaisons for it and persuade it to forsake the air, where it rules by great majorities, and join with other elements.[57] But electric power will do it — see Ford and Muscle Shoals — and nitrates for explosives and plant food, for poison gas and ladies' toilet instruments will not be lacking. Though Chile nitrates will still be dug for arsenals and farms over the world, the crisis of the nitrogen supply is past, and the main problem now is finding uses and extensions for it into this already too explosive world.

And chemists juggling their pet molecules have built another world of new synthetic products. Germany not long ago celebrated the 50 thousandth new creation of the chemists' fertile formulas. America and England could do almost as well. From cotton seed, for example,[58] come mattresses and lamb's wool underwear, varnish and smokeless powder, writing paper, cattle feed, lard, soap, artificial silk and leather, roofing and collodion and dye and a hundred others. The strange shift and instability of creation has settled on it. It is raw material of a world. Old and new metals, perfumes, drugs,[59] new stuffs for building come in huge numbers from the laboratory, not one half of which are yet assimilated into our living system. Nature has huge potentialities not yet realized or created, and man as assistant creator is doing fairly well.

Cement is pouring on the world in long ribbons like a patent tooth paste for our cars to travel on; in mighty lumps and structures, from bridges to wheat elevators; and cement supplies are almost inexhaustible. In America more than 137 million barrels of cement [60] were made in 1923 to be joined forever with sand in some desired shape. Today America turns out 155 million barrels of cement, lays 12 million cubic yards of concrete roads, and pours 91 million cubic yards of other concrete structures in a year. That, says Harper Leech,[61] is 34 pyramids of the best Egyptian period and almost equals an annual Chinese wall. It took 100 thousand slaves some twenty years to build one pyramid. Each slave laid the equivalent of thirty cubic yards in twenty years. On a modern concrete job thirty cubic yards are laid for each man in the crew in sixty hours. Science applied to power resources has dynamic consequence.

And superpower grows towards the world's rebirth.
Economies of power and distribution, democracies of
effort and control lie in it. It is perhaps the keynote of
the future age. In 1919 steam roads produced 37 billion
horse-power-hours at eight pounds of coal per horse-
power-hour; but central stations, Jackson says,[62] produced 53 billion horse-power-hours at one and one half
pounds of coal per hour. And so it will go on: Power
production will be concentrated; power consumption
will be more and more distributed. The long lightning
of those slender wires will redistribute man.

On man the effect of sciences applied is not less than
a new universe. His time is new. His space is rearranged
and amplified. His mobilities are enormously increased.
His experience of material things is nearer saturation —
if there be a saturation point — and his life swirls
through a dense world with wide frontiers.

His foods are changed and the material of his living.
His life is organized on a larger scale. Great industries
and professions rise around a science pointed at some
field of human action. Science in agriculture lowers the
labor necessary to a pound of flour and raises the pounds
per acre. Science in medicine lengthens man's life some
twenty years or more, reduces death at birth, keeps men
physically more efficient, and adds no doubt fully twice
as much to the quantity of a life as man possessed
before. Science in engineering adds to the instruments
of work and transportation, shelter and defense, efficiencies and powers that have multiplied in fifty years
man's mechanistic capabilities not less than 250 times.[63]
They make of him an animal of enormous power. Two
hundred thousand American engineers work towards
those new potencies, and their aim, says Beyer,[64] is
less and less concerned with wringing power from nature

as with adjusting power to legitimate social needs. They build alliances with nature.

Our climate even is affected by the modern burning of great fires. The annual combustion on this globe of 1,000,000,000 tons of coal produces 3,670,000,000 tons of carbon dioxide gas that returns mostly to the atmosphere. Like glass or water vapor this gas admits the sunshine to the earth but prevents to some extent its radiation off again. At present rates this gas will double in the atmosphere in 800 years, not long as climates go, and unless some counteractive factor intervenes, the climate will be warmer.[65]

On every side science impinges on the modern life of man. And though the effects of science are socially universal, the knowledge and control and applications of it are relatively too narrow. Natural catastrophe or reaction may easily destroy science, as the classic culture was destroyed, though it seem impossible, or use it to destroy human life and progress. And there is only one defense: the spread of scientific knowledge on broad and democratic bases of control. Making science popular and broadly known is an important function. Science never should be left solely to a narrow, priestly class of theorists and technicians.

In many fields the tendency of science and its applications has been socially too centripetal. In control and operation and above all in knowledge it has never been distributive enough for full security. Modern industrialism, the huge product of applied science, is subject to that danger.

Man's life has followed closely on the course of power production. The momentum of stone axes, the spring and potential of a bow, the domesticated power of animals and slaves, the leverage of wheels and levers, the push of winds on sailing ships, all were utilities and ways of organizing power to his advantage. It was a slow advance up to the first boom of gunpowder. In dynamic terms the world till then was in an age of power produced and consumed distributively.

Then gas explosions were domesticated. Gunpowder, steam, gasoline banged and pushed all for man's glory and aggression. Their huge energies were hitched to engines of destruction, construction, locomotion. Power production became concentrated, and around those concentrations and machineries gathered laborers and consumers in massive aggregations called industrial towns. Today those desperate densities of population by far outnumber, in the western world, all of the rest. It is an age of concentrated power production and consumption.

The newer age, of which light streaks now appear on the east horizon, will be an age of concentrated power production, but with distributive consumption. Man may return then to the soil that loves him without the sacrifice of power and benefits and joy that now depresses him there. Rural life without its isolations and futilities will gain renewed prestige, and man — granting his intelligent desire — may regain once more life's natural conditions to which he physically and psychically is adjusted.

Highways of power will stretch across the land from coast to coast in continental systems of electric superpower.[66] Into power trunk lines will run feeders from the plants built at the coal mine's mouth or by reservoirs of water, feeders from the waterfalls and from the winds and waves and tides, the inner heat of earth, and the sun engines of the desert spaces. And from those trunk lines power will be tapped wherever it is wanted, for industries and agriculture, for electric curling irons and for locomotives and canal boats. The use of power will not be limited to the locale of its production.

There are problems, to be sure, before that age can come, and the cost and conductivity of copper wire is not the least of them. But man, like the chimpanzee, is primarily a problem solving animal and these are not insuperable. Already the electric power consumption of the United States per capita is more than 400 kilowatt hours per annum.[67] Great lines are hooking up from Wisconsin to Kentucky, from North Carolina to Alabama and Tennessee, from Washington to California. In California 1200 kilowatt hours of electric power are consumed per annum for every member of the population. Of this 41 per cent is used by manufacturers, 21 per cent by railroads, 16 per cent by agriculture, 16 per cent for lights and domestic uses, and 6 per cent by mining. In the United States, central electric stations in 1922 used more than 20 million horse power to generate more than 40 billion kilowatt hours of power for human consumption.[68] There will be growth in that.

Man's power problem is mainly to defeat old Carnot's law of the irreversibility of process; and though man never can defeat it, his steps in that direction have marked the progress of his material affairs. For the energy that comes from all his engines available to his use must always be a good deal less than what goes in. His efficiency, and that of all his engines, is measured by the energy he saves or makes available. America is a monstrous engine; and the reckless waste of resources and of men, of power, of soils, of forests, oil and coal and iron, is the measure of our inefficiencies and failures. The energy that we take out for human purposes is low compared with what goes in. Conservation of resources and power is an aspect of the super-engineering that must appeal to statesmen and constructive men. This national engine is in their hands for running or for wreck.

With this chapter the long account of universal process

comes, in a sense, to an end. It began — after some attention to the structural ideas of the world, space, time, matter, energy — with the tale of cosmic process, the birth of suns and solar systems, the earth and soils; then living process, plant and animal and its evolution; then behavior and the mind of man; then ancient man down to the age of writing; modern man of the historical period; and now the evolution of modern power and human energy. The line is dynamically continuous from nebulæ and the shock of colliding stars down to eight cylinder automobiles. It is one evolution, for all process is an evolution, and though our human interests lead us to select only one aspect of it, namely, the line that leads to man, it is continuous, we may assume, and orderly throughout.

In this chapter man's inventiveness was first mentioned; then the basis in liberalism of all modern science and its applications; an inventory of energy and an account of the resources of modern power in coal, water and the like; the material resources of the world in iron, soil, and their effect on life; modern problems of materials and energy, rubber, nitrogen, cement, and the like; how science must be made enduring; the next age, superpower and conservation. It is a massive situation that modern man has come upon.

But there are further futures, and a violin's singing now, or a girl's laughter, will reach as far into the being of the world as all the crash and mechanism of man's industry. Our solar system is none too safe, the experts say, for Jupiter may grow in time to be a mighty star. There will be burnings then and terrible perturbations; our piquant little earth will slip into the sun; the dunes at Saugatuck will drift away in mist; the band at Potawatomi will play no more; the St. Charles corner drug store will never serve again a tall, brown Coca Cola; the hills will melt; the town pump will be consumed; the steel mills of Gary will blaze in cosmic crucibles; and

Jupiter and our sun will turn about each other as a stellar binary.[69]

Man has his place in stellar systems; he has his cosmic value; but his scale is hardly in those terms. He must create his values. He must find worth within. An atom after all has all the world, all time and space and motion inherent in its pattern. It is a cosmic order, and events within it have all the import of events among the stars. And within his system man too is a significance and a power; for the power of life has no mean import in the universe. The nature — and the value — of a thing depends, as Einstein well might say, upon its field of reference.

Industrial Society

MAN too is a natural resource. The power of the
white streams, of winds, of strands of coal woven
deeply in the meshes of the earth, of tides and sun is after all only the junior in alliance with the power of life.
Though economists will call these[1] "land" and man
power "labor" they are different only in a point of view
and valuation invented by ourselves. The mobility of
man, his strategy and calculations, his control of crucial
situations among the surface forces of this earth give an
advantage. He coördinates their energies to some extent
into one system. He is the cosmic catalyzer whose presence somehow will reorganize the rest. He is an enzyme
floating in the streams of natural energy. Ferments
begin and new adjustments come.

This power of life is no mean thing as superficial
energies go. It does something to the environment, says
Dewey,[2] "as well as has something done to itself. There
is no such thing in a living creature as mere conformity
to conditions, though parasitic forms may approach
this limit. In the interests of the maintenance of life
there is transformation of some elements in the surrounding medium. The higher the form of life, the more
important is the active reconstruction of the medium.
This increased control may be illustrated by the contrast of savage with civilized man. Suppose the two are
living in a wilderness. With the savage there is the
maximum of accommodation to given conditions; the
minimum of what we may call hitting back. The savage
takes things 'as they are,' and by using caves and roots
and occasional pools leads a meagre and precarious
existence. The civilized man goes to distant mountains
and dams streams. He builds reservoirs, digs channels,

and conducts the waters to what had been a desert. He searches the world to find plants and animals that will thrive. He takes native plants and by selection and cross-fertilization improves them. He introduces machinery to till the soil and care for the harvest. By such means he may succeed in making the wilderness blossom like the rose.

"Such transformations are so familiar that we overlook their meaning. We forget that the inherent power of life is illustrated in them." And in industrial society today this power of life finds a magnitude and muscularity of expression without parallel in the history of man. With gases captured and their expansive strength added to man's arm, with other natural powers convertible to electric energy, a machine age is made possible, and the power that man directs can drive tools and huge implements, like the printing press or the steam shovel or the 100,000 horse power engines of a battle cruiser, where his arm alone, or slaves or horses might find it difficult. This well nigh catastrophic increase in man's power of arm is the dominating factor of industrial life and of our western social problems. For our habits and our customs, our institutions and societies that even half a century ago were organized with some stability about an average man whose strength from outside sources was not much more than two tenths of a horsepower, now crack and strain about a man of five horse power additional.[3] The life engine of today sits on a base built for an engine of one twenty-fifth its power.

For with stronger arms man can produce more; he makes more things for his enjoyment; he saves more. As his capacity for enjoying wealth can hardly keep in stride with his increased productive power huge parts of what he makes are saved for more production and the pyramid of modern life endlessly piles up. It is in the nature of machinery, power driven, to do this. Its rumbling bass is the dominant motif of what economists call capitalism. For machines and manufacturing plants are concentrated savings from the wealth of things produced, for the sake only of more production.[4] They are a form of capital, in concentrates of operation and control; they are those main productive implements that make this modern period what it is.

Great quantity of production marks the machine age,[5] for machines are mostly repetitious mechanisms, doing over fast and untiringly what they have done once; so long as power and raw materials hold out, the quantity of their output is determined almost solely by the amount that can be sold. This has increased with the advance of industry, with greater populations and the wider area of consumption on the part of every modern man. Steel production in America from 1891 to '95 was 23 million tons, for example, but from 1916 to '20 it was 200 million tons.[6] That growth in steel with war and higher living standards, is four times the corresponding increase in our population.

To the repetitiousness of power machines, however, not all industries are easily amenable. Agriculture and some elements of house keeping, dairying and breeding, building to some extent and silk production, for example, are not easily put on a large scale basis; and in consequence our economic system has strange bulges and distortions. It is steatopygous after the manner of a Bantu carving. The effects of quantity production are differential. Some industries have grown to huge size and profits. Others have not kept their corresponding place.

In the manufactures and in transport and in communications such as newspapers and advertising the transformation has been greatest. For their costs decrease with large production, where agriculture, beyond a certain limit, may increase in cost. And with more integration around great groups of power machines the

number of establishments in many of these fields has
grown fewer as the decades pass while the wage earners
and the capital and product have respectively increased.
In Germany, to quote Taussig,[7] the per cent of persons
in establishments employing more than 1000 hands
increased between 1882 and 1907 from 3.5 to 8.1 while
the persons doing work alone decreased from 25.2 to 10.1
per cent. The twenty years since 1907 will show increasing shifts in this direction in most of the western world.

Horizontal combinations between like industries,
vertical integrations between industries and their an-
tecedents or successors in the productive organism,
have taken place impressively. Ford owns his coal and
iron mines, his railroad and his shipping, his repair and
selling systems. The Bell Telephone spreads laterally
in a copper mesh over the continent. And U. S. Steel
is both broad and deep. In many industries, no doubt,
these concentrates of management and operation and
of power tied to great machines will remain economically
most needful.

And to watch the work of interstitial adjustment in
all industry comes a man who is neither laborer nor
engineer nor direct producer.[8] He is the business man;
he often takes the risk; he directs; he has his hand on
many things, some foolish, some sublime, some selfish,
some a sacrifice; he works, but many name him T. B. M.
He works in terms of money; he very likely wears a
derby hat; and it rests with him "to make or mar the
running adjustments of industry." He, with trade and
commerce, as well as the laborer and the operator, with
industrial production, is focused on the cities; for the
growths of machine industry have been largely urban
growths. With the new age has come a differential
development of the great town and of the country. It
is lop sided in the former's favor. The 1920 census found
America with the majority of her people in the cities.
The towns increased in tonnage, population and in

consumption for each resident. The country not much more than held its own. In ten years the people of our cities increased more than twelve million while the rural districts gained less than three. The margin of nine million souls roughly represents the human premium that accrues from industrial organization and modern business methods. Like capital, like engines, machinery, manufacturing plants, it too is saved, as it were, from the surplus of production beyond the limits of immediate enjoyment.

The derby hat is not a unique absurdity in the lives of men, and though it can claim fairly to be the classic instance of what fools these mortals be, its funnyness is like a congressman's, it represents the rest of us. For the hat will be fitting souvenir of an age when industrial standardization reached a maximum. Its trim and sober mediocrity, cut as it were by one thud and stamp of a derby hat machine, suits our modern style and quantity productions. It is man standardized in head gear amid the repetitious roar of his machines, in contrast with a woman's Easter ecstacies.

For machines do one thing in endless repetition, and that repeated thing of course becomes the standard of their product. Such standards and equalities of value are inherent in all trade and currency,[9] and machines producing quantities of undifferentiated output increase the natural ease and speed of trade. New "currencies," as Wallas says,[10] are created when iron, sugar, rubber, or any new commodity is standardized and enters the world market; the chance of trade and mobile speculation is increased. The machine technique has entered business all to the latter's glory. It has increased the multiplicity of objects for the market. It has reduced their inner differences and perversities of value to bases

of comparison and trade. Denotatively the machine
technique has enormously increased our world. Con-
notatively it has perhaps impoverished it. Extrinsic
multiplicity, intrinsic similarity, in such a world, trade
flourishes and bankers now grow fat.

Production and enjoyment of wealth must run in
standard channels when both are concentrated near
machines, and derby hats and massed societies ensue.
It is a world susceptible to the organizer's will, and its
parts, from commodities to labor, can be shifted and
transposed with a new ease. For standard things are
not hard to mobilize; they are predictable and a given
force applied will always have the same result. The
fluidities of this modern world come in great part from
man's increase in power and the machine process.
Movement is its principle; and fast turnover, more than
old time thrift, is the way to get along. And progress,
what is progress in these modern mobile terms? The
question is "not how long can you keep a thing," says
Owen D. Young, "but how quick you can economically
scrap it. That's progress." And thus the absolutes
decay.

Currencies are elaborated in this mobile world in
huge complexities; and men, sometimes called "the
bankers," who control their concatenations acquire
power and an unique import. For currencies of gold or
standard wheat or pig iron are abstractions through
which man can manipulate the shift and sale and making
of his goods. They are artificial standards, and their
stability depends upon their common usage and our
discipline. To fix our currency so its general buying
power will be stable through the shock of war and industrial upheaval is the prime problem financially of
the world today.[11] For with the dollar, or the pound or
mark or franc now at one hundred buying power, now
at sixty, now at forty-three, back and forth, up and
down, in fickle oscillations, investment is a risky bet,

saving is a dangerous gamble, and the general faith in our economic structure is undermined.[12] In all this modern world of measurements and standards, of accurate machines and industrial organization our money still remains in real value quite unstandardized.

The trouble, says Irving Fisher,[13] is the dollar's too narrow base, for a fixed quantity of gold cannot keep stride with the average "buying powers" of massed commodities. And the answer is, he says, a new "goods-dollar" made of gold in quantity that varies according to the range of prices, or "index number," at the time. He would load his dollar with a ballast to be taken on or off according to the index number of a group composed of farm, food, clothing, fuel, light, metal, lumber, building, drug, chemical, furnishing and other goods, and the result no doubt would be a dollar more seaworthy than we have today. Though Keynes [14] says that in control of bank rates a non-metallic money standard already has slipped in unnoticed this hardly would replace reforms as fundamental as Fisher's.

Economically this is a liquid world and the once stubborn properties in land, or capital or enjoyment that seemed sometimes well nigh inalienable and hard to concentrate are now transferred time and again in accumulated pyramids by a mere pen stroke or a broker's nod. It makes easier the control of land and wealth by the adepter few, and a workman's only property for his job today may be a pair of overalls. The real point in industrialism, says Earl Dean Howard,[15] "is that men are laboring to produce useful and beautiful things, which except by rarest chance, they do not hope to enjoy." They are less men than labor units abstractly figured in production costs; and machines inevitably control the limits of their job and status. They are standardized by the machine — called fixed capital; their jobs are limited and accurately defined, and replacement is less hunting for a man than for a spare part.

It is an urban situation. Only there, can so specialized a life be forced on general purpose man. It comes mostly of machines and of cities that grow near them; and when energy can be distributed once more, perhaps by "superpower," the condition may be bettered. The dangerous abstractions of today's production may be ameliorated, and "hands" and jobs will have their connotative interests as well as their ulterior values in money and new power.

For the age that builds the one piece derby hat, the fountain pen, the patent player of pianos, the predigested breakfast food purveyor, the gas log, the accurate weigher of a wad of gum, elaborate dried beef cutters, bread slicers, mechanical hair driers and cobblers' singing lathes for men who have a secret love of all machines beyond their mere utility may yet flame into culture and imaginative context above mere quantity production. Machines have their beauty and their humor and their humane possibilities. Socially they as yet are undigested, and if man can somehow readjust their raw emphases on labor specializations, on urban life and crowding, on the brass and emptiness of a life too standardized he may find the decencies of living through, not in spite of, his machines. The outcome will depend on the purpose that man holds before him in his economic life. Today his aim is barbarous.

"For what gives meaning to economic activity," says Tawney,[16] "is the purpose to which it is directed. But the faith upon which our economic civilization reposes, the faith that riches are not a means but an end, implies that all economic activity is equally estimable, whether it is subordinated to a social purpose or not. Hence it divorces gain from service, and justifies rewards for which no function is performed, or which are out of all proportion to it. Wealth in modern societies is distributed according to opportunity; and while opportunity depends partly upon talent and energy, it depends still more upon birth, social position, access to education and inherited wealth; in a word, upon property. For talent and energy can create opportunity. But property need only wait for it."

Waste, wild and disastrous, is one consequence of the unsocial purpose that dominates our modern economic life. And it is waste that counts, for man's exploiting power has grown to dangerous size. Wastes of resources and of men, of products whose destruction will advance the market, follow in our wake like sharks. In lumber and in oil and probably in coal, says Stuart Chase,[17] the output of end-products could probably be doubled while the rate of exploitation could be reduced. In making patent medicines and drugs, in commercial vice and crime, in adulterations and in fakes, gambling, speculation and in some wars, fashions, advertising, sports and luxuries our wasted man power totals eight million and perhaps a good deal more. There is child labor and there are other wastes, social and economic only less savage. All must be attributed to the "divorce of gain from service."

For industrial society itself is not unlike a closely organized machine that drives its way across the terrain of life heedless of other things save somehow "getting there." It is strong engined but it lacks an engineer to realize and exploit its proper function. Its own mechanism hardly can decide how man should use it best; it needs domestication. It tramples us where it should serve. It often overrides our human happiness and the natural ways of life where it should aid and strengthen them. It is decisive against thrift on the part of workmen, Veblen says,[18] in "the fact that modern large organization of industry requires a high degree of mobility on the part of employees. . . . The working population is required to be standardized, moveable, and interchangeable in much the same impersonal manner as the raw or half-wrought materials of industry. From which it follows that the modern workman cannot advantageously own a home. By force of this latter feature of the case he is discouraged from investing his savings in real property, or, indeed, in any of the impedimenta of living. And the savings-bank account, it may be added, offers no adequate substitute, as an incentive to thrift, in the place of such property as a dwelling place. . . ."

Thus the workman loses much of his interest and respect for property. He finds the home, for forty thousand years the seat of his security and ownership, less appealing as a source of comfort and of strength. To him the natural right of property no longer means so much as it once did, and he turns to trade unionism for support. That is "a concomitant of industry organized after the manner of a machine process;" and it may abrogate to some extent the "natural rights" of property and single bargaining already lost elsewhere. It is clear from these chaotic areas both in capital and labor, among employers and among workmen, these subversions of men's natural tendencies and hopes, that machine industry has not yet been assimilated in our civilization. It is far from that, though it is not impossible. Three industrial phenomena: quantity production, standardization and minute division of labor all have their social bearings and their dangers still unsolved. The world most needs, perhaps, a technological development that will favor distributive industry, energy and ownership; and the "superpower" idea seems the most hopeful for such results.

Today our greatest industry in America, namely, house keeping, is still distributive; and agriculture, also distributive, is not far behind.[19] Homes, and their diversity of manufacturing, from boiling beans to mending Bobby's breeches, still take twenty million able bodied folks to run them. Of workers gainfully employed in America there are more than forty million; and of these, ten million are on farms. But the pressures of the modern age are not favorable to farms and households. Ten million women have left the communistic industry of the home for gainful work outside, and the farm drifts to the town with increasing impetus. In the factories and mines, in transportation work and in communications, more than fourteen million workers earn their daily food and shelter. A new world is upon us; new energies are in our hands. Our problem is to save this newer world and adjust it somehow to man's ancient nature.

In the peripheries of our industrial life lie problems and enigmas half hidden by the smoke of general prejudice and fear. Problems of politics and morals, of man's growth and living, are involved and their statement is confused and difficult because their nature is; truth may not always be clear and logical.

For industrialism can arise only in communities prepared for it and its march onward will be deflected one way or another by residual characters and influences in those groups. Industrialism demands in a community, says Russell,[20] first, "large organizations of workers devoted to a common task;" second, a willingness in those who direct the labour of the community, "to forego present gratifications for the sake of greater wealth later;" third, a government so orderly and stable that those who make this postponement will be able to reap their reward; fourth, a large number of skilled workers; fifth, scientific knowledge to make and use mechanical inventions. And the fifth is by far the most important. Today is the child of science for all its perversity and grime, and our hope for it and the tomorrows following is less in intervention in its nature than in giving full expression to it. Science built the towns and industries and the big businesses of today, but the wastes and fighting, the poverty and injustice, the horrid crunching of gears that do not mesh are hardly scientific. It is a cold and cautious parent, it may be, without the generous enthusiasms that we demand of heroes, but science bred all down the line of modern problems would save the wreck and tragedy that now confront us. That cannot be perhaps, but if it cannot be, industrialism must possess strong traits that are not scientific.

In this energy and drive to power that students call industrialism are tendencies that one by one trickle hotly down the diverse ways of life like lava streams from an overwhelming source. Their nature,[21] lies in the fact that industrialism makes society more organic. But there is more than that to note, for the organism is dynamic, and it endures because it can absorb and use more energy than can the scattered parts. The new organicism of society is a function and a consequence, as it were, of man's accession to new energies and greater natural powers.

A truly scientific system would mean coördinated energies and their use down to the last erg. It would abhor waste and conflict, for science, if nothing more, is a category involved in systematic order. It would cut the great depressions and the panics to an unimportant minimum, and periodic losses, now called inevitable, would no doubt disappear.

For "progress towards greater total production and resultant higher standards," say Foster and Catchings,[22] "is retarded because consumer buying does not keep pace with production;" corporate and private savings make for increasing differentials between production and demand, and "chiefly because of shortage of consumer demand, both capital and labor restrict output;" depressions threaten; there is unemployment and still less buying power, and nations "engage in those struggles for outside markets and spheres of commercial influence which are the chief causes of war."

In a scientific system those strange anomalies and failures — when panics come with shelves and elevators overloaded and families starve and freeze by thousands beside production plants far greater than our needs — would not be. But the modern age is not solely scientific, and within its general organism wild powers clash and jar sometimes with terrible concussions. Reason is highly localized in our social system. There remain, and no doubt always will remain, refractory and perverse materials, shock and nature's prejudice and the raw thrust and headlong drive of men. The tendencies of industrial society cannot always be consistent.

The tendencies inherent in the industrial system, Russell [22] says: are extreme division of labor and hence much trading; a sensitiveness, like any other highly organized being, to wounds and destruction, and in consequence a strong government to protect it from criminal attack and other dangers; a loss of liberty from increasing government, but a gain of liberty in the less labor needed to provide the necessaries of life; an increase in education in order to provide efficient workmanship, and a concomitant political democracy of some kind; a decline in individuality and in personal freedom but an increase in the freedom of the community in relation to nature and her pressures; a decline in personal passions and in art and romance, but an increase in collective passions such as war, sanitation and elementary education; the break-up of the family and of marriage with woman's economic independence and the care of children more and more by public agencies or the state; the decline of religion and the tendency to value things for uses rather than intrinsic worth; and with all the increase in governmental functions and the decline of family individualism, socialism in some form, says Russell, will evolve from our industrialism.

It is rich with isms, but who denies that many if not most of them are correctly named? Of all of them, the impact of industrialism on our governments is the first, if not the most important, aspect of the modern situation.

Socialism, communism, anarchism, syndicalism, guild socialism, and individual exchange are six ways to answer the riddle of industrialism. And even then no doubt it would remain unanswered, for industrialism like nature is sometimes not responsive. Around these answers the weeds and flowers of human bitterness and love have grown. Sacrifice and killing, cruelty and devotion, greed, beauty, hatred and compassion surround them with strange, pungent mulches and heated earths. Man usually burns with passion, when he should be calm.

Socialism means communal ownership of land and capital.[23] It would dedicate to some democratic form of government the natural resources and the means of production, and distribute wealth therefrom according to the general good. From this common threshold socialists wander down a diversity of paths, as different as the elements of human nature, and arrive at mild or militant conclusions. They believe in parliamentary forms of government, and when they come to power, as in England, Germany and France, their procedure is not widely different from their predecessors. They regard "capital" and the wage system,[24] "as a means of exploiting the laborer in the interests of the possessing classes, and hold that communal ownership, in one form or another, is the only means of bringing freedom to producers." But they rarely advocate a revolution or wealth redistribution by violent or unnatural means.

Marx, it is true, father of socialism, saw in the "class

war" one of three main principles of socialistic theory, and Sorel says [25] that this is the essential element of his doctrine; but modern western socialists are less militant and usually find in economic methods, the strike, the purchase of industrial stocks by labor, collective bargaining, labor banks and by the vote and other peaceful efforts, a surer way to gain their ends. With experience and with transplantation to a western continent where class has neither fixity nor tradition nor an economic cause, the "class war" of Karl Marx has been much ameliorated.

Two other Marxian principles, the materialistic interpretation of history, and the law of concentration of capital have gained more under the scrutiny of time, until the usual professor of conservative economics now accepts the first as uncritically as his daily bath, and the second as a normal economic evolution to be taught to freshmen.

And within its causal category, namely economic behaviorism,[24] the "phenomena of human society have indeed their origin in material conditions;" while politics and laws, religions and philosophies are but expressions of régimes in current economics and of material conditions of man and his environment that underlie them. Meanwhile the concentration of capital proceeds per program. Free competition lessens; the number of businesses and of capitalists declines; and fewer and bigger businesses, fewer and bigger capitalists, and more wage and salary earners take their places. But what Marx took to be a course fixed finally by things in general may well be but a technological phenomenon inherent in the present nature of machines. When improvements come in that machinery, perhaps some "superpower" or sun power publicly controlled, there may return, with energy distributed, new individualisms and capital decentralized.

Communism, a word for diverse things from calm Amana, deep in the corn and prayer meetings of Iowa, to the red rage and sufferings of Russia, means the holding of all property in common. From Plato, classic communist, and Sir Thomas More, to Owen, Fourier and the Americans, Brisbane and Horace Greeley,[26] the communist tradition comes in various literary and social forms. It differs usually from socialism in its broader prohibitions of private property.

In Russia, huge communistic laboratory, a vicious and corrupt autocracy was broken, the peasantry was given land; and though it hardly was a communistic act, it gave the revolutionary government strength to fight off five invasions from abroad. After a moment of pure communism distilled from Marxian manifestoes Russia swung ponderously into the first great stage of socialistic progress, namely oligarchic socialism. This, say students of the situation, is bound to be the case in undeveloped and industrially undisciplined peoples; and though in Russia it reveals despotic management of the mills and mines and factories, and rigid censorships,[27] it still is for the people, if not by them; and with the educational work now under way, it may well develop into liberty and more democratic forms — or fail.

Anarchism, red, and most horrific, holds with socialism that land and capital should be owned in common, but unlike socialism, it distrusts the state, fears its growth of power, dreads its tyranny and meddling in the private lives and tastes of men, and would abolish it.[28] Its apostles, Bakunin and Kropotkin, aristocratic Russians, would do away with private capital, wage systems and compulsory labor. They would sweeten industry by science, make a few hours' work a day do for each man, and make the work attractive so he would like to do it. Anarchism trusts that man, without much law, will live as he should live, provided only that he has "half a chance" under ameliorated conditions.

Syndicalism, another dark brown word, opposes socialism and its belief in parliamentary government.

In this it is like anarchism. It is a French doctrine arising in French trade-unionism,[28] and its essence is the class war promoted not by political but industrial methods, as the strike, the boycott, the label and sabotage. Its aim is to destroy the state which these believe is made to terrorize the workers, and they wish to see each industry self-governing.[28]

Syndicalism is organized around industrial unions as opposed to craft unions. There is a difference; for craft unionism, says Cole,[29] "unites in a single association those workers who are engaged on a single industrial process, or on processes so nearly akin that any one can do another's work." But industrial unionism "may follow the lines, not of the work done, but of the actual structure of industry." All workers on one commodity may be one union, and the basis of organization may be neither the craft nor the employer, but the service on which the worker is engaged. In America the I. W. W. is organized by industries, while the A. F. of L., under the late Mr. Gompers at least, is based on crafts.

In England guild socialism has built a modified and non-inflammatory doctrine from elements of French syndicalism, American I. W. W., and English common sense. And the result, in the hands of Cole and others, is one more interesting effort to find the proper synthesis between machine industrialism and human nature. The guilds, or industrial unions, in this system would represent producers in the government. Parliament would represent [30] consumers. These two co-equal powers in government (occupational and regional representation) would refer in turn to a joint committee of parliament and guild congress. For the political problem of industrialism, say the guild socialists, is to reconcile the interests of consumers with producers; and the answer is to have a house in government for each group. It is based like other socialisms on state control of the means of production, and therein differs mainly from our present capitalist régime.

Individualistic exchange, our present system, is less
a theory than an aggregate of practices, and it gains and
loses both because of it. It is spontaneously coöperative,
says Deibler;[31] it rests on enterprise; it depends on
private property as a stimulus to private enterprise; it
is tied together by free contract; it operates through
competitive effort. And capitalist production, he continues, is organized around: the entrepreneur or captain
of industry; division of labor; large scale production;
risk, for production anticipates demand. It is a system
built in great part in a trading era when industry was
still distributive. It is full of evils and injustices that may
wreck it. Its fate lies solely in the hope of altering it to
liberal dimensions to fit this modern age. But in spite of
dangerous evils it remains the most flexible, perhaps, of
any. It is bad, but it is human.

If the various socialisms remain impotent because their
appeal is on a too narrow base, capitalism gains, with
every concentration of power control and wealth, more
potential foes. If agriculture and the soil and some other
private properties cannot be socialized effectively, industrial concentrations and mass production on the other
hand would indicate where socialism is possible if not
already nearly an accomplished fact. The socialist depends too much on cataclysm and hard times, and the
"masses" that he reaches are not the real masses of
thoughtless, fairly happy citizens who still have hope, at
least in normal times, of somehow getting on. But the
capitalist is likely to ignore or to repress the restlessness
and discontent of millions whose struggles for a better life
get them nowhere. For five per cent of American families
take thirty per cent of American income.[32] The average
income of 95 per cent of American families is far below
the annual $1700 required — according to U. S. figures —

for subsistence in the cities of the land. And the average for all families is considerably below that level.

The sudden loading of our industry with coal and steel, with new energy and great machines has upset our economic balance. Distributive production loses in the readjustment, and concentrations and the cities gain. Tariffs protect the smoke and roaring of industrial towns; prices are high and wages rise to meet them; while the farmers, buying goods and hiring labor on one level, must sell their produce on a much lower one. It is but one example of unbalance in our system, but in the lives and homes of all America and of all the world there are many others.

Where the machine, on which this world is riding, is about to go no one can say. It will have its natural movement in the future as in the past, and its course will be directed partly by the iron evolution of its own nature, partly by the needs and habits of the men who live on it. It may ruin; it may save society. For power man must have in even greater ratios if he will hold his grip on life and natural things; but power in pools of legalized control, in all engrossing concentrates of private property and privilege may well be poisonous to the human race. Power must run in rivulets and irrigations between the common furrows of this human field if it would nourish an enduring race.

Distributive society is old fashioned now; Denmark is sweet but quaint; Sweden is not powerful; but distributive society is more than likely necessary to man's endurance on this earth.[33] The new age, through mechanical development such as "superpower," must retain the hold on power production, but provide for distribution of our power [34] and its attendant privileges to the broad and wholesome soil and to men who live thereon. Deflation of the cities and return to land is the program of the coming era. Man will take his city with him to the rural districts and there have both.

In this chapter the power of life and the modern quantities of production are noted; standardization and our unstandardized currency; specialization and the dangerous separation of gain from service; inherent tendencies in the industrial system; proposed forms of control, socialism, anarchism, syndicalism, guild socialism and individualistic exchange are discussed, and the need for a distributive society through further evolution of machines, such as "superpower" is briefly mentioned. Here in industrialism is the vortex and the burning of the modern age. There are fumes and smoke and great fires, and what is making there is hard to see.

CHAPTER TEN

Society Today

TODAY, for many men, is a drunken yesterday. It is yesterday in form, content and reaction to the world, but it is hugely stimulated. It reels down man's ancient course with a strange howling. It ricochets in massive skips along the old paths of time, and its difference from days before is only in its jostling and rush. For these men the modern age is the age gone by but going faster. The change is not in structure but in speed.

And they are right, perhaps; but new speed means new social vehicles to absorb it, new roadbeds, new conceptions, new human beings tuned to a greater power. Increased mobility, a greater social turnover, will alone warp and wrench society into new configurations, and a nation whose wealth increased in fifty years preceding 1910 from $500 to $1500 per capita, and whose business turnover grew enormously, cannot remain the same.[1]

Business dominates American society today. It is the bulging factor in this modern life that determines social readjustments. It is exchange, and the rapid turnovers made possible by the energies and new mobilities that man has found through science and raw resources, has raised exchange to new prestige and power. Though in itself business is but a crackling emptiness, it is dynamic, it is the shift and movement of a restless age that wants always something that it has not got, and as pure changing it gains to some extent a philosophical finality.

Because business is an abstract thing that works from offices and ledgers, boards of trade and banks without close contact with the stubborn stuff of things and workmanship, of engineering problems and the laboratory, it too often lacks creativeness; its imaginative context is impoverished; it treats life denotatively; its terms are quantitative and extrinsic; and the world in being businesslike often is pumped dry of being. To this mechanistic emptiness America is subject, for business or exchange is after all abstracted usually from the vitalities and motions of steel wheels and pistons, of the long arms of dredgers, of the thrust and mighty hammering of electric drills, and as the nation's engineering outlook is subordinated to pure business it will suffer correspondingly in reality and richness. Business is dynamic mainly on paper and in hustling personalities.

By partitioning sales, financing and larger management from the fixed capital such as machines and the labor managed, by abstracting the controlling forces from the things controlled, by absentee ownership and like methods of industrial concentrations, big business has impoverished its outlook. To be big it has encelled itself in well nigh watertight compartments, and it suffers from the narrow despotism of specialists in profits and manipulation. It must be highly organized, but it is, no less, overorganized for human good. It grows in the great town. It sits in that center of the specialties. Its threshold is the city, and the city is its home. Business and the modern city have grown coördinately. The prime circumstance of today's society is the growth of cities.

In the half century preceding 1910 America's population trebled but the growth of cities was more than three times that. And while the independent farmers decreased in number, clerks, salesmen and typists increased more than nineteen times; transportation workers increased sixty times; miners, nine times; wage earners, six times; banks, more than twenty times, and corporations more than nineteen times. Today two thirds and more of our national wealth is owned by corporations.[2] It is the city and its accessories moving in upon the nation. Its great feet press the soil. Its breath is a dusky fog over the sun.

For the modern city is the social correlate of industrial concentration, and the coal and steel that made it lives

in its streets and buildings. Machinery and its power,
improved communications and transport, disease control,
and printed matter put out cheaply, says E. A. Ross,[3] are
factors making for the growth of cities. Cities are the
grimy whelps of science. Man sought objective order in
his world and what he found gave him skill and tools to
build this latest urban age.

In the city, says E. C. Hayes,[4] labor and capital and
not land are dominating factors. In the city young people
come and give the urban population a progressive tone
and speed. Home ties are fewer, the people are more
shifting. In the city nature and the out-of-doors give
place to artifice; there is intense stimulation and the never
ceasing interest of fellow man's activities always finds an
object. Extremes are there of wealth and poverty, of
brains and ignorance, of art and ugliness, and from
overstimulation men come to live on mental surfaces
without deep meditation; mob style is easy; fads and
fashions flourish. In the city "quarters" form, China-
town or Ghetto, financial district or red light; men live in
deep anonymity; they take their niche; few know them
personally. In the city, lastly, the individual is more
dependent on communal life and action than when on the
farm, for the urban regions must be greatly organized to
survive. Man's life there is special; he depends for much
on others. And so it goes: the city is a pressure and dis-
torting influence on human life, a thrust and strain like
the powers that compress rocks and turn limestone into
marble and granite into gneiss.

Today the towns lurch on, like blind elephants through
a jungle. Land is high, and buildings soar the higher.
Five-story towns add fifteen stories to their height, and
streets that once were made for five must carry four times
that. Subways, elevated tracks and increased speed pile
people into town during rush hours; buildings go still
higher and people crowd to fill them in wild toppling
ratios of absurdity and crowding. In the accurate sense,

says **W. L. Bailey**,[5] there are no great cities in the western world today: there are sprawls and aggregates of things and business, that must be organized, concentrated, condensed, unified by huge trunk avenues, built higher in the modern method, on the one hand, and redistributed, resegregated and carried out in regional colonies around its margins on the other. Somewhere, no doubt, a human limit lies, beyond which men will not increase congestion, but it is hard to find. Urban distribution can hardly wait on what humanity will stand; an earlier hope is some technical achievement, such as superpower, perhaps, working to distribute, as today's technique works to concentrate the people. Group cities already are developing over many miles in area based on correlated industries; and suburbia for homes is gaining confidence in an enduring future.[5] With industrial decentralization, and with suburban residences, the needful concentrates of commerce and of business in the cities can proceed without great risk. Commercial concentration, industrial and residential decentralization is the hope of our great towns.

Crime grows there now, and its bitter weeds stain the crop of human happiness and order with disasters. Graft and corruption are normal modes of government in America's larger towns. Pay for protection and the defeat of law goes on, and government in these urban districts becomes less a general, systematic order than a shifting set of pressures (drives) now here, now there according to the local need, or whim or public outcry for a stricter regulation. It is a dynamic notion of control that has at least mobility and the energy of attack, but it is often personal and prejudiced; it is uncertain, like a hasty parent; it is always open to corruption or bamboozlement. To the legal absolutes of Anglo-Saxon minds, the law technically exact, inflexible, a principle absolutely real regardless of the concrete situation, this comes as a dynamic contrast. In a new world of massive mixtures and conglomerates in which law, technically absolute, does not fit; drives are compensatory efforts, failing, to be sure, but doing more, perhaps, than government could do without them.

For the growing point of modern life is less in government and politics than in industry and business, and where power is, there will be headstrong will and chronic, particular rebellions against control. Business in America always wants its own way; it is traditionally a law somewhat to itself; it has an anarchistic strain; and exemptions from inspection, as well as privilege, pull, and headlong energy down its own path are accustomed hopes and attitudes. Law in the cities is less a principle than a minimum necessity, and city government remains our greatest failure.

Murders and manslaughters in London in 1918 were 37; in New York City they were 221; in Chicago they were 222; burglaries in all of England and Wales in 1917 were 9,453; in New York city they were 9,450; in Chicago they were 5,623; and so it goes,[6] from rape to speeding, from arson to hip pocket liquor, the savage lawlessness and violence of these great towns rides on without much hindrance from year to year. Though the criminality of a country, as Ellis says,[7] "is a by-product of its energy in business and in the whole conduct of affairs;" though it "is a poisonous excretion," but an excretion in the "measure of vital metabolism;" though "we cannot be sure that we ought not to regard the most criminal country as that which in some aspects possesses the highest civilization;" still crime is a sign of break and fracture in the social system. It thrives mainly on the discontinuity between modern industrialism and government, between politics and business. With the one sapped of its energy and pride in favor of the other; with strong men finding their rewards in industry and in private order, public order and the town in general suffers.

There are more specific reasons for the crime in cities, but they trace in great part to industrialism and its certain shock to social systems. The heterogeneity of our population, Fosdick says,[7] makes control difficult. New York has nine times the foreign population that London has. In New York 41 per cent are foreign born, in Chicago 36 per cent; in London 3 per cent. In New York are 340,000 Italians, 485,000 Russians, 267,000 Austro-Hungarians, 280,000 Germans, and so on; the streams pour in from many different hillsides, and the waters are not clear.

And the law's delays, its technicalities, the abstract rights of every citizen held here to the placing of a comma, are more reasons, Fosdick adds, for crime. Light penalties and pardons, a fickle, sentimental public, and overdone publicity add further difficulties. Too many laws, laws that cannot be enforced, weak courts and corrupt lawyers are no small part in governmental weakness. They accumulate our failures. They are evidence in general of our social pluralism, our disunited politics and business, our clashing purposes in industry and good government.

But society has its code and standard, and if they are not legal, or written ponderously in official documents, they are no less valid. For modern life toes the line of an abstraction with a discipline and rigidity that written creeds and laws cannot command. It has made a standard of living — as all societies must — and it lives to that established standard with a fervency that churches and governments rarely can arouse. It is a standard set communistically to a given key, and its nature will depend on population factors, on wealth distribution, power and resources per citizen, education and on other elements of the social complex. It is an organic principle in society of supreme importance, and though it is determined more or less unconsciously, it is definite and in every general group no doubt unique.

The "standard of life," says Ely,[8] is "the number and character of the wants which a man considers more important than marriage and family," and though this is a modification of Ricardo's dictum on the "minimum of subsistence" it still tells pungently of the conflict in man's wishes between sex satisfactions, the securities of family life and the personal demands and comforts of one person.

Never has that standard been so high as in America today; never has the individual so trespassed on society's primal synthesis, the family. Late marriages or none result, sex instincts find expression increasingly outside of wedlock and its responsibilities. Marriages and children "do not pay" so well in the great towns, and there are fewer of them. The families there that maintain high educational or economic standards usually are soon extinct.

To keep five in a family on the "subsistence level" in these towns required $1700 in 1920, according to the Department of Labor, and to keep a woman worker, living away from home, took $800, but in this standard, low as it is, there are necessities that a century ago would have been high luxuries.[9] To keep a family with what are sometimes called the "finer things" would take two or three times the $1700 needed for subsistence, and there are therefore fewer families formed. "More life" to the individual in the form of high standards usually means fewer individuals.

Every automobile, someone has guessed, displaces a baby or so in America's life procession; and every raccoon coat no doubt puts marriage off for someone a few more months. These joyous properties, coats and cosmetics, cars, cabarets, designed to give prestige and beauty and the bright flare of life to those who use them, and surely requisite in some fields to competitive success in getting married, have their paradox. For they cost money, effort, time; and life with them requires economic power that few prospective householders will have before the age of thirty.

Young wives, perhaps, but older husbands, not so many babies, men loose living before they can afford to marry, widows, free divorce, venereal disease — now the most threatening of human ills — and arising from these situations, a new morality, perhaps, a more sound adjustment to this sudden world that the old codes alone cannot well handle: these are implications in high living standards. "Too wide a difference between the standard of living of the laboring classes and the successful middle classes," says Hayes,[10] "causes population to be recruited more from the former and less from the latter. The 'business' standard of success which measures social position, not by services rendered nor by personal culture and character, but by scale of expenditure, is a genetic curse." But prolonged education, cultural sensitivities and like accessories of the higher standard have these effects as well; for man's expansive powers of enjoyment have everywhere a tendency to reduce some of his productions, such as babies.

"The labourer," says Malthus,[11] "who earns eighteen pence a day, and lives with some degree of comfort as a single man, will hesitate a little before he divides that pittance among four or five, which seems to be but just sufficient for one. Harder fare and harder labour he would submit to, for the sake of living with the woman that he loves; but he must feel conscious, if he thinks at all, that, should he have a large family, and any ill luck whatever, no degree of frugality, no possible exertion of his manual strength, could preserve him from the heart-rending sensation of seeing his children starve, or of forfeiting his independence, and being obliged to the parish for their support." And this is true not only of the laborer's eighteen pence but of the engineer's or doctor's eighteen dollars, where the prestige of consumption overbears the need for forming families. For food may increase in arithmetical ratio while population may increase in geometrical ratio; but man's wants have an expansibility that is no less than explosive; and given the enthusiasm, the urge to them and the hope, they alone will act as checks and compensators to population growth. Levels of living and their population densities are by no means measured solely by the needs of minimum subsistence. There may be more food than families. In the city, for example, it statistically is rare for any family to exist for more than four generations.[12]

Unchecked the population of this earth would increase geometrically: a thousand men and women would produce the present population of the globe (say 2,000,000,000) in two centuries and a half; the progeny of Eve and Adam — had they existed — would be two million billion people, says Swinburne,[13] or more than a thousand people per square yard over land and sea. Though man's physiological fertility is seven per cent or so a year,[14] an actual increase of less than two per cent would double population in forty years. External causes of one kind or another, high living standards, war, celibacy, pests, abortion, education, birth control must operate to check man's too great increase. They always have operated to check it; but today is rather different. Man may choose to some extent the kind of check. What shall he choose?

Continence by married people will not reduce the population rate, for married people never will be continent, if conclusions both of Malthus and Professor Raymond Pearl [15] are right; nor can celibacy of the unmarried be expected as the economic pressure against marriage and more babies continues; war, pests, Chinese infanticides, famines, as deliberate agents of control can hardly be considered; and higher living standards, educative progress, with birth control by contraception, remain the more intelligent means of regulating population densities.

For "male and female created he them;" and new or old societies designed for sexual prohibition will not much change that basic biologic fact. Our population projects must conform to, not obstruct, that instinct, and build therefrom a wholesome social life. With large areas organized together the densities of population of the parts, says Pearl,[16] may be greater than before. But there are limits, in any case, where more density is undesirable and that limit precedes by far the limits of subsistence. In A.D. 2100, Pearl predicts, the United States will have 197,000,000 people living within its borders.

Historically, says Reuter,[17] "children have come as an undesigned result of sex satisfaction," and "so far as a desire for parenthood exists it is largely a socially engendered thing, which requires constant stimulation and so varies with the historic situation;" "but if knowledge of means of family control be at hand, the sex need of the persons may be satisfied without their being hampered by children in the realization of desires that may outweigh the desire for offspring." This modern separation of sex satisfaction from natal consequences is a new and highly critical condition in the growth of populations; for contraceptive methods, known through science to important parts of our societies, are bound in time to spread to all, and population maintenance or increase will depend not on the drive and urgencies of instinct but on a more deliberate choice.

Our future populations, in a word, must rely on social pressures for their being, on the use and need for children in the economic and the social scheme, and a scheme, like modern urban life, that penalizes those who have a child by a lower living standard, cannot endure. For contraceptive secrets have intense importance to the average individual, and the knowledge of them cannot be withheld from him for long. Increase in family will then be voluntary in a sense that it has never been before; it will depend on motives solely social and institutional; and unless it can be made a directly social and an economic asset, society will die. Birth control once for all disrupts the automatic ratio of population to the food supply, and in man's economic life and social institutions it will have profound results.

Today the well-to-do, the competent, the better educated families can control their increase; while the poor, the ignorant and often the unfit breed heavily of their kind. It is a dangerous differential. Only forty-five per cent of college women marry before the age of forty as compared with ninety per cent for all women [18] of the United States. The fertility of women of foreign parentage in America is almost twice that of women whose parents are native born. The professional and educated groups of our society are relatively sterile. The well-to-do rarely reproduce themselves. High living standards and an undistributed knowledge of contraceptive methods throw the burden of our population maintenance on those least fit to bear it.

A nation of 200 million people living well is no doubt better than a nation of 500 million living miserably. For America with all its braw vulgarities is better off than China, India or Europe. High living standards and wide powers for every citizen are not impossible for a race that can control its natural fecundity, and industrial gains, inventions and increased productive powers will not then be absorbed entirely in creating larger populations; they will raise the living levels and augment creative leisures of the citizens extant. This has in part happened in industrial societies. But the scale of human misery is not much less than it was three centuries ago, and though there are more people, and more people living well, and larger, lazy leisure classes than this earth has ever known, the power and betterment from new energies and machines has not been fully liquidated. The ills, mostly, of this modern world are from industrialism imperfectly assimilated.

For modern industry carries on its back a huge accession to the populations of the western world. In England

this industrial margin is not far from 30 million people.[19]
In Germany this surplus set on industry is no doubt more.
All Europe in 1760 had not more than 130 million people,
but 450 million folks were there in 1915; Japan in 1871
had 33 million people and had been stationary for a
hundred years or more; then came doctors and industrialism, wage systems and foreign exports, and Japan, not
much happier than before, now has 53 million mouths to
feed. And America by a synthesis of circumstances,
partly industrial, partly free lands, has gained in a half
century more than 70 million people.

With the industrial revolution came huge increases
in western populations and, with the world to draw from,
massive gains in food supplies and power. It is an added
population living largely by its hands, without lands or
capital, flexible and restless, and immediately dependent
on subtle organs of great industry, on transportation and
on far supply. To give this mighty margin stakes in the
new order, property, or other stabilizing interests in
their place and function in this new world is not the least
of social problems. For in American corporations in
1924, less than five per cent of the stockholders owned
more than 75 per cent of the total stock,[19] and concentration in corporation ownership still increases. The
current move towards the distributive ownership of
stocks, employee ownership, labor banks, and coöperative stores and housing are hopeful signs of democracy in
industry; and if they are not loaded dice played for some
other purpose, they will be, when more developed, strong
buttresses to the modern system.

And to the cities recruits came from the farms first of
New England, from Ireland struck by hunger, landlords,
and potato blight, from peasant fields of Germany and
Sweden, from Russia and the fractured states of central
and south Europe, from southern Italy and dark browed
Sicily, from Polish ghettoes and south Russian pales,
from Spain and Syria, from Mexico and from shanties on

our cotton lands, shuffling in millions down to work under
the roar of great machines. It is a migratory world, and
what America does now industrially and socially, the
world will very likely do before the age is past.

To the work of cities and to better wages, to free institutions and to farms sometimes, the peoples of the
western world have moved in mass migrations. Four
waves of them have overswept the United States: first,
in the decade following 1845; second, in the years after
our Civil war; third, in the late seventies; fourth, in the
late eighties in a rising curve to the great war in Europe;
and but for recent laws restricting immigration, a fifth
and overwhelming wave following the war would now be
lurching over us. In one hundred years more than 33
million immigrants came to our shores.[20] In 1914 alone
more than one million aliens entered.

They came in motley companies, hopeful, alien, many
tongued, and as they came pressing down upon our living
standards,[21] holding wages down, huddling in undigested
turmoil in our towns, the birth rate of our native stock
declined in rhythms corresponding to their influx.[22] The
result of heavy alien immigrations "has not been a net
increase to American population but has been a substitution of foreign for native stock."[23] This theory of survival advanced by Walker and supported generally by
Hall, Commons, Bushee, Fairchild, The Industrial
Commission, Ross, Marshall and Fisher,[23] has favorable
and strong bearings on America's quota immigration
laws. Without arrogance and without claim to race
superiority, our people may still protect its living standard, its wage earners, its homogeneous tradition and its
racial stock from further raids and mixtures. In 1900,
more than a quarter of a century ago, 46 per cent of
America's population was of alien birth or the children
of those of alien birth.[24] If folk unity has humane and
social values, as most Americans believe, the problem is
great enough by now without a further aggravation.

For emigration from an overcrowded country helps that
country little; [24] low living standards do not rise and the
fecund populace promptly lifts the human tide to the
level that it reached before the emigration. Europe could
send many times the migrants to our shores that she has
sent without lowering her numbers or raising living standards.[24] China, India, Japan could inundate America
with cheap labor imported by our manufacturers, miners,
employers in general, but China, India and Japan would
not be greatly helped. By western science, sanitation,
hygiene and the humane impulse to save life the oriental
populations have increased by large margins. With the
west as midwife to the colored stocks of the world, says
E. A. Ross,[24] unbalanced populations have been built
that will try to emigrate. Without lowering their birth
rate or raising living standards, they will press out upon
new frontiers. But migrations will not help the senders;
they harm the nations that receive. Immigration is a
one way problem. America must solve it for herself.

In the backwash of the nation, buffeting the wake of
industries and great towns comes agriculture and our small
town life. They are nearly lost today in the smother
of great undertakings. Tomorrow, some tomorrow it
must surely be, they will emerge again. For life near to
land, where the native brush and hedgerows are not too
far away, and the streams scour their banks in the
eagerness of Spring, is man's most natural need; and an
existence permanently in urban regions abstracted from
the soil means only mobs and cynicism, disillusionment,
social disaster.

With new communications, with facilities of transport
much improved, with the social prestige of the city somewhat declining, the great town as a center of enjoyments
is no longer so essential as it was. City life is virtually ex-

tended now to many rural districts and a further growth in that direction is more than probable. The large town is not so necessary now to the consumption of the finer goods. Consumption may become distributive, and when production can likewise be diffused somewhat, the curse of towns will be removed.

For production and consumption are abstractions that economists manipulate too much. No human action can be solely one or other, it is a natural synthesis of both; and when the modern era finds it out, men will be more concerned in joining "life" and business than they are today. They will want consumption values or enjoyment directly in productive work. They will refuse the sharp dichotomy between their pleasures and their job; and will return in some degree to the land and natural stabilities to which man is physically and mentally adapted. In the small town city and country will eventually be joined.

But the way is still long to distributive society, and to "superpower" or other instrument that may make it possible. Today the farmers are depressed by mortgages and upstart prices. They must buy high to pay the tax to industry and cities, labor is hard to get, land is high, and they must sell low for lack of coöperative agencies and skill. Tenancy increases on the middle western farms, and great rural regions, such as Iowa, decline in population. Small banks fail throughout the agrarian west; and a life long farmer deeply invested in the soil, in live stock and in buildings does well to get an income equal to the income of his brisk young daughter who types letters for a business man in town.

The farming population of America, some 30 million souls, has probably a larger income per family [25] "than any other equally homogeneous group of individuals of anything like the same size anywhere in the world." But with taxes and interest on debts deducted not much cash is left. Net earnings before the war were \$724 for the average farm family, and of this $322 was earned by the capital invested in the farm and $402 by the labor of the farmer and his family. These $724 of net earnings were received by the family as follows: $303 in cash, $35 as fuel, $125 as rent, and $261 as food furnished by the farm.[25] Today the farmer's place relatively is even worse. Tenancy in Illinois is nearly fifty per cent. Farm boys become the fodder of great towns.

To lift himself to economic levels set by "industrialism" the farmer must give up to some extent his decentralized activities. He must make a compromise away from his distributive system, as the industrialist must make a compromise towards it, in order to come at last upon a common synthesis and a workable adjustment. Coöperative farm marketing is a start that has high promise, and a closer organization of the farmers, from land and living to seed time and crop sales, must come in time. Already the fruit growers of the west have found success in this, and when general farmers overcome inherent difficulties in personnel and method, they too may find it. A fruit exchange in the far west reduces costs of marketing from ten to three per cent of the sale value.[26] That is only one example of coördinated farming.

In the small town — yellow dog of the modern system, kicked about from cities to the farms and back again — is the best hope of future social synthesis. Here may be the foci of distributive production in the future; here urban folks can live out of work hours; here farmers may reside or come in during busy seasons from their farms nearby. The future offers economically no insuperable objection to a small town system; and when the town becomes attractive — as it well may — many will wish enough to live there to make it socially a dominating fact. Its development will hang on the rise of the farmer's economic level and a further distribution of industrial production. From the right and from the left two streams will join to make it.

Americans and American democracy are constructed generally on a small town basis, and our social methods, our public opinion, our free speech, press, assembly, our attitudes towards property and welfare take strange, distorted forms when removed from that foundation. In a nation of neighbors our forms and institutions were conceived; in a nation of strangers, aliens, city mobs and polyglots they are less effective. Where the tomorrows of this world may lead us no one can tell, but among the brighter possibilities is a cyclical return to much modified small towns. The conservation of "America," her eagles and their screams of freedom depend on it.

Today the opinion of our public is not the virile, stubborn power that it was once before great cities mastered the earth.[27] Newspapers were not then industrialized; editors in 1776 almost without exception were revolutionaries, for they were humble artisans and printers. Only one in all the colonies of that day had ever kept a carriage, and he was Tory.[27] Would the great and prosperous press today stand solidly behind the ragged patriots, the farmers and workmen of the towns, as it stood when America was founded? It would not.

For the press today, and the greater part of public opinion, is standardized [28] perforce by the instruments of its production, by quantity creations and "modern" methods. It lives on advertising and the reader who receives a paper costing several times its purchase price cannot expect old fashioned independence of it. Though the press in citified United States rarely is corrupted, its scales inevitably are loaded on one side; it represents the managers of great capital; and where their interest is the nation's welfare the press usually is right, but where their interest and the nation's welfare may diverge the press usually is wrong.

And this under our conditions, is about the only kind of urban press that can exist; for by Gresham's law of currency, depreciated money will displace good money, and a sensational, complaisant press will push out all the others.[29] Begotten of industrialism, nursed on the milk of advertising, the urban press today is usually true to its heredity and education. It carries advertising, partner to great industry's mass production and wide spread sales, and incidentally must amuse and draw the reader. News, is still important, though technically it no longer is the main consideration. In spite of all, however, the press remains one of the potent educative forces in this country.

Other teachers are the radio and movies, sports, jazz, dancing; advertisements are a vivid university; automobiles, schools, labor unions, colleges, soap box orators, all have a place in America's education; all help to build our ideology; all standardize our type. And which is most important is not an easy question.

Officially our schools and colleges bear the torch of learning ("a 15 watt cast brass piano lamp with red silk tassels is given free with each four year subscription"), but a huge, unofficial periphery also has much to do with education. The clink and rattle of our educational machines sound through the country; grades, credits, degrees, more grades, credits, degrees, mark our quantitative standards of the inner light; America is as busy educationally as a machine for sorting fruit when the orange crop is ripe. For if the press is mechanized and lost to greater things, our educational institutions in general are even more so, and the reasons are about the same. They are controlled by the instruments of their production; standardization, mass production; the method, in whatever field, will give about the same results.

And to the universities and high schools students come to live the life, to drink the fiery wine of love and music, to find release in the great games and joyous energies of college yards, and to study when they must. Careless, sweet, deceitful, lovers of life and the direct beauty of humane associations, they come to college for the education that America has promised all her children, but the learning that they get is not the learning that educational authority intends. They are forever loosing quail in learned councils. They ride through the hours of college untouched by professorial dust. They sift across the drone of classrooms like bright and shifty gold and emeralds from a spendthrift nation's hand.

Not all are thus, nor are all newspapers flatulent and full of nerveless noise; not all opinion in America is standardized per specification, nor is our whole vitality focused in the cities and big business. For America — and America is most characteristic of the modern age — is after all diverse and contradictory. It is bewildering and rich. It bewitches all analysis. For under surface sameness lie naïve depths and love and differences, innocent profundities that poetry and music and philosophy have yet to sound.

This chapter skirts the edges of ten social situations of today: business life, city life, city government and crime; living standards, population, birth control, industrial population margins, immigration; journalism and public opinion, education. There are many more within and without these problems. Their drift at least suggests the currents of today and tomorrow's destination.

Society Tomorrow

BUT tomorrow is a gesture and a beckoning; it is a wish for peace and the resolution of today's disasters, and a hope for new struggles and new problems. It will take this age as raw material, and in some cosmical refinery extract the purer stuff and leave the slag in smouldering piles behind. Tomorrow is our problem more and more as the race grows older, as society expands its time horizons into the past and future, and the sources and resources of this energy, that we call life, become a more direct concern.

A new world, says Charles E. Merriam,[1] "in which space and time are fundamentally altered," a new world of wide spread leisure, of universal education, of scientific methods and results, a new world where a race of beings are master of nature's forces in greater measure than was before deemed possible, a world where the bulk of the community participate in its decisions, will bring with it new politics. They must be more scientifically adjusted to the modern time. For politics are but a system of relationships, and old systems do not always fit new facts. Parties grow old and sclerotic governments fumble the energies and life of a new age that they can never comprehend.

Parties grow senile and retire with age from ideas and public policies; they clinch desperately at life, and seek by any means to hold a personal power for purely personal advantage. It is the lean and slippered last of a party's six or seven ages. Ideas become a liability, and in a country standardized by school and press and by the giant roaring of machines, by mass productions and expert distribution it is not hard to utilize mechanical and psychic means of industry for ends political. Party or-

ganization becomes dominant and the quality of personnel and public policy declines. Ideas find fewer vehicles
in an aged party system. They turn to outer means, from
Lenin's revolution to Gandhi's noncoöperation, from
fascism and the Ku Klux Klan to the Nonpartisan league
and labor groups, for their promotion and estate.

These are passing rivulets no doubt running towards
the sea, but they glisten with the eternal sun; their splash
and clatter is the resonance of ages; they indicate the
conflict and the inner movement of all life. In India
Gandhi[2] seeks reversal of industrial development. He
would abandon concentrated power, break the machines
into small tools that fit the hand, retire to the land, and
weave, spin and manufacture things in rural family
groups. From the empire of Britain and the far thrown
net of politics, organization, armies, that has caught all
India in its mesh, Gandhi would remain aloof. He would
not coöperate. He urges India to live its own "pre-industrial" life, without violence, without caste, without fighting or hatreds, and with folded arms defeat the troops and
governments of the island power. And he has come near
to it. He is the great meekness of the east, the power of
India, and to many Indians a god.

Without Britain, what might come to India is hard to
say: fighting and despotism perhaps and a quick recession to high mortalities and cyclical disaster, or maybe to
a better state built not on national lines. With Britain,
Indian women labor in the mills and industrial towns for
a joyless wage, and feed their children opium to keep
them still during a day's work. Of the mothers in the
mills, says the Manchester Guardian, more than 96 per
cent feed opium to their children — pills bought until
recently from the British government. With or without
Britain, India sees no happy future. It is a dark and overcrowded land not built for happiness: and children must
be born, all India believes, to serve and pray for parents.
It is a land where man takes the defensive. While we

seek materially the maximum, India lives the minimum. That is her faith and discipline, and Ghandi is her prophet. Though not a "Christian," he leads in spirit and in doctrine the purest Christianity of this modern world. He may not win; with death, his teachings well may follow him into silence and ineptitude; but Gandhi is our greatest Christian.

For Gandhi, Tolstoi, Jesus and others of the type are revolutionaries in the accurate sense; they would return to old and sweeter styles; they would abandon concentrates of power and outer discipline; they would ignore massive organisms and prides that give this western world its form. Their only politics are love and firm simplicity. Gandhi is the modern revolutionist; Lenin is revolutionary in method, not in end.

For Lenin would develop power and machine production to what he deems their ultimate conclusion. He would direct their evolution to higher concentrates of state control. He would abandon private property as the workers have — perforce — abandoned it beside the new machines; and though historically his greatest deed may be the return of land to the private hands of peasants (some 85 per cent of Russia's population), his doctrine is capitalistic evolution [3] from personal to state control. Lenin is no more Christian in his methods than is Germany or France, England or America. He uses war, civil and external to break down threats against his evolutionary capitalism,[4] and as he lies in state in Moscow, the silent father of new Russia, Asia and all eastern Europe stand at arms to recall power from distant overlords.

If Mussolini and Lenin converge, their starting points at least are far apart and their aims are even more so. For fascism is violent reaction to maintain an economic *status quo*, to give order and rigidity to government, to work the old machine of imperial expansion and war in greater ratios of efficiency. It abandons faith in democratic government. It rules out representative systems.

Though it leans towards syndicalism — and this is most significant — its order and its motive are still romantic violence, special privilege and personal and private power. It rides on censorship, force and the suppression of all liberties that may encroach upon it. Its ends are speed, immediate efficiency and personal and national aggrandizement.

Where bourgeois Mussolini, where Lenin, the aristocrat, are both radical from their respective points of view, MacDonald of the English labor party, is for liberalism in labor and in labor's hand in capital, as Lincoln, Roosevelt and Wilson stand for liberalism in politics. In England labor slowly moves towards a new age where private property, no doubt, will never be extinguished, where the greater instruments of production will be more and more in public hands, and a people, now 78 per cent city dwellers, will find an economic balance between public and private control, between concentrated and distributed production and consumption, that will fit the needs and special situations of the time. It is English muddling through, but if the pressure holds towards liberal labor progress, it will be the best for England.

Wilson represents democracy resurgent. He is one more effort to restate this world in terms political and democratic. In domestic politics he won in part; in foreign fields he failed.[5] His programs, from the League of Nations to his plans for Russia, are political superimpositions on a world where other energies are dominant. Where politics today are usually an adjusting instrument, Wilson had in mind creative politics, prime producers in a world of facts and energies that Wilson never knew. He belonged to an old group, psychologically, that gave ideas a place in material causation. He looked to politics for creative energies, and here was superficial, for they lie far deeper. With Wilson, much, if not most, of American opinion lies in this early nineteenth century bayou of "intellectualism," stagnant and inept.

For Wilson's brave fight for American democracy, though in part successful, lost from this failure to appreciate dynamic factors lying deep in politics and government. To him it was a world of words and concepts, and the reaction following him in such men as Andrew Mellon, the reaction towards undemocratic power and private concentrations, owes much to Wilson's failure to dig deep to the energies of life. His political democracy, in part, broke down.

In the rise of popular intelligence, in the higher standard of living, in weakening religions, says E. A. Ross,[6] are great reasons for modern development of democracy. And these in turn are deeply implicated in the growth of cities, in wide use of machinery, in improved transportation, in the mingling of races and of cultures, in the use of scientific methods in all inquiry, in the belief in evolution. Democracy is no frail thing built by its laws. Politics cannot make it; they express it.

And no less sturdy are its enemies. They too are implicated in modern energies, mechanics and materials; and the struggle for democracy against them will be deep and broad, vertical and horizontal; it will be on many levels and plateaus; and in particularities as well as wholes it must fight through slowly in deep struggle and in solemn wrath.

Internal democracy, external strength is America's dual problem. A correlated decency and power has been long an obvious goal of statesmanship rarely attained. For modern states are aggregative clots of energy and men, that here are black, there white, there brass or silver, and their net decencies may barely top their ugliness. For America strength lies in her democracy and its maintenance against the odds of concentrated power production and great cities. Rewards must more and more be based on service, and a man's true earnings should determine in greater measure what he receives. Though it is hard to tell always what men earn, and liberal interpretations of it must be made in formulating the upper brackets of the income tax, it is clear that most of those inheriting great wealth have never earned it.

Drastic inheritance taxes are of critical importance in the maintenance of our democracy, and beyond a half million or a million dollars, say, inheritance should be made impossible. The passing on of massed estates and fortunes with their privilege and power, their accessory prestige, their baronial contempt and snobberies to men who have not earned them is not American in spirit. It is not safe. With the end of free lands, with increased ratio of our wage earners, with the pioneer occasions for independent business enterprise closing rapidly, with our economic life more rigid and inflexibly in the cement of age, such inherited lines of wealth in the United States will be a curse and a disaster on the nation. Nor need such taxes disrupt business continuity. Death is always discontinuous. The managers and editors of the Chicago Daily News are buying back today the paper that they helped make during long years of service, because the owner on his death left it to his estate; but the Daily News goes on without an interruption.

Labor banks, profit sharing plans, stock held distributively by consumers and employees are other movements toward democracy of no small import; but the world waits for a technical development, such as "superpower" publicly controlled, that will make distributive energy consumption worth while. Science by its applications, its machines, threatens democracy; and science by this further evolution may make the world once more safe for democracy.

If internal democracy is America's first aim, external strength is second. For in this world — as is — without one the other never will endure. They are reciprocal: A free people, without great inequalities in wealth, is the sole foundation of our strength; and without defensive power against the military and other pressures from without we cannot long be free. For America, with high living standards, with wealth in gold and resources and fixed capital, with a controlled birth rate, restrictive immigration laws, high wages (and high tariff) and with a stake in the liberalism of other countries, can maintain her higher living levels against the equalizing flow and swash of the world currents only by the tacit threat of force. It is not nice to say so, and pacifists and many liberals do not relish it, but power or potential power is requisite to maintain America in her present station, and granted the right of that, our navy is well justified.

It is not sure that the cause of life is always hurt by war, nor is conquest always unjustified. For an eternal *status quo* will not fit on this humanity, its development is differential and changes good in the long run, though legalistically unallowable may need force to be effective.[7] Though war always is a risk, both to winner and to loser, dogmatic absolutes against it are dangerous too. Its justification must be measured by criteria pertaining to the time, the place, the specific situation where it brews. Though war mongers, 100-per-centers, Lusks, Palmers, espionage acts and "National Security leagues" are to-day among the most immediate threats to our democratic government, to our freedom and our American toleration, the case does not justify — even with their dangerous existence — an absolute and dogmatic intolerance of war. War or the threat of war may still be necessary, and the navy may yet need the oil looted at Teapot Dome.

Tomorrow, Russell says,[8] Russia and America, and perhaps a European block, or China, will be the dominating powers. They are strong defensively, and their indifference to offensive policies will leave them free from crushing armaments and the wreck and weariness of foreign wars. They are self-contained industrially; they are continental in area and population, and beside them other states will dwindle like saplings by the trunks of trees. Moscow, says W. L. Bailey,[8] and Chicago will become the greatest cities in the world, and the latter by 1950 may have some 12 million people. Of the great two or three nations America, with wisdom and democracy, may overarch the world.

This the English forecaster does not hope to see until wars have scourged the earth and imperialisms have climbed to greater heights than now. Japan he says will fight America and be crushed as Germany was crushed. Russia will form an Asiatic block perhaps including India and China. Europe will integrate and control Africa or will break, with the western half subservient to America and the eastern part, perhaps from the straits of Dover, perhaps from the Rhine or the western line of Poland, subservient to Russia. The world hangs on the edge of universal politics and of world states of hemispheric size.

To nationalism America is now lashed fast by ties emotional and institutional, and though it has its evils — such as Mitchell Palmer — it is still, no doubt, the most feasible of vehicles for American development. It is an integrative influence (ofttimes dangerously so) and in this continental area and mixed and mobile population, that is important. It gives character and energy to our common deeds. It makes sacrifice a glory, and if our democratic principles can be maintained, the new America will go to heights unknown in man's history. It is the focus of our racial tone and culture. It is the assimilative center of our stock; from it a people of the future, the Americans, will arise.

Race remains a violent and tender dynamite in our social system that may at any moment tear foundations loose. Though some deny its place or try to mould it over into purely economic terms, it has, in fact, an importance that is critical in the change and progress of many of the world's departments.

What "race" precisely is has not been well defined, but whatever it may be is significant and burning in the field of modern problems. There are three ancestral stocks, presumably: white, black and yellow, whose common trunk ended long before history began. Of whites there are 900 million more or less; of yellows, 650 million; of blacks, 140 million; of others, not definitely classified in any of these three, there are some 70 million human beings.[9] Correlated with these ancestral strains are biologic differences, slight but noticeable,[9] that usually are thought of as primal differentiations of the races. And deposited on these slightly varying stocks are long accumulations of culture, tradition, language, institutions, that may vary widely. "Race" as a dynamic factor in man's crowded living is an aggregate of all these things. It bulges into social life. It is thick, stubborn, irrational; it is humane; and emotional cohesions bind it in rigidities that mind and common sense cannot dissolve. Our way to race distinctions has been long and positive, and though they sit, ostensibly, on a minor biologic difference, such as color of the skin, hair, eyes, a two or three ounce nose, thin lips or thick, their import and their circumstance is ancient and very often honorable.

For if race, as an effective factor in human history, arose through segregation and detachment, it is also true that man's specific progress has been down lines more and more divergent as they receded from ancestral stock. To this centrifugal development of man has come in the later centuries of written history, and particularly in the last fifty years, a catastrophic shock: The sudden limits of the earth were reached; by means of new powered transportation, the world shrank, two, three, ten, twenty times, in terms of travelled distances, and peoples once remote were next door neighbors. "Thanks to overseas commerce and colonial exploitations," says E. A. Ross,[10] "races which lived in ignorance of one another's existence have been jostled together and have to make up their minds whether it is to be peace or war."

In a world where civilizations have developed differentially through divergent channels, where the sweetness and the flavor of their cultures inheres in great part in divergence, the sudden mechanizing of society has sometimes aspects of disaster. In the raw thrust of physical and emotional contact their cultures cancel out each other, and only the lower strata common to both may endure. Chinese and American family life, both beautiful, cannot be juxtaposed without a mutual searing and destruction. It will be so in many other fields of life. If the peoples of the world are to be re-shaken and re-fused, like the brisk ingredients of a "chocolate malted milk" in a power driven mixing machine, there will be preliminary destructions and decadences of a vast extent. There will be more Port Saids, more Syrias and New Yorks, more Alexandrias and the muck of crossroads over the earth than there are today. There will be long dark ages before the world rebirth.

If, as Flinders Petrie says,[10] the source of every civilization has lain in race mixture, "it may be that eugenics will, in some future civilization, carefully segregate fine races, and prohibit continual mixture, until they have a distinct type which will start a new civilization when transplanted. The future progress of man may depend as much on isolation to establish a type as on fusion of types when established." A world unit of race and civilization that escapes such differential growths and conflicts will come only through darkness and travail, hardship, doubt, perhaps destruction.

To give up "race" and the homogeneous cultures hammered out in the little smithies of the world may be inevitable, but the prospect of it is not altogether satisfying. What we shall get may be far from what we want. Because the roots of our civilizations join in the dark soil of the past may not mean that their tops will join gracefully in the future. There well may be uprootings and if science and machines survive them, plantings again on a general scale.

For a century or two, says E. A. Ross,[11] a bifurcated world will be man's hardest problem. On the one side 600 million western peoples with high living standards, low birth and death rates, free women, and an individual-istic Weltanschauung, will hold desperately their fron-tiers against an Orient with lower living standards, high birth rate but low death rate, subjected women and a clan, or family, point of view. From the Orient huge streams of emigration will break massively on our coasts, and they will cease only when Asia becomes liberalized and balances her birth rate. Restriction laws, says Ross, are necessary for the support of western standards, but with free exchange of culture and of culture bearers, such as students, between the east and west, war may not be necessary. It remains a threat inherent in the racial lay-out of the world.

Science, machinery, general finance, as well as Edward Bok and other League of Nations men, favor internation-alism, and it may come in ways we think not of, but race is a stubborn spirituality that will die hard and fighting, for the unique cultures of a people are not easily over-borne. Tariff walls stay up and self-determined nations multiply like pups across the map of Europe. In America an internationalism of race and governments soaks in the assimilating fluid of our national state and culture and is harmonized thereby and made slowly one. It is a method of slow and good natured assimilation by a dominating culture that may well become world wide.

But even in America — the ideal test for international-ists — race is no solved problem. Of the four minority races in this country: The Indians have been answered by reservations and extinctions; there were in 1920 about 243,000 Indians left. The Asiatics have been answered by exclusion: there are about 172,000 eastern Asiatics here. The Jews (if rightly a minority race) answer the problem for themselves, whether we like it or no, by interpenetration, the capture of strategic points in our economic scheme, and by superior business energy and shrewdness. There are some four million Jews among us.[11] The negro has been answered by political discrimination, by mobs and lynchings, by economic pressures and new serfdoms; and of negroes in this country there are nearly eleven million. Mixture goes on illicitly by cohabitation of white men with negro women, and the mulatto dusk creeps higher in the faces of our people. About one third of the negroes of the United States have traces of white blood.[12] They will replace the pure blood blacks eventually and approach, no doubt, to a color level not well distinguished from the whiter stocks.

In America the race problem is far from answered. It hangs like dark and sultry storms waiting to break over our politics. It predetermines public issues in the south. It holds the Democratic party artificially together by an outside pressure and keeps it thumping persistently and irrelevantly for reaction against progressive measures. It fortifies thereby reactionary elements in the other party and makes progressive politics consistently impossible. There are signs of fracture in the old parties; problems of the farm, of prohibition, of the negro may soon break them; but the liberalisms of America's last half century have themselves broken time and again on the negro problem.

And the problem has not now an adequate solution; for preaching to the southerner to treat the negro as his brother will do no good. Race prejudice and oppression in the south is a human fact that will remain as long as liberal treatment of the negroes there will threaten white control. "If the Negro progresses, acquires a competence

and the means to leisure and education," says Selig-
mann,[13] "he at the same time assimilates the white man's
culture and manners; he threatens to become fit to asso-
ciate with white men on the basis of any test which white
men may erect, except ancestry — and even in the veins
of many persons of color flows the blood of the most distinguished white men of the nation's past. The conception of race relations represented by the emphasis upon
sex is given extraordinary currency by the press, by politicians who always seek to rouse men's least governable
impulses, and by white persons who have absorbed it as
part of the credo that clings with all the tenacity of
impressions and beliefs absorbed in childhood. In a sense
the favorable development of race relations in the United
States depends upon the supplanting of this over-sim-
plified issue of sex by other more varied and more immediately pressing considerations." But despite Seligman's
brave analysis, race prejudice and oppression will endure
so long as the two massed peoples live together in the
south. The sole answer, and that is doubtful, lies probably in other distribution of the negro stocks.

With war and immigration laws and the great suctions
of machine industry a negro current has begun to flow
out of the south to industrial centers of the north. By
hundreds of thousands the negroes have moved northward, and if the stream continues the great black belts
of America will be broken. Small white farmers then may
penetrate the south. The negroes may find advancement
in the north. And the "solid south," for all the country's
good, will at last disintegrate. But the race problem in
America — America, example of inner internationalism
— and in the British Empire, has not been answered.
When that answer comes the more ambitious schemes
outside may be more feasible.

Of foreign whites in America there are nearly 15
million, and though they have aroused a nest of poignant
situations, from native birth declines to labor difficulties,

the problem, as it stands, will not be permanent. Of these foreign born, twelve per cent are German born; almost twelve per cent Italian; eleven per cent are Russian; eight per cent are Pole; seven per cent are Irish and six per cent are English; [14] with prosperity and peace and the present immigration laws America can no doubt digest this racial garden truck without great hardship. The severer race problem lies elsewhere.

As population thickens, says E. A. Ross,[15] "we mark the genesis of sects and clans, each of them a natural community which forbids society to remain a natural community. The sect being a true social cell enjoys a natural order. It monopolizes sympathies. It becomes the object of devotion. It instigates heroism. It has its martyrs. It has, in fact, everything that society ought to have, and yet is only a segment or fragment of the mass. Hence the antipathies of sects threaten to tear society to pieces. The drawing apart into opposing camps of poor and rich, capitalist and worker, functionary and citizen, civilian and soldier, as well as the race enmity of white and black, or yellow and white, or Christian and Jew, summons society to act or perish. The folk mass becomes a dangerous compound ready to explode at a touch. Unless the all-inclusive group finds means to assimilate and reconcile its members and weaken the ties that bind men into minor groups, the social order will be disrupted. In the struggle for order, therefore, the group is not always pitted against the person, the social against the individual interest. It is often the big group against the little group, society against the sect or clan. And the danger is from fanatic and sectary, zealot and partisan, as well as from the egoist. Society must muzzle Jesuit and Mafiote, conspirator and anarchist, as well as the man of prey."

Ready made into America groups have come by immigration whose lines are rigid and whose souls — racial, religious, political or social — are deeply alien to

America's *motif*. Of our population in 1920, says Lotka,[14] 53 per cent was composed of immigrants since 1790 and their descendants. They have come here undissolved; but America's good health and inner continuity depend on their solution. Our mobilized society, its ceaseless shift; our 20 million automobiles (in 1926); our public schools and the general tendency still to send all children there; our sports, movies, radios, newspapers; our slang and dancing, our songs and hair pomades; our styles in clothes and chewing gum; new drinks and corner drug stores and the ceaseless press and shoving of advertisements, the army and militia, labor unions and other groups that lie across our racial segmentations indifferently, all are dissolving acids of importance. For human nature as Ogburn says,[15] "is very elusive; our ignorance of its laws is great; measurement is difficult; and prejudices are strong;" and its influence and development in society and civilization can be seen more clearly after the cultural factors and progressions are better recognized. They change and rearrange their pressures; they find new seats and centres of new distributions. The new small town, where urban zest and flexibility is not lacking and where the soil is not too far away is best no doubt for life and social continuity in America.

A distributive society, flexible and mobile, is no doubt necessary to an enduring American life, and this, even with twice our population, may well be realized. Crop areas, says O. E. Baker,[16] can be increased one third, the acre yield can be increased a third, and with diet changes, less meat and more plant products, fully 200 million healthy Americans can grow where 100 million grow today. The high concentrates of population in the cities with the bled out rural districts of today probably are not the best adjustment to support the largest national population. A new agriculture leaning heavily on dairy products will come, says Harper Leech,[17] and that with a new industrialism of "superpower" may well make modern social readjustment possible. For economic reasons, as well as social, technical, racial, eugenical, America will move eventually no doubt towards a distributive society.

But the enemies of race are not all aliens or outsiders. Within are armies of defectives, feebleminded sons of Uncle Sam, free to breed their kind and to increase at rates greater perhaps than those of sound Americans. It is an estimated army of 400,000 low grade minds,[18] weak, often criminal, usually diseased, born to a sub-social status and capacity, and without power through education or experience to rise to citizens' responsibility. Crime finds its roots in these defective minds — most criminals if not all, says Hickson, psychiatrist for Chicago courts, can be detected in their youth before their greater crimes begin. And rotten strains of race find perpetuation through them.

The problem of eugenics is primary and important, and though programs scientific or artistic to promote the intercourse of human male and female may never have weight, some restrictions can be put on mating that will save the race much woe.[19] The feebleminded members of communities can be segregated, treated well, made happy, given work suited to their capacities, but kept from crime, mating and the free wandering of a normal man. It would empty many prisons. It would reduce disease and vice.[20] It would raise the level of our stock.

Voluntary sterilization of the unfit is a second, although secondary, practice that may protect society somewhat. Eugenic and hygienic education can do good, and protection from venereal disease do better. In America there are two million syphilitics, and Americans with gonorrhea are in far greater numbers.[20] They lead diseases in disaster. The so-called ills of women are nine times out of ten from gonorrhea. Were venereal diseases done away with, fully half of our institutions for defectives, says Fisher, would be no longer needed.[20] No threat of guns or foreign armies, no imminence of famine or of wreck, was ever a greater danger than this enemy within.

A weak state means a strong family system, say social experts, and a strong state means a weak family system.[21] Where the family is strong, Müller-Lyer continues, the position of women is bad; and where the family is weak the position of women is good. This with the usual exceptions, scholarly qualifications, emendations, checks, balances, hems and haws, is no doubt true enough to suggest a background and one reason for the moral astonishments and changes, sexual and institutional, that assail the modern world.

For a strong state is more or less inevitable in this delicately organic industrialized society, and the family as an industrial system rather self-contained has been replaced in great part by larger social mechanisms. They take industrial production — spinning, weaving, canning, curing, sewing, cooking and the like — away from home, and women follow them to factories and business offices, or live in somewhat parasitic ease on the earnings of their men. As organized society takes over home productions, home training of the young and other functions of the family life, women gain more freedom. They learn to work for wages and their comparative independence economically releases them from male control. That alone is bound to jar sex and marriage customs from many of their most sacred moulds.

For men are out of balance sexually, says Charlotte Perkins Gilman. They are over sexed. They want more than women care to give.[22] They burn; they always hunger, Ward explains;[23] and their restless explorative nature as compared with that of women, upsets a peaceful social pattern that might otherwise be reconciled to prosaic, routine facts. For man's sex restlessness supports the "double standard" with its complement of female prostitution and disease. He enforces chastity on the females who depend on him, and from their easy continence he turns to those "outside" for fuller satisfaction. It is exogamy of "sin" and it correlates completely with the fixed and classified high virtue of women who are "nice." [24]

In a system where men's marriage and economic maturity come from eight to fifteen years later than their sexual maturity there are years of stress and wandering and exposures to venereal disease — said to afflict at some time three fourths of all unmarried men — and the double standard flourishes.[25] But with woman's economic independence this will change somewhat. Sexual relations will be more flexible and free, and the demi-world, that in America now includes 200,000 to 500,000 prostitutes [26] and costs annually about $628,000,000, will gradually decline.

Already marriage customs show the move towards freedom. Marriage is more brittle, and the difference between parenthood and mating is better recognized. For the good of marriage [27] is primarily to protect children and their mothers and to hold restless men responsible as well as women for the consequence of love; beyond that good, marriage in the modern economic system need have little weight. Divorce increases daily. It means new flexibility and freedom between sexes of preponderating benefit. In Wyoming there is one divorce to 3.9 marriages; [28] in California, one to 5.1; in Oregon, one to 2.6; in Illinois, one to 6.8; in Pennsylvania, one to 10.2; in New York, one to 22.6; in South Carolina, none; but the differences are more in laws than in fundamental habits or in points of view. In America in 1922 there was one divorce to 7.2 marriages. It is a situation far more wholesome than that of countries where divorce is hard to get.

The ends of human living are no doubt eternal but the rules for finding them must vary with the time and place.

Marriages and moralities and the brass bound conventions of our lives are after all but rules made to defend what man has found worth while, and when rules like these become the ends of life, they lose their moral value. They obscure the light of being and the spirit; they distort the human purpose and become in an accurate way dogmatic immoralities. The shift and change and flexibility of our moral codes of conduct in this modern age are signs of their vitality. The good will is man's first moral principle, and the good will carried into action in a world of new industrial conditions, of great cities and machines, of highly organized production, of wage earners and concentrated capital, will have new paths to break, new rules to build, and old conventions to forsake.

And the church, ancient aggregate of rule, form, sham, love, of pharisee and Christ, of dogged externalism and the inner life, of petty regulation and obstruction and the breath of being, shakes down amid the quakes of modernism and great machines like an old pyramid too thick to fall. As a leader in that first of all moral problems — the importation of good will into the deep structure of industrial society — the church has not been dominant. It has lost itself in many cases in instruments and forms, creeds, authorities, externalisms and forgot its end. It has become too often — unlike Jesus — an obstructionist, protective more of property, and of one conception of it, than of the human spirit.

Three parties, says Kirsopp Lake,[29] quarrel for precedence in the modern church. The fundamentalists sit pat on four traditional doctrines: the infallibility of the scripture, the deity of Jesus, the blood atonement, and the second coming of Christ. The institutionalists accept with their mouths what they must of fundamentalist doctrine in order to preserve the churchly institution, and at least believe more fashionably with the scientific current of the times. The experimentalists abandon "revelation" so far as fact experience is concerned and entrust the development of stated truth to scientific observation. They coördinate religion — so far as it is practical and rational — with science,[30] and predict, with justice, that the church will pass away as a dominating institution in society, if this adjustment of belief to modern thinking is not soon made. Let belief go to the scientist for authority and let religion be a path for living says Experimentalism. "It is promising and powerful," says Herbert Croly,[31] "only in so far as it accepts all the risks and assumes all the responsibility of envisaging Christianity as a way of life rather than a body of belief. . . . The essential business of religion is not the submission by individuals to a particular formulation of the truth, but the choice by individuals to govern their lives by the truth, no matter what it is, and the willingness on their part to discover what the truth is by means of methodical conscious experience."

In the practices and rationalisms of man's modern life there are divers ill adjustments, from church to business, from property to government, and most of them come from the new science and its mechanisms thrusting in upon old habits and outworn institutions. "Modern industrial civilization is, of course, based upon the achievements of science and the more effective control of man over nature," says Croly.[32] "The surplus economic value on which the hope of human liberation depends is the product of the inventor, the machine and ultimately of the scientific investigator. But the existing economic system has not, until recently, been able to make any sufficient use of scientific methods, and the capitalistic machine has been indifferent and even alien to the scientific spirit. Science is patient, deliberate, critical, organic and disinterested. The organization and methods of business have been impatient and amateurish, and its purposes have been selfish and hidebound." And the church, the governments, the police and crime control, state and domestic institutions, as well as business, need

a completer penetration by science. So far as life must
deal with instruments, with rules, forms, reasons, dogmas,
tools, causes, externalities and objective fact science is
the safest measure and the surest guide.

But the ends of life are a rather different matter, and
before them science and industry, business and the massive institutions laid stone by stone through history have
less arrogance. Enjoyments and life's consummations
deeply within themselves are not developmentary, and
though the instruments and arts may change, the ends
are final. The tools of pleasure, and the means to realize
life have grown with industrialism. Sports have become
self-conscious and commercial. Arenas with their fifty
thousands scar America's terrain with giant hoof marks.
The radio and drinking; the movie and the dance; the
amusement colonies, Coney islands, Riverviews, leaning
like dishevelled, careless girls against the stark sides of
cities; motoring and surf bathing; camping, canoeing,
hunting; bridge and football; travel, flirting, catching but-
terflies; reading the fiction of the magazines; comic strips
and singing; hunting wild women, church socials, talking,
eating, dressing, drama, checkers, metaphysics, coasting,
poetry, love, prayer, painting, cross word puzzles, music,
they all unroll endlessly men's enjoyment; and though
they and their pleasures hardly are life's consummation
they point fingers to finality and to man's wish for being.

The "economic man" is nowhere found, says J. A.
Hobson.[33] "Actual man, as many anthropologists depict
him, appears to begin with luxuries and dispenses with
conveniences."

The good life at heart is not life's instruments but life's
ends. Man looks for being. His deepest interest is finally
to realize it.

The tomorrow of politics, of democracy, of America's

race and nation, of culture and agriculture, of sex, of morality, of religion has been touched here, but the new day may rise without much reference to the problems of the present. History has its discontinuities, and society today cannot promise society tomorrow.

BOOK THREE

Studies In Personal Values

The World of Appreciations and Æsthetic Interest

"and at last the vision is revealed to him of a single knowledge, which is the knowledge of beauty everywhere."

— PLATO

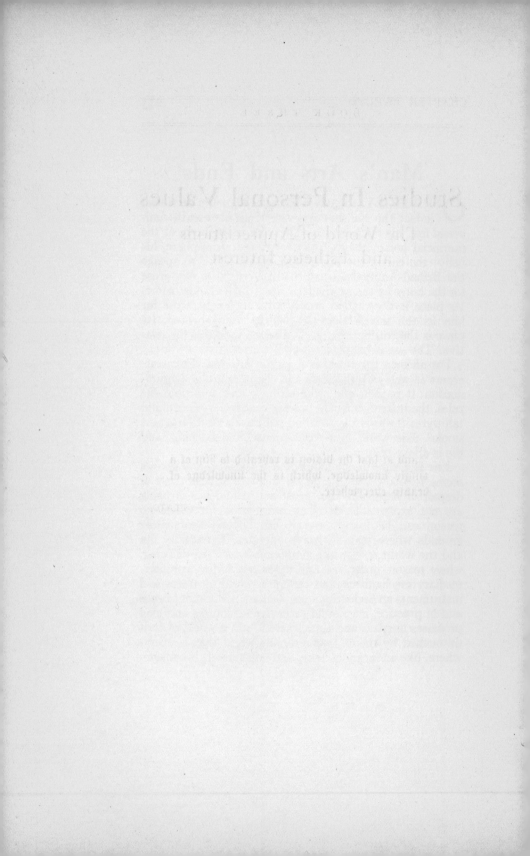

Man's Arts and Ends

OM! VERILY, the dawn is the head of the sacrificial horse; the sun, his eye; the wind, his breath; universal fire, his open mouth. The year is the body of the sacrificial horse; the sky, his back; the atmosphere, his belly; the earth, the under part of his belly: so speaks the Bṛihad-Āraṇyaka Upanishad.[1] Verily, the day arose for the horse as the sacrificial vessel which stands before. Its place is the eastern sea. Verily, the night arose for him as the sacrificial vessel which stands behind. Its place is the western sea. . . . The sea indeed is his relative. The sea is his place.

For all men the world is a sacrificial horse. For westerners as well as Indic seers and chanters it is a consummation; it is their end. The struggle and ambition, the rules, the instruments, the science and society that build tall pyres towards the sky find realization in its fragrant smoke. The world is a sweet smoke and burning, and life is a love of fire.

Life is a flare in our hands and a gratuity, and no one seems to know why we go on living. For regardless of despair or happiness the thrust and confidence of being are not explainable. It is an affirmation for which no reason can be found; and it lies beyond the middle grounds where reason always operates. Eventually life and the world rest on the simple push and yea of being, where reason, order, use and other relativities are intermediary mechanisms, and though a world of means and instruments and scientific formulations, a world of science and of practice, may build extensive structures and long processes in space and time, there is still a world of ends untouched by them. It is a simple world that is everywhere, like an incandescence, and nowhere. It is consummate in being. In beauty, love, religion in the spiritual sense, it is real and final.

The sciences, says Schopenhauer,[2] consider nothing more than the relations of things, "the connections of time and space, the causes of natural changes, the resemblance of forms, the motives of actions," — merely relations — and science is distinguished from ordinary knowledge merely by its "systematic form," "by the comprehension of all particulars in the universal, by means of the subordination of concepts, and the completeness of knowledge which is thereby attained." But art finds a world that is neither rational nor relative, and with it man breaks free from wanting; he escapes his little individuality; he rises into the object of his contemplation; it loses its relationships and externalities, and he finds in union with it a finality that science and utility cannot give. By artistic intuition he may find the eternal form, the being, that Plato calls the *idea*. By love or religious aspiration he may rise into the real sun. It is a simple "yes" at heart. The world is a spiritual affirmation.

Though science and society as a making process, as Ellis says,[3] may be one with art there remains between them the deep difference in mode or vision of the world that lies between reason and the spirit, between the behavior and the being of things, between their measurements and relations and their inner affirmation of the real; spiritually we face the east; practically, scientifically we face the west. Men know which way is west, but the east, though its flame consume them, is seldom recognized.

War and laughter, love and marching, play, music, football, dancing, poetry, friendship, prayer, philosophy have their infinitudes and beauty. They affirm existence, and men find in them appreciative interests and finalities that are unassailable. The world has its intrinsic and its extrinsic aspect, and though the former can never be explicit or defined, it is immediate and real.

Nature herself is content in a fair and self-conscious vision, says the delicately mental Plotinus,[4] and by man the Absolute is found threefold in the æsthetic contemplation of beauty, of the one and of the good. Beside religion and beside morals he puts æsthetics and, in æsthetics, art. It is a contemplation, highest of activities, and of it all human creative activity is a by-play. For the more realistic Bertrand Russell,[4] on the other hand, art rests on human impulses, and of them there are two kinds: the possessive and the creative. The one is of property and leads to conflict. The other is more harmonious and brings into human existence something eternal. Be it play or dancing, love or cutting marble, that in some sense is art.

From means to ends is a spiritual revolution. From business to love, from matter to being, from reason to the spirit, from science to art is a deep crossing and conversion, and those who do not see it find it anyhow in life.

The arts traditionally have defined frontiers that aliens may not cross without much questioning. There is poetry, an art of time and sound suggestions and of words that penetrate dimensions of experience that the senses cannot probe. There is painting, an art of space and color and plane surfaces, of line and light. Sculpture is a spatial art, of contours and of volumes, of shadow and of mass, and of an enduring moment, as Lessing says,[5] that must "express nothing that can only be thought of as transitory." Music, purest of the arts, without burden of representation, rides on time and pitch, on tone and harmonies. Its mystery and wonder remain unanswered. It comes without cause or compulsion and without need. It burns with the sweet scent of being. Like a god it is gratuitous and complete. Music, says Schopenhauer, is the naked will. And dancing is music buried in the flesh, an art of space and time and movement.

Dancing and building, says Ellis,[6] "are the two primary and essential arts. The art of dancing stands at the source of all the arts that express themselves first in the human person. The art of building, or architecture, is the beginning of all the arts that lie outside the person; and in the end they unite. Music, acting, poetry proceed in the one mighty stream; sculpture, painting, all the arts of design, in the other. There is no primary art outside these two arts, for their origin is far earlier than man himself; and dancing came first."

For the arts are neither separable nor finally defined,[7] and space and painting, time and tone values, dancing, words, cathedrals, songs, are only beaten paths over a plain. They are ways, but there are no doubt others. Art, says Santayana,[8] "is the plastic instinct conscious of its aim." But all life, all things, are plastic, and in all there may be art.

Poems are bowls of being; they are cups in which a deep and universal liquor shines; if the rims are trimmed with gold and decorations or raw clay, no one minds, who knows the drink within. Poems send words like bees to the hearts of things and life, and many flowers and many carriers build one sweetness. They seek the final juice and vigor of the world; and they find what cannot be articulated, what no one points to, what no one explicates, and they bear the burden of it with joy and urgency and a faith in just found being.

How curious! how real!
Underfoot the divine soil, overhead the sun.

Words are motley bearers of reality, and these of Walt Whitman are naked coolies bearing precious loads.

For words have various duties. Language has values both direct and indirect. It is an activity first of all, and as a form of action possesses muscular or kinæsthetic values that relate it to the dance and singing and the like. It is behaviour, and poems as behaviours will not be unrelated to the poet's type and musculature.[9] They are implicit kinds of action, and they bulge with biceps and the round or rugged shoulders of their makers. Language as sound is an added instrument to a poem's symphony. It is tone and pitch and sonant value added to the kinæsthetic rhythm of the dance, and music joins hands with words. Language as a vehicle for other things, as a representative for all articulate experience, carries in its pack a universe of objects, things, relations, ideas, images, whatever makes this world, and lays them down at a man's bidding.[10] Muscular values, sound values, conceptual values, all are involved in language.[11] All may be found in poetry; the last alone is found in prose. In poetry is the incandescence and suggestion of a world beyond articulate expression.

Poetry is suggestive. Prose is informative. Poetry awakes realities already immanent in the reader. Prose carries fact or other rational material from one mind to another. The form of poetry or prose can have no dogmas. Used in its kinæsthetic and musical sense language increases in suggestiveness; and with this in view formal technique is designed. But form in itself can never be a true criterion of poetry.

Literary patterns, sonnets, blank verse, dactylic hexameters in time acquire dignity and value in themselves. An intrinsic fitness and beauty somehow illumines them; and the poet finds his problem less in creating a free form to suit his impulse and material than in selecting and manipulating his material to suit the form. Content becomes sharply distinguished from form, and an artificial but spirited controversy arises over their relative values.

Against this ancient and disastrous movement towards external standards modern poets have rebelled; and the limitations of the older forms and of the rather stereotyped material suitable to those forms are at will abandoned. For doctrinal authority in literature as in religion is a phenomenon of a medieval stage of evolution which will pass away before a new enlightenment. Until poetry and poets can outgrow the artificial distinction between form and content they will remain immature. For such differences and controversies are external to the deep suggestion and the intimate reality of great work.

To the region where words are not as yet emerging above the threshold of consciousness, says Bliss Perry,[12] belongs "the strange feeling, witnessed to by many poets, of the fluidity, fusibility, transparency — the infinitely changing and interchangeable aspects — of the world as it appears to the senses. It is evident that poets are not looking — at least when in this mood — at our 'logical' world of hard, clear fact and law. They are gazing rather at what Whitman called 'the eternal float of solution,' the 'flowing of all things' of the Greeks, the 'river within the river' of Emerson."

Poetry is intuitive, imaginative, spiritual. Prose is discursive, rational, objective. The difference between them originally was not great, but with the growth of science and our increasing ability to analyze and organize our environment, prose has grown in importance and distinction. As language becomes representative of objective, verifiable phenomena, its symbolism hardens; it becomes standardized and exact; its connotations become rigid, permanent, denotative. The practical symbolism of prose supersedes the fluidity and suggestiveness of poetry.

The break and merge of ancient forms today is not limited to space and time, physics and atoms, matter and politics, marriage and ecclesiastical dogma; it has come upon the arts, and the old distinctions — romantic,

classic, form, content, subjective, objective, verse, prose,
emotion, reason — are giving way before deeper and
more intimate realities. In Whitman and Carl Sandburg,
in Tagore, Frost, Shakespeare, Yeats, and other modern
men the new poetry burns with youthful joy and courage.

With Whitman being bulges up from the level lands of
America in giant rhythms; the poet celebrates the earth
in uncouth joy and majesty. For he is naïvely metaphysical in temper: being shocks him with urgent thrills and
electricities. To Walt Whitman the deep identities of
self with every thing, the pressures of existence, are
enough for halleluiahs. Reality indeed is a massive halle-
luiah that he draws somehow into his utterance. It is a
glad imperative. It is the mystic *yea.*

Was somebody asking to see the soul?
See, your own shape and countenance, persons,
          substances, beasts, the trees, the running
          rivers, the rocks and sands.

I will not make poems with reference to parts,
But I will make poems, songs, thoughts, with
          reference to ensemble,
And I will not sing with reference to a day,
          but with reference to all days,
And I will not make a poem nor the least part of
          a poem but has reference to the soul,
Because having looked at the objects of the universe,
          I find there is no one nor any particle of one
          but has reference to the soul.

And I will thread a thread through my poems that
          time and events are compact,
And that all the things of the universe are perfect
          miracles, each as profound as any.

And in the spiritual oneness of all things Walt
Whitman [12] finds the democratic thesis that stirs and
rambles through his Leaves Of Grass like a thick and
stubborn wind. For America merges with the man; his
friendship for the world becomes Walt Whitman. In
"Spontaneous Me" he finds friendship, love, sex,
America, democracy, being, the universe, all implicit:

I celebrate myself, and sing myself,
And what I assume you shall assume,
For every atom belonging to me as good belongs to you.

But all poets at heart through all time sing much the
same song. And all men in their spiritual wonder, in their
love, in their appreciations and identities with being are
poets. Poetry is never cumulative and expert. It is not
built up like science on its past. Poetry is its own past
and future, and its past and future are poetry's today.
It is a warm flame on the world, burning, repeatedly
observed. It is as fresh as living and as old as life.

Tagore comes frailly out of ancient India and the
reveries of the east. Beside Whitman and his burliness
and this raw America he stands strangely quiet and
reserved; he is cool, delicate, mental; but what he sees
and sings is what Whitman sees and sings:

Thou hast made me endless, such is thy pleasure.
This frail vessel thou emptiest again and again,
and fillest it ever with fresh life.
        This little flute of a reed thou hast
carried over hills and dales, and hast
breathed through it melodies eternally new.

Have you not heard his silent steps?
He comes, comes, ever comes.
        Every moment and every age, every day
and every night he comes, comes, ever comes.

Emerson sits in his white house where the road forks in Concord, prim, ministerial, tightly New England, and burns in the same flame of being: "For poetry was all written before time was," he says in one of his poems that usually are called essays, "and whenever we are so finely organized that we can penetrate into that region where the air is music, we hear those primal warblings, and attempt to write them down. . . . Words and deeds are quite indifferent modes of the divine energy. Words are also actions, and actions are a kind of words."

Sandburg, with lank hair and the slouch and toil of great towns in his gait, finding a story for the Chicago Daily News, jabbing down a ragged movie criticism, eating ham and fried potatoes with a friend under the roar of the "elevated," comes with the same burning and the same thing to say:

A bar of steel — it is only
Smoke at the heart of it, smoke and the blood of a man.
A runner of fire ran in it, ran out, ran somewhere else,
And left — smoke and the blood of a man
And the finished steel, chilled and blue.

In the blood of men and the ink of chimneys
The smoke nights write their oaths:
Smoke into steel and blood into steel;
Homestead, Braddock, Birmingham, they make
     their steel with men.
Smoke and blood is the mix of steel.

Fogs push and swirl across his work; there is humane cursing; there is the scratch and howl of car wheels on the corner, lullabies and metaphysical moonlight.

The sheets of night mist travel a long valley.
I know why you come at sundown in a scarf mist.

What was it we touched asking nothing and asking all?
How many times can death come and pay back what we
    saw?

In the oath of the sod, the lips that swore,
In the oath of night mist, nothing and all,
A riddle is here no man tells, no woman.

Blake and the Vedic hymns, Dante,[13] Langland, Herbert, Browning, Shakespeare, Wordsworth, Keats,
Goethe,[13] Schiller; all men are poets in their hearts, the
list is endless. Shelley, slender and intense, comes with
words soaring to the selfsame sun. Of Adonais:

> Peace, peace! he is not dead, he doth not sleep —
> He hath awakened from the dream of life —
> 'Tis we, who, lost in stormy visions, keep
> With phantoms an unprofitable strife,
> And in mad trance strike with our spirit's knife
> Invulnerable nothings. *We* decay
> Like corpses in a charnel; fear and grief
> Convulse us and consume us day by day,
> And cold hopes swarm like worms within our living clay.

> He is made one with Nature; there is heard
> His voice in all her music, from the moan
> Of thunder to the song of night's sweet bird:
> He is a presence to be felt and known
> In darkness and in light, from herb and stone,
> Spreading itself where'er that Power may move
> Which has withdrawn his being to its own;
> Which wields the world with never-wearied love,
> Sustains it from beneath, and kindles it above.

Thoreau tramps across New England pastures, builds
his hut under the hard woods by Walden, and in nature
finds the utter smoke and loveliness of being: "This is a
delicious evening," he says, "when the whole body is

one sense and imbibes delight through every pore. I go and come with a strange liberty in Nature, a part of herself."

Lindsay comes howling in mellow jubilation at the world and finds in central Illinois the Congo and a golden track to all reality. There is Yeats with Ireland singing in his verse. And Lincoln in humane understanding finds the universal epic written on an envelope. Robinson prods carefully at the world and excavates sharp lined eternities. Frost writes of walls and birches, the calm whiteness of a winter, of New England men and women. His ability, says Llewellyn Jones,[13] to "dispense with sensational subject matter and yet achieve undoubtedly poetic effects by the simple ability to come close enough to daily living to get under its skin of accustomedness, brush from its aspect the artificialities of practical life — as one would brush from one's vision of a country the artificial lines of meridians and parallels — and exhibit it in its original movement," is his most general characteristic:

> Something there is that doesn't love a wall,
> That sends the frozen-ground-swell under it
> And spills the upper boulders in the sun;
> And makes gaps even two can pass abreast.

De la Mare comes neat, careful, mystical; Eliot, taut, cranky and perversely sweet; Bynner laying being like old carnelians in his Chinese lines; Fletcher, bright with words; Sarett with pipe clay on his cheeks; Leonard, poignant, proud; Millay, girlish, sprightly and profound; H. D., hard, delicate, refined; Lawrence, with tumescent verse, sexual metaphysics, love and the flushed unities of flesh and worlds. He says:

And who has seen the moon, who has not seen
Her rise from out the chamber of the deep,

Flushed and grand and naked, as from the chamber
Of finished bridegroom, seen her rise and throw
Confession of delight upon the wave,
Littering the waves with her own superscription
Of bliss, till all her lambent beauty shakes towards us
Spread out and known at last, and we are sure
That beauty is a thing beyond the grave,
That perfect, bright experience never falls
To nothingness, and time will dim the moon
Sooner than our full consummation here
In this odd life will tarnish or pass away.

Masters writes grim histories of death. He builds biographies of gloom and the dark truth and decadence of rural life in Illinois. "He is mordant and denunciatory," says Amy Lowell,[14] herself a poet, he "resists with every fibre of his being." He is "more preoccupied with sex than any other English or American author has ever been, and in a different way." He sees life "through the medium of sex, and sex for the most part cruel, untamed, perverted, tragic." "D. H. Lawrence is also greatly preoccupied with sex, but in his work there is a certain rapture, sex is treated as a burgeoning of the mental and physical life, he throws over it the transparent and glittering cloak of joy." But Masters and Strindberg, says Miss Lowell, include all that is coarse and revolting in sexual life.

But sex whether treated realistically or ecstatically, is after all a prime solvent of the universe, and in its molten ore all things dissolve. In it and in the grim toughness of humanity Masters finds the one:

We quarreled that morning,
For he was sixty-five and I was thirty,
And I was nervous and heavy with the child
Whose birth I dreaded.
I thought over the last letter written me

By that estranged young soul
Whose betrayal of me I had concealed
By marrying the old man.
Then I took morphine and sat down to read.
Across the blackness that came over my eyes
I see the flickering light of these words even now:
"And Jesus said unto him, Verily
I say unto thee, Today thou shalt
Be with me in paradise."

And of Anne Rutledge:

Out of me unworthy and unknown
The vibrations of deathless music;
"With malice toward none, with charity for all."
Out of me the forgiveness of millions toward millions,
And the beneficent face of a nation
Shining with justice and truth.
I am Anne Rutledge who sleep beneath these weeds,
Beloved in life of Abraham Lincoln,
Wedded to him, not through union,
But through separation.
Bloom forever, O Republic,
From the dust of my bosom!

New movements in poetry blaze and fade, for routine
and custom in poetry is almost surely bad. Our hope is
continuity in new burnings, and in America now the flare
of literature is high and glorious. The prose of Occidental
writers, of Conrad, Anderson, Joyce, Proust, of Cather,
of Shaw, of Rolland, Dreiser, Galsworthy, Lewis, O'Neill,
White, Gale, Wells, of Tolstoi, of Hardy and others, the
poets and the news men all add fire to this world. To
Harriet Monroe, to William Reedy and to other brave
explorers, the discovery of new literary continents is
due; and free verse, and free men unknown before, Sandburg, Frost, Lindsay, Masters and a score of others owe

them much. But poetry has a wide diffusion. In slang [15] and funny stories, in cowboy songs or in epics of Paul Bunyan, in energetic gayety and love, in tunes and poetry, America will find a unity and being of her own.

Arts are a sun to all peoples, and the soils of China and Ceylon are warmed as well as those of Illinois. But music is less arrogant than words and is meaningful to all in spite of different harmonies and new modes. Music, of all the arts, is least allied with the incidental uses which give the other parts a place in the functional organization of man's life. What justification it has is in itself, and for this reason music is the best, because the simplest, subject of artistic analysis and at the same time the most difficult.

The import of music is hardly in its representative power, for as a practical means of communication it is not much. What emotional suggestibility it may have is probably irrelevant to its value as music. It is not utilized to any great extent in the world of social and discursive relations. Its value is intuitive; its immediate significance is its sole significance.

That a pattering of sounds on the ear, says Santayana,[15] should have such moment "is a fact calculated to give pause to those philosophers who attempt to explain consciousness by its utility, or who wish to make physical and moral processes march side by side from all eternity. Music is essentially useless, as life is: but both have an ideal extension which lends utility to its conditions. That the way in which idle sounds run together should matter so much is a mystery of the same order as the spirit's concern to keep a particular body alive, or to propagate its life. Such an interest is, from an absolute point of view, wholly gratuitous; . . ." For music is an experience and a living in itself. It is a consummation and is parallel in this way to the experience of life or of activity. It motivates and makes useful an entire series of interests that subserve it.

For if the stock yards are one expression of the reality that is America, if the steel mills and the southern gardens, the prize fights, the Vermont pastures, the cabarets, the country schools, the coal mines are expressions, our music is equally a real thing that somehow carries in it the being of America. Jazz, says John Alden Carpenter,[16] finds its basis in American life in athletics, in negro music, in the dance. It is an American release, like athletics, from the restrictions on art of the early Puritans, and it will tend to identify itself with what Clive Bell would call the "significant form" of American life. Jazz is America's unique contribution to music.

From Tin Pan alley, from singing waiters or from Irving Berlin's studio, tunes come with the gay buzz of summer and the rhythmic slide and shuffle of ten million feet. They are clipped and throbbing tunes, here like bright ephemera. They are blossoms that give way presently to another crop. From *Alexander's Ragtime Band* or *Who* to George Gershwin's *Rhapsody in Blue* or Gruenberg's *Jazzberries* [17] or Deems Taylor's *Circus Day*, jazz moves from simple melody to more symphonic stuff, but its blunt and vivid realism is the same; the raw drive and din of life, the sweet savagery of living carries it on. Jazz as yet has found no accurate notation, and jazz orchestras can do what no notes can signify. Jazz inventors are many, but jazz masters able to write it down, to orchestrate it all, to build more massive structures out of these elemental dance tunes have not appeared.

Western music, perhaps all music, is an evolution largely of the dance tune, and jazz no doubt is the first turn of a new cycle of western music. For the formal structure of the tune, the very tune idea indeed, from which symphonic complications have developed is found in Bach, in Mozart and Händel resting on the dance. To this Beethoven brings dynamics and a high charge of human life and power. In him music becomes apostolic. A divine smoke and grandeur envelops it, and the voice of Jehovah is singing in its midst. Wagner builds in epic forms, and the lyric voice of tunes and melody becomes less constant. Strauss moves on from Wagner towards dramatic mass and color. For the patterned melodies of the classics are declining and Wagner, Debussy and Stravinsky, says George Dyson,[18] embody our more rhapsodic ideals of today. Masses of sound supplant the lyric line of melody. Texture and tonalities interest the composer where line and architecture held him a century ago; and Scriabine, Debussy, Goossens, Delius, Ravel, Bartòc, Schönberg, to name but a few, move more or less in order down this line of evolution.

Today the twelve note system, the major and minor scales, the old harmonies and forms are toppling, like Euclidian geometry, from preëminence, and vast diffusions and relativities, quarter notes, third notes, sixth notes, Orientalisms, new experiments and upstart scales,[19] arise beside them. For they are arrogant and artificial categories, after all, derived more or less by accident; and when the new world finds realities, not suited to their forms, new categories will come. In music and poetry, in geometry, physics, in space, time, chemistry, in painting and dancing, in religion, in politics, in trade and sculpture, the old forms shift and deliquesce and new formulations of the world appear. Today is a crevice between two worlds. Perhaps every day is that.

Music in America, from McDowell to John A. Carpenter, from the jazz hounds of Paul Ash to Whiteman and more formal orchestras, is varied and full of promise and accomplishment. Though the American composer's most complete failure is intellectual, says Deems Taylor,[20] intellect after all is only a musical auxiliary. Dance music America has in massive proliferations. It has the scent of strength and mastery upon it. It is America in no slight sense; it no doubt will carry on to more mature things.

Whenever beauty is really seen and loved, says Santayana,[21] "it has a definite embodiment: the eye has precision, the work has style, and the object has perfection." And in painting, sculpture, the graphic arts and architecture, forms — of whatever school — are spatial finitudes that somehow glimmer with infinity. For it is the business of modern art, like that of the more spiritually minded of masters of the past, "to get at the deeper reality that lies beyond realism," says Sheldon Cheney; [22] "the rediscovery of 'form' is matched by a life-quality that is of today." Art reaches inward for a world that science cannot know; it is fused with being; it is tinctured with eternity.

In the advertising columns of the magazines and papers there are steel machines and energies depicted with a truculence and line of truth that is not mere description but the inner being of the age. There are sleek limbs of steel and fire on those pages, and engines with their nickel plated hearts surge on to great destinations. In them an industrial civilization finds a form that is significant sometimes in itself. It has roots below the surface of utility and size and shape and weight, and in that reality, like all other things perhaps, is beautiful.

Modern art so far as schools and conscious critics represent it is primitive, intense and non-imitative. From Cézanne it rises, and back to Cézanne it continually returns. To the modernist and to modernists of days gone by, Aristotle and his "imitation" doctrine [23] are anathema, and the ebb and flow of classicism, romanticism, naturalism across the history of the arts are but lifeless drift upon the surface that mean little. There is in modern art a quest and seeking, an attempt to "realize" — as Cézanne said — the essential form of things. It is intense and petulant; it is intolerant of another's point of view; it is arrogant in its knowledge of a quest for something that it may rarely find; its dogmas and productions are often narrow and ridiculous; but its aim is deep and its methods are ascetic and sincere. Where it will end is hard to say, but its trying is worth while.

From Greek [24] primitives to the Byzantines, to Giotto, El Greco,[24] Rembrandt, Velasquez, Rubens, Poussin, Claude [25] the way to modern art comes down to Cezanne. He is the founder of new movements. Post-impressionism, cubism, futurism, dadaism, vorticism, synchromism, abstractionism, mobile color, expressionism; the litter is large and not all of it can live.

Two slopes of art in the western world lead down from the great primitives to the bogs and flats of representative art and "nasty naturalism," says Clive Bell; [26] and by slope he means "that which lies between a great primitive morning, when men create art because they must, and that darkest hour when men confound imitation with art." The Greek primitives of the eighth century B.C. are the top of the one slope; thence it declines to the richer and more naturalistic Periclean period; thence, says Bell, to the accomplished prettiness of Praxiteles; and thence to "the long sands and flats of Roman realism" where it is lost forever. The Byzantines of the sixth century A.D. are the top of the other, or Christian, slope, and for 700 years art kept the "greater tradition — the tradition that held the essential everything and the accidental nothing." "From the peak that is Giotto the road falls slowly but steadily," says Bell; Leonardo comes; Raphael, the mighty Michael Angelo, Titian, Tintoretto, Veronese, the renaissance and the "taste for round limbs," the Dutch painters, Turner, Corot and gradually down to antiquarian pre-Raffaelites of the nineteenth century. With the æsthetes such as

Whistler and the impressionists, Monet, Renoir, Pissarro, Manet, the Christian slope seems to end. For impressionism is the Hume of art; it is the ultimate sensationalism, and light is its subject matter. It is the instant world of color shrewdly seen. It is realism in its last retreat; it is the impression of an utter surface. Cézanne ends that with revolution and a new era. He looks within a thing for its realization and its form.

His post-impressionism is an ascetic art, intense and contemptuous of nature's forms and realizations. It bores in by burning intuition beyond the crust of natural appearance; it penetrates nature, as Cézanne says,[27] to its dynamic essence; and though it fears natural beauty with a taut and grotesque bigotry it reaches deep into the dungeon of the real; it burns with the constant fire of creativeness that is being. Simplification, design in which color and drawing are inseparable, an unconcern in natural realism and detail or explanatory irrelevance, these characterize Cézanne [28] and the post-impressionists who follow him.

Gauguin from south sea isolations finds form again, and like Van Gogh his fellow post-impressionist, fears no distortion or suppressed detail as he tries to realize it. Where form in Cézanne is four dimensional, a reaching down beyond a natural observation, Gauguin, says Cheney,[29] moves towards decoration and a world of two dimensions, towards "sensuous appeal arising out of balance, rhythm and flat color rather than moving color and organizational color."

Matisse follows Gauguin and Cézanne as well as the impressionists and from them builds new structures and new forms. This painter, says Faure,[30] "is the one who, least of all since Cézanne, causes one to think of the subject which his works represent. They tend untiringly to organize his universe from the angle of painting alone, absolutely delivered from the attraction of sentiment or of the picturesque in the object. At bottom they express no object. At all events, the object is, with him, no more than a pretext for the creation of new organisms, which a powerful love for form is alone capable of imagining." Design in him is almost an arabesque, in which things somehow may be captured.

Cubism came, tied to Picasso's leash, stretching to step in the footprints of Cézanne. It is geometrically inclined; it analyzes an object into planes and reassembles them in harmony with a more complete and final vision.[31] It synthesizes all aspects of an object, front and back, right and left, inside and outside; it tries to show them all conceptually in one work of art, and the results, though often shattering, usually are sincere. Cubism in some painters becomes two dimensional and colorless; it has other ramifications, doctrines, dogmas and geometric theses, but its value in the end will lie no doubt mainly in its influence towards structural strength in later art.

Futurism, Marinetti's child, is not Cézanne descended. It returns to representation, and what it tries to represent usually is motion. Nothing is immobile, say the futurists,[32] and to prove it they paint the successive motions of an object in one picture. They seek to see the object from within, and from there to represent its motion.

The vorticists, founded by Ezra Pound of Idaho and England, say that every painting must be slightly representative, but "you cannot convey the emotion you receive at contact of nature by imitating her, but only by becoming her." [32] The vortex is the form out of which it is drawn; it is the artist's will that engulfs the object.

Dadaism, says Cheney,[32] "aims at novelty, sensation, shock;" it is war in the mind and war's ruins. It is disorganization, chaos. It is a "cultural reign of terror." Dadaism with its deliberate disorder and insanity, is an art, evidently of protest and of ultimate cynicism. It is a metaphysical clown; who in this post-war day can deny its truth?

Synchromism is another creed out of Cézanne. Every

color, say the synchromists, has a physical property.[32]
Some approach; some recede; and formal compositions
may be built upon this color law.

The abstractionists, led by Kandinsky, a theosophist,
divorce visual art wholly from material actuality.[32]
Marin, American, stops just short of complete abstraction, Klee, O'Keeffe, Ray, Seurat, Redon, Heckel,
Grigorieff, Kuhn, Davies, Kent, Hartley, are artists of
this and other schools. Mobile color organs, sound correlations; the world is still experimenting. Old forms and
old articulations disappear. Despite rebellion and can-
tankerousness of many artists in regard to them, the new
machines and the new energies under human hands will
affect our art. Space, time, motion, matter, things,
cruelties, events, affections have new cleavages; the old
articulations in the nature of things are less well defined
and new crevasses come. New mechanisms and instruments of art, new distributions, new materials will affect
man's facility of expression. The movies, the radio, the
newspapers, all the wild froth of modern things, will build
new eternities of meaning. The intrinsic nature of the
object, the artist's imagination, the nature of the material
all enter into "form," say the modernists, and they are
right in that.

Expressionism follows post-impressionism and grows
from it, as the most significant of recent schools of art.[33]
It is German built in general and with German vigor
"wades through nature" with the ruthlessness and intensity of a search not to be satisfied with pretty surfaces
or arrangements. It seeks reality in a deep, "structural,
organizational" form; and in the work of Kokoschka,
Heckel, Nolde and others it attains something of that
reality. Prettiness, grace, representativeness, harmonic
unessentials are sacrificed in the new expressionism to
"structural feeling, compactness, profound organizational
movement." From Cézanne the movement comes, but
it becomes more masculine than France. As a general

term, says Cheney,[33] expressionism denotes all modern
art that has given up the interest in correct representation
for "something in the nature of æsthetic reality or ex-
pressive form." In music, painting, literature, dancing,
sculpture it has its influence and its modern power.

In sculpture it sweeps on to new expressions of the age
old stuff and wonder of the spirit and the flesh. There is
the dumb, primitive stone of Gaudier-Brzeska or the
nervous formalism and abstractness of Lehmbruck.[34]
There is the massive sweetness of being, power, repose in
the marbles of George Grey Barnard, and the serene
distortions, the cruelty, the hard fulsomeness of Gaston
Lachaise. Brancusi lays abstract and subtle eggs and
hatches from them beautiful and strange forms and projects. There is Berlach building movement and eternity
in wood; there is the wrought strength and reticence of
Duchamp-Villon; there are great Rodin and Paul Man-
ship, Maillol, Gill, Saint-Gaudens, Metzner, Mestrovic,
Borglum and the more illustrative marble cutters. Jacob
Epstein takes London by the ears with spare, resurrected
Christs, soldiers, women, spirits, and being burns somehow deep in their frail masks of stone. Archipenko's
carved and rounded rocks come like calm extrusions from
the earth, moulded in the twist and coil of ages, modeled
under hands that know the smooth indifference and spa-
ciousness of abstract form. From sentiments and realisms and life's decorative details these men retreat. There
is a greatness in their aim if not always in their productions.

For reason is a eunuch that guards their doors sometimes with too much strictness. The cramp of arrogance
and dogma often seizes them. They may fail to find the
being that they say is beauty because they will not go
where beauty lies. With a theory or a formula to guide
them they canalize their world and know of nothing
beyond those narrow shores. For neither reason nor emotion is the end of art, nor as guides are they infallible.

The waiting spirit, and a willingness to look wherever the light may burn is better. Men wait to be consumed, and their reasons or emotions or the effects on men themselves make little difference.

Building has returned in modern times to a new dignity, and the thrust and power of engineering works, of machine design, of steel and concrete construction, glass, stone grows in new cycles towards the confident expression of this dynamic age. The slow, grim gnashing of the bascule bridges; the slide of ships along the river, the massive silence of them or the gaunt music of their whistles; the curve and glint of motor cars, their stripped speed under the shadows of buildings; the soar of steel into the air, the lift, the thrust upward of great buildings; it is all a vast design, a crackling dynamism and brocade, an austere arabesque of life and steel, of sound and bitter articulations, of movement and of light.

Buildings rise out of the dance and restlessness of the street, and builders now have learned to strip them of their ornament. They lean against the sky like naked athletes waiting for the rubbers and the showers. They are stripped and towering and their lines of steel and stone bear little frippery and falsehood. Sullivan, Wright, Helmle and Corbett, Holabird and Roche, Saarinen, Hood, Gilbert, Rogers, are among the architects and builders of the age. There will be more. They will learn to build less for front and more for native structure.

And the theatre shifts with the change and restlessness of the new universe. With the other arts it discards to some extent crinolines of sentiment and detailed realisms and in men such as O'Neill and Craig and the Moscow players moves towards its own expressionism of words and scenery. And the dance, mother of arts, finds new forms and being. There is Isadora Duncan and Ruth St. Denis; there is the Russian ballet, Fokine, Pavlova, Mordkin. To the cruel sweetness of jazz, to rhythmic sentimentalism that lies like paper lace and valentines on the surge and silence of the currents of the sea, the world is dancing at the cabarets and dance halls and dinner parties of this tidal age. The universe, says Ellis,[35] is a dance. The stars surge with its rhythm.

For all the arts and all the world's activities are but different figures of one rhythm. They are but dancing steps. They have been departmentalized too much. They have been articulated falsely; their separations have been fixed too long. Art is a point of view; it is a junction with the one reality of things. Creeds and rituals and definitions destroy it in time, for their value is not final. The ends of life though found in many things are one. Art is a way of life.

In this twelfth chapter a transition from instruments to ends is first attempted, and the world as an end, a contemplation, a sacrificial horse is at least suggested. What are life's consummations; where is being? The arts would answer, and are in part successful. Poetry, music, painting, sculpture, a bit of building and the dance and drama are touched briefly in their modern aspects and their meanings. But art is deeper than these specialized departments. It is universal.

The Finalities of Life

ALL PERVADING is the great Tâo! It may be found on the left hand and on the right, says Lao Tse,[1] philosopher and mystic of ancient China. "All things depend on it for their production, which it gives to them, not one refusing obedience to it. When its work is accomplished, it does not claim the name of having done it. It clothes all things as with a garment, and makes no assumption of being their lord; — it may be named in the smallest things. All things return to their root and disappear, and do not know that it is it which presides over their doing so; — it may be named in the greatest things."

What the Chinaman has seen all other men have seen burning in their lives; and though they may not know it, all outer objects, mechanisms and utilities are beside it only smoke and shadows. Chinaman, Hindu, Christian monk, Greek, Russian, American all live on the same earth, look at the same stars, breathe the same air and find spiritually within them the same finality and being. They bathe in one stream of living. They are mists from the same sea.

In cold exegesis the finalities of life are meaningless and strange, for the language of logic and science is only a sieve to carry water in; it is an iron cage to capture sunlight and the warmth of living, and never can be adequate. Of the inner worth of things, of living, of beauty, love, religion, such language has no comprehension, for they are not comprehensible; they are immediate and final in themselves. If men find worth while the blunt and simple fact of being, the things and activities that seem beautiful, love, wonder, communion with the universe, joy and action, and vitality for its own sake, they have stepped beyond the reach of scientific explanation; they have crossed the threshold of a world where the externalisms of science and utility cannot be applied.

A different mode, a new approach to being here ensues. It takes things in their intrinsic worth, instead of their relationships. It is simple. A man in love cannot calculate its value in respect to other things. Beauty is not relative. Living is not a utility. Laughter is not scientific or practical. Beyond prose, beyond science, beyond "common sense," lie man's consummations. There is timelessness in every instant of his life. There is infinity in every step. "Where is what you call the Tâo to be found?" asked Tung-kwo Tze; and Kwang-tze [2] answered, "Everywhere."

What the finalities of life may be is hardly answerable, for they are shown less in objects and comparisons than in an attitude. They are involved in values, but they transcend values. They reside in things but they sink to profound depths beyond particular things. Each thing is, as it were, a well that sinks ineffably to the absolute. Each value viewed intrinsically may be final.

But the finalities of life are rarely the stark and gasping ecstasies of emotion that romanticists would have. They are, far better, an experience in normal living. They are appreciative. They are consummations found in things scattered from dawn to dark, from dark to dawn, from shore to shore of our daily lives. They are a constant mode. They are an insight into things and a finding of one being there.

In terms popular but hardly valid (namely: 1. value; 2. not-value; 3. outer relations; 4. inner being) science is an approach to things through 2 and 3; practical life is an approach to things through 1 and 3; spiritual life is an approach to things through 1 and 4, or, more profoundly perhaps, through 2 and 4. But such anagrams

and puzzles will bear but little scrutiny; they may help
to mark the ways whereby we come upon the real; they
have no other meaning.

For the significance of our attitudes is still a question.
There are means, we say, and ends. The one we tolerate,
not for itself, but for relations called external to other
things. Its reality for us, as means, lies only in that ex-
ternality, relationship and "otherness." We make no
postulate of being for the means itself. We want no union
with it. Our will towards it, our urgency and fiat that says,
"This is; this is not," gives it no subsistence of its own.

But the "end" we take somehow for itself. We charge
it with the bitter strength of being. We find in it finality.
As end it does not hang on things external to itself. Its
value is within, and its reality, by that inevitable command, is self-sustained. Value is a way of projecting our
experience into orders, chains and series. It organizes
life and things on ends. There are means; ends; we know
their meaning organically, externally; but what they
really mean is hard to say.

We know only that in ends there is a thrust and affirmation that men are wont to name being. There is the
lift and self-assertion somehow of a real thing. There is
a certainty that no rationalist dare question, a direct
appreciation of whatever stuff this world may be that
no one can dispute. We lean against these ultimates in
every moment of our lives, but no one can explain them.
There is finality in every instant; there is a consummation
in every living deed; there is beauty in every breath we
draw; but reason can tell little of it. Reason, and science,
is only draughtsmanship upon a plane surface of the
universe. Being, and the finalities that men know, escape
its comprehension. Their dimensions are far deeper.
They are spiritual.

Beauty, love, religion are three finalities of life that
may not be at heart different from each other. They are
primal affirmations, and the things here, there, every-

where in which we find consummate being may be expressed perhaps in terms of all or any one of them. They are high romantic words, but the last, ragged commonplace of living is charged with them.

Beauty lives in many houses and rides with many friends. She associates herself with joy or sorrow; she rides upon disaster and good fortune; she finds herself alone with thought or with sensation, with philosophy or laughter, with small or great, with old or young or death or living quite indifferently. Beauty no doubt resides in everything, could we but find her.

Beauty itself, of course, is but a word, but things are beautiful. They glimmer with a light that men have always seen but never can explain. "It 's well known by now," says Llewellyn Jones [3] rather overconfidently, "that beauty is not an objective property of bodies or even of nature," and if he means that beauty cannot be subsumed under the code of naturalism; of mechanism, of externals and of reason, he no doubt is right. But to say that beauty is a psychic matter, merely subjective and emotional is to accept the selfsame code, from its other side, with no less innocence and risk. For beauty spiritually is beyond our local minds and emotions. It is beyond the individual; it is involved in being; and in it persons lose their letters and distinctions.

"What is the significance of anything as an end in itself?" asks Clive Bell. [4] "What is that which is left when we have stripped a thing of all its associations, of all its significance as a means? What is left to provoke our emotion? What but that which philosophers used to call 'the thing in itself' and now call 'ultimate reality'? Shall I be altogether fantastic in suggesting, what some of the profoundest thinkers have believed, that the significance of the thing in itself is the significance of Reality? Is it possible that the answer to my question, 'Why are we so profoundly moved by certain combinations of lines and colours?' should be, 'Because artists can express in combinations of lines and colours an emotion felt for reality which reveals itself through line and colour?'

"If this suggestion were accepted it would follow that 'significant form' was form behind which we catch a sense of ultimate reality. . . . On this hypothesis the peculiarity of the artist would seem to be that he possesses the power of surely and frequently seizing reality (generally behind pure form), and the power of expressing his sense of it, in pure form always." It is unfortunate, Bell intimates, that "reality" cannot be cancelled out, and (in creating works of art, in seeing things as they might be artistically created, or in contemplating the works of art of others) that the emotions cannot be felt for pure form regardless of anything behind it.

But old stereotypes inevitably intrude on him and on all others who would tabulate reality; for "behind and before," "emotion *for* a thing," "subject, object" and the like are hardly valid categories in the realm of ends. Reality is not a dark and monstrous mystery remote from our appreciations. Its being is its nearness. It is intimately there. It is the significance of form; it is the thrust and pressure of beauty and the spirit on us, and its compulsion. Emotion *for* a beautiful thing we cannot have; we are that thing. We enter spiritually into its being, and emotion is but the play and quiver of a light upon the surface. What we love we spiritually become; what we worship, what we find beautiful we are; and there find being and the absolute. It is commonplace enough. It glows in every homespun moment of our lives. It is the stuff of living, and tall words and abstractions, such as the above, only obscure it with a smoke. It is the warm, wilful, concrete being that permeates all things. We know it directly, intimately. Art helps to realize it. Beauty is its shine and burning.

For things that are called final, beautiful, or ultimately worth while are authorized not by our persons or particularities or psychic bents and lists and wanderings but somehow in themselves; and the test of æsthetic experience, if tests there must be, is in their infinitude of being, their benign indifference, their gratuity, their freedom from outer relations, their completeness. All things are beautiful, but our seeing it depends on many minor things. Even Santayana, critic of the absolute, poet of man's sacred limitations, escapes this final cup of quietness and glory that mysticism offers him only by preliminary postulates.

We are not obliged to assert that all gradations of beauty and dignity are a matter of personal and accidental bias, says Santayana.[5] "The mystics who declare that to God there is no distinction in the value of things, and that only our human prejudice makes us prefer a rose to an oyster, or a lion to a monkey, have, of course, a reason for what they say. If we could strip ourselves of our human nature, we should undoubtedly find ourselves incapable of making these distinctions, as well as of thinking, perceiving, or willing in any way which is now possible to us. But how things would appear to us if we were not human is, to a man, a question of no importance. Even the mystic to whom the definite constitution of his own mind is so hateful, can only paralyze without transcending his faculties. A passionate negation, the motive of which, although morbid, is in spite of itself perfectly human, absorbs all his energies, and his ultimate triumph is to attain the absoluteness of indifference.

"What is true of mysticism in general, is true also of its manifestations in æsthetics. If we could so transform our taste as to find beauty everywhere, because, perhaps, the ultimate nature of things is as truly exemplified in one thing as in another, we should, in fact, have abolished taste altogether. For the ascending series

of æsthetic satisfactions we should have substituted a
monotonous judgment of identity. If things are beautiful
not by virtue of their differences but by virtue of an
identical something which they equally contain, then
there could be no discrimination in beauty. Like substance, beauty would be everywhere one and the same,
and any tendency to prefer one thing to another would
be proof of finitude and illusion. When we try to make our
judgments absolute, what we do is to surrender our
natural standards and categories, and slip into another
genus, until we lose ourselves in the satisfying vagueness
of mere being.

"Relativity to our partial nature is therefore essential
to all our definite thoughts, judgments, and feelings. And
when once the human bias is admitted as a legitimate,
because for us a necessary, basis of preference, the whole
wealth of nature is at once organized by that standard
into a hierarchy of values. Everything is beautiful, because everything is capable in some degree of interesting
and charming our attention; but things differ immensely
in this capacity to please us in the contemplation of them,
and therefore they differ immensely in beauty."

But dialectic is a dangerous acid that will scarify and
eat the humane relativities that Santayana offers as well
as those finalities that he repudiates. It is sceptical in
outcome and no standards, humanistic, relative, pragmatic or absolute will withstand it in its field. Despite
the cogency and penetration of Santayana's humanistic
argument, it rests after all on what he naïvely posits
over against the naïve absolutes that others posit. And
by the test of æsthetic experience, by the authority of
spiritual intuition, which after all is all we have, beauty
is beyond relatives; æsthetic experience is just that
simple passing from human limitations to the final stuff
of living and of being. Difference in beauty need not
mean ascending scales and hierarchies. What democrat
could think it? Finding the "identity" of being in all

things need not mean monotony, except in terms of repetitious systems of the outer world.

Science, naturalism and the like always are relational; reason is their code; and from space and time and Forest Moulton's super-galaxies to sales and money making, a whole in that world is always part of something else. Beauty and the world of spirit however are of another mode: any part may always be the whole. The rose, the petal are equally complete within the world of ends. The girl's hand, somehow, or a wandering lock of hair becomes spiritually an entirety. A gesture and a swerve of limbs caught in the marble is the life of all athletes and the love of power.

To Schopenhauer, that mystic fish who slips somehow through the nets of Kant, a thing called beautiful is "an object of our æsthetic contemplation, and this has a double meaning; on the one hand it means that the sight of the thing makes us *objective*, that is to say, that in contemplating it we are no longer conscious of ourselves as individuals, but as pure will-less subjects of knowledge; and on the other hand it means that we recognize in the object, not the particular thing, but an Idea; and this can only happen, so far as our contemplation of it . . . does not follow the relation of the object to anything outside it . . ., but rests in the object itself." [6] And since every given thing, he continues, may be observed apart from all relations, everything is also beautiful. Only because some things make pure contemplation easier than others do we call them more beautiful.

To Croce, Italy's philosopher, art makes none of these departures from common sense and sane particularism; it is expression. It is experience — caught by the artist before intellect or morals have cracked it into parts and categories — expressed somehow in a work of art or in implicit imagery. It is expression of the artist's intuition, and intuition for Croce [7] is a form of knowledge "obtained through the imagination" not the intellect, in images, not

concepts. "By elaborating his impressions," says Croce,
who is technically an idealist in philosophy, "man frees
himself from them. By objectifying them, he removes
them from him and makes himself their superior. The
liberating and purifying function of art is another aspect
and another formula of its character of activity. Activity
is the deliverer, just because it drives away passivity."

Art from this point of view is an activity, and its formulating power, its creativeness, is its value and significance. For beauty, here, is created; "natural beauty,
which an artist would not to some extent correct does
not exist;" [8] " and to enjoy natural objects æsthetically,
we should withdraw them from their external and historical reality, and separate their simple appearance or
origin from existence." In this position those modern
artists, and they are many, who deny the representativeness of art, find their authority. They combat Aristotle,
with his doctrine that art "imitates," nature, and they
substitute: "nature so far as it attains beauty, imitates
art." It is a significant following out in art of the doctrines of dynamism and human activity, that in recent
years have stirred science and philosophy, religion,
politics and human thought and institutions — from
pragmatism to the new atom — into new cycles and pre-
sumable achievements.

Contrasted with Croce, Ellis and others, for whom art
is activity, and beauty a created form and purity rather
remote from natural things, are the more logical idealists
derived from Kant and Hegel and represented well by
Puffer. The beautiful object, she says,[9] "should inform
the æsthetic subject with that unity and self-completeness which are 'the forms of reflection' of the Infinite.
. . . Not because I behold the Infinite, but because I
have, myself, a moment of perfection. Herein it is that
our theory constitutes a complete contradiction of all
'expression' or 'significance' theories of the Beautiful,
and does away with the necessity those theories are under

of reading sermons into stones. The yellow primrose needs not to remind us of the harmony of the universe, or to have any ulterior significance whatever, if it gives by its own direct simple stimulation a moment of Unity and Self-completeness. . . . The beautiful object possesses those qualities which bring the personality into a state of unity and self-completeness."

There is Tolstoi [10] with his art tied to morals, and Taine [11] with his imitation theory; Pater [12] and his art for art's sake; Shaw,[13] with art to promote ideas; Santayana with his "beauty as objectified pleasure"; Schelling,[10] Hegel, Baumgarten, Plato, Guyau [11] who says, "The Beautiful is perception or an action which stimulates life within us under its three forms simultaneously (i.e., sensibility, intelligence, and will) and produces pleasure by the swift consciousness of this general stimulation"; Schiller, Aristotle, Bell, all take their solemn shots at beauty and load their guns for more. It is a pleasant exercise, if we realize its futility. Rational artillery will never bag the moonlight. It may kill the bird; it will not collect the song. Reason may articulate a skeleton; it will not find life. It may pile up tools and capital and the sombre steel of six days of the week: It never can enjoy.

In the world of things and systems and societies, art and capital are at opposites. The one is solely means and instruments, the other is concerned with ends. Capitalism does things to matter for a practical purpose. Art — in the plastic field at least — does things to matter for the thing itself. It alters the material world for a spiritual purpose. It creates.

In sculpture for example is the synthesis of architecture and dancing. The structure so significant in architecture here is implicit in sculptural form. Motor moods and dynamics not possible in building are brought in. The emotional texture of a human gesture and a body's pose are carried into marble. Here building moves and the

stone of great houses is a dance. Art is a way to worlds
that are always new; beauty is beyond time.

Art has its forms, but the forms and rituals of love are
only less impressive. They intervene in art and mutually
reciprocate, and the art of love, in social ritual or in
frozen institutions, in speech or solemn sighs or dance or
gesturing is never far in mode or motive from the meaning of all art. In art, religion, love, men try to fix finality
somehow in outer forms. They would import absolutes
into time and space and by externalizing them in finite
form suggest the world beyond. Of all of them love is the
most recalcitrant. It resists particulars and material
restraints. It retires like a noonday's warmth from the
fixed and frozen forms of the cold night.

Love, says Santayana,[14] "is a natural metaphysician";
and every lover, it would follow, can no doubt penetrate
the universe more profoundly than philosophers or scientists. Love sets the world somehow into new modes and
rhythms, but it cannot use the old. It can move unregulated, like an ineffable ghost across the ordinary planes
of common sense reality, and still avoid the age and old
rigidities of experience. It can realize new dimensions of
the universe, like a magician pouring into things strange
illuminations, lifting from the incandescent core of life
the stony crust and cover of external forms and observa-
tions. It is a longing, says Schopenhauer,[15] "which proceeds from the primary source of all being, and exhibits
itself in the phenomenal world as the lofty passion of the
future parents for each other, paying little regard to all
that is outside itself . . ."

As an end and finality of life love has its deeper meaning, for it sinks below the surfaces of casual emotion, of
feeling, of happiness, to profound realities. Beyond possession, and personality and play — not against them —

love penetrates to realms that intuition finds ultimately
real. It seeks identity with being; it wants divine approach. For the world is but a woman with all her mystery and loveliness; and though we may attend her as if
we were physician, scientist, business partner, love will
go quicker to reality than these and find the inner being
of the world. Reason is a glass, but love is nearer being.
Reason is carried beyond personality into an universal
mode in science. Intuition — whatever that may finally
mean — moves beyond personality into an universal
way in art, in love, in religion. It moves toward Platon-
ism.

Platonic love, says Santayana,[16] is the "transformation
of the appreciation of beautiful things into the worship
of an ideal beauty and the transformation of the love of
particular persons into the love of God . . . We are
often Platonists without knowing it. In some form or
other Platonic ideas occur in all poetry of passion when
it is seasoned with reflection." For, he continues, "all
love that does not lead to the love of God and merge into
that love, is a long and hopeless torment"; and the
essence of Platonic philosophy is "the application to
passion of that pursuit of something permanent in a
world of change, of something absolute in a world of
relativity." It is the same quest that every man takes up.
It is the quest for ends and ultimate reality.

For the deeper mystery of love, says Plato,[17] is to find
that the "beauty in every form is one and the same";
and the lover towards the end "will suddenly perceive a
nature of wondrous beauty (and this, Socrates, is the
final cause of all our former toils) — a nature which in the
first place is everlasting, not growing and decaying, or
waxing and waning; secondly, not fair in one point of
view and foul in another, or at one time or in one relation or at one place fair, at another time or in another relation or at another place foul, as if fair to some and foul
to others, or in the likeness of a face or hands or any part

of the bodily frame, or in any form of speech or knowledge, or existing in any other being, as for example, in an animal, or in heaven, or in earth, or in any other place; but beauty absolute, separate, simple, and everlasting, which without diminution and without increase, or any change, is imparted to the evergrowing and perishing beauties of all other things. He who from these ascending under the influence of true love, begins to perceive that beauty, is not far from the end."

"And remember," Plato adds,[18] — and this is the crucial twist of all the metaphysics of love and of the spirit — "how in that communion only, beholding beauty with the eye of the mind, he will be enabled to bring forth, not images of beauty, but realities (for he has hold not of an image but of a reality), and bringing forth and nourishing true virtue to become the friend of God and be immortal, if mortal man may." In this mode lies final being. The real at last is spiritual. Art, love, religion all will attest it.

But Sally's kiss for Philip under the shadowed doorway of her home last night was not notably ontological; and she clung to him in the ecstatic dusk and timelessness of evening without a thought — Thank God — of corroborating Plato. She does, as Plato did, find her eternities in living; and though no proctors stand around to define or analyze, to classify, to give cause and utility, to say why she does it or what for, Sally does not miss them. Those are but secondary, external things, biologies and instincts, psychologies, sociologies, systems of æsthetics and religion of which she very likely never heard. For her the moment is eternal in itself. It is enough. There is no more. Its beauty asks no questions; it needs no answers. And that intrinsic meaning of it in her mind is authority sufficient for a world of spirit, for religions, arts, realities.

For religion is but a step from art and love. It is an "inner" world. It lives. "Religion, like art, is concerned with the world of emotional reality, and with material things only in so far as they are emotionally significant," says Bell; [19] and though his interpretation in terms of "emotion" may be hardly adequate in a spiritual world that would reach far below those psychic and emotional levels, his synthesis is true. "For the mystic, as for the artist," he says, "the physical universe is a means to ecstasy. The mystic feels things as 'ends' instead of seeing them as 'means.' He seeks within all things that ultimate reality which provokes emotional exaltation; and, if he does not come at it through pure form, there are, as I have said, more roads than one to that country. Religion, as I understand it, is an expression of the individual's sense of the emotional significance of the universe; I should not be surprised to find that art was an expression of the same thing."

All things — as in China's Tâoism — may be ends, and to the spiritual eye "God," "the universal principle," "being" — the names are various — resides in every thing. For the democracy of God is all pervasive. The stones are burdened with him; the little birds bear him in their songs; the clouds are heavy with his presence; and every part of life is all of life. Of Walt Whitman, America's religious singer, prophet of God and fellowship, of love, democracy and the inner worth and being of all things irrespectively, Santayana says,[20] "Never, perhaps, has the charm of uniformity in multiplicity been felt so completely and so exclusively. Everywhere it greets us with passionate preference; not flowers but leaves of grass, not music but drum-taps, not composition but aggregation, not the hero but the average man, not the crisis but the vulgarest moment; and by this resolute marshalling of nullities, by this effort to show us every thing as a momentary pulsation of a liquid and structure-less whole, he profoundly stirs the imagination."

Mystic and democrat, artist, lover, Whitman reveals the spiritual foundation of democracy. Forms are external; class, privilege, rigid inequalities, vain differences and prides are superficial flotsam of a life, and like dead scum upon the stream absorb and kill the glitter of the sun. For Whitman there is God in all, and the living warmth of every thing is proof of its eternity and worth. In every citizen America resides beautiful and everlasting. Whitman's values are intrinsic. His view is spiritual.

What is worth while? One says, action; another, emotion; another, knowledge; happiness; peace; death; life; one says, the composite hints and mixtures of experience that we call the living situation; one says, being. "Pleasure," says one; the ultilitarianism of Mill and Bentham, says Robert Morss Lovett,[21] "is an attempt to rationalize individual values in terms of pleasure and pain into social values." What is worth while? "God and work," says Carlyle;[22] "God and the church," says Newman;[22] for both reject Mill's rationalism for a mystic and a supernatural justification of conduct and asceticism.[21] The "ethical value of life to the individual in terms of service to society"[21] is George Eliot's and Huxley's[22] scientific formulation of finality. And "man's joy in his work" and in nature are the ends of Ruskin[22] and Morris. There is Arnold's[22] doctrine of culture and Pater's living as a fine art and art for art's sake. There is the "realism of experience" of Henry James and Butler,[22] and the pragmatism of William James and Dewey: "Life," says Lovett,[21] "is taken for granted as activity, of which the sanction is experience itself in the forms of realistic adventure, of persistent education, of perpetual discovery and testing of new conceptions of the good, the true, and the beautiful. . . . Pragmatism, with its empirical doctrine of knowledge and its realistic ethics gives an intellectual character to the present age certainly as marked as utilitarianism gave to the early nineteenth century."

They come on, one by one, each with a new world in his eyes and a new religion on his lips; but in the hearts of all burns the same being. They formulate new aims and universes; but the stuff of which they make them is all the same. It will slip back, when the times and localities wear off, to the same simple being and the same God. The finalities of life are simple. They are one. They are always in our hearts.

In this chapter the intrinsic worth of things as contrasted with external relationships is suggested as the core of final value and reality. Then, What are finalities? rises as a question, and beauty, love, religion press for consideration. Beauty in art and elsewhere is discussed. Love and Platonic love are given inexpert attention. Religion and the goodness that resides spiritually in all things is spoken of. The next book will be devoted to the great summaries and codes of the universe; and three, the scientific, the practical and the spiritual will receive attention. The following chapter — first of the next book — will suggest, most inadequately, what the spiritual approach to the world may be.

BOOK FOUR

General Ideas of the World

This screen that thou hast raised is painted
with innumerable figures with the brush of
the night and the day.

— TAGORE

The Spiritual Approach
to the World

HEREBY shall ye mark this: says the Theologia Germanica,[1] "There is an inward sight which hath power to perceive the One true Good, and that it is neither this nor that, but that of which St. Paul saith; 'When that which is perfect is come, then that which is in part shall be done away.' By this he meaneth, that the Whole and Perfect excelleth all the fragments, and that all which is in part and imperfect, is as nought compared to the Perfect. Thus likewise all knowledge of the parts is swallowed up when the Whole is known; and where that Good is known, it cannot but be longed for and loved so greatly, that all other love wherewith the man hath loved himself and other things, fadeth away. And that inward sight likewise perceiveth what is best and noblest in all things, and loveth it in the one true Good, and only for the sake of that true Good."

And let no one suppose, the ancient German book continues, "that we may attain to this true light and perfect knowledge or life of Christ, by much questioning, or by hearsay, or by reading and study, nor yet by high skill and great learning, yea, so long as a man taketh account of anything which is this or that, whether it be himself, or any other creature; or doeth anything, or frameth a purpose, for the sake of his own likings or desires, or opinions, or ends, he cometh not unto the life of Christ."

And in these quaint profundities of human spirit and expression there is the light and the timeless longing for a final world, for a unity and sureness and a being that in every human heart finds only wide words and dim, uncertain symbols there to say it. For most men the world somehow is one world, could they but say it; and if they operate in two or three in practice, they remain spiritually, they hope, one world men. They want no string of universes hung on time orders or on shifting moods and interests in the mind. They want no part-time worlds and cosmic severalities. They avoid such confusions with a naïve faith. "Several worlds somehow are not the way that things should be" — and their innocence and intuition may well be right — "it is not natural." And with this in mind most men want just one.

A man's monism is nearly as sacred as his monogamy. If 85 per cent of his fellows are in fact very unmonistic persons who move casually from a world of science to a world of action or to art with no notion of relationships between them, or of other unity, that he would say is but an incident with little bearing on the principle. That the world at times looks suspiciously pluralistic he may admit, but appearances not always are realities.

Russell [2] suggests that a medieval wish for tidiness amid the care and sprawl of a dark age gave us our bent towards a single systematic universe. The Greeks popularly did not have one; neither did the Romans. From Parmenides on down a search for one reality behind change, illusion and particularity has persisted; from the ache of prayer and wonder in the primitive to the cold questing, say in science, for a general principle, men have hoped somehow, illicitly or otherwise, to find the golden core of things; but such adventures for the Greeks were left more or less to spiritual buccaneers and altered little the Grecian world convention and Weltanschauung. The ancients were content with plural worlds and the raw unhemmed edges of a universe beyond their fields and tilling. The spiritual imperialism of modern thought driving on towards systematic unity rarely mastered them. Where the rule of monotheism and the elevation of one God to power was necessary, no doubt, among men for whom moral administrative efficiency was more important than diversity and freedom, the Greeks were for freedom. The one world idea with one autocratic God is hardly Greek in type. Nor is it easily compatible with all of modern life.

A plural world, says William James,[3] is a universe in which the parts may have only external relationships to each other. They compose a "pluriverse," he says, and the inner being of them all, the basic singleness of their reality, the identity that one world and one God would have, is not in them. But a world where things may not be fitted to a common scale, where actions have no final end, no pattern, where outside relativities are no sign of identity within, where God cannot be absolute because there is no absolute, is not the kind of world that men today will usually choose for permanent investment. It lacks workmanship and finish. It has too little style. In our life in many worlds the yearning for the one persists. The aggregative worlds of pagan times and of our common sense are not easy to accept.

But pluralistic temptation remains vigorous, and we cannot tell for certain that the ways of pluralism are unmitigated evil. Moses, indeed, no longer calls the people back to one God, and if he did no one might listen, for polytheism of the ancient period is not now a menace. But philosophical Moseses are arising here and there to call us back from many worlds to one, and with more right; for with a predilection for one world most men in practice deal with several. They suffer what the scholars and academies might call, "epistemological pluralism" — which sounds serious. They are hesitant. Whether impulsive quests for one or practical and discursive contacts with many be the right way is not always sure.

A world in general may be more to many men than the sum of its details. It may be more than arithmetical complexity and scatter such as James suggests. It may be more than that organic unity of cosmic plumbing that the rationalists and some idealists would install. For some men, such as Hindus and the Quakers, for all men at heart no doubt, the being of the world is not in parts but only in the oneness of the whole. Though it seem obscure and no doubt unimportant, the yearning for the one persists. From without, the world may well press manyness upon us; from within, as the old German book might say, it names it one.

If the pluralistic world of James is the "universe" of brisk activities; if the organic world of reason and phenomena is the world of science; then the deep being of the world, the mystic probably will say, is the world of spirit. Language always is inadequate in this, for no word can say what is beyond articulation; but the Hindus and the Quakers and all other men in deeper moments will appreciate the phrase, "identity of all being," for it suggests the flare and thrust of all eternity that lies in every thing. In the whole — whatever that may mean — is a value that no sum of particulars can supply and an intimacy with being that no part can give. The first problem and the foremost motive in philosophy and religion is this world in general.

When Vâshkali besought Bâhva to teach Brahman to him, the sage was silent, says an ancient Indic book of God and wonder; for Brahman means "the eternal principle of all Being," and words fail before it and become nothing. "A second and third time this request was repeated," says the old Oriental scripture.[4] "At last Bâhva said: I am teaching it to thee, but thou understandest it not; this Âtman is silent."

For those who want one world this silence of the "soul," or Âtman, is final and complete. It is the last recession from the brittle things and pluralisms of a varied life. It is the mystic's utter monism and absorption in the world's one being. It is the spirit in its final citadel beyond the clamors and the efforts and expressions of an outer world that seems real only in the dust and chaos of diversity. As the fundamental thought of this Vedânta system of the Hindus is "the identity of Brahman and the soul," and as Deussen says,[5] this soul, this true essence of each one of us "is not a part, an emanation of Brahman, but wholly and absolutely the eternal, indivisible Brahman Himself," so in every man there is this mode of stillness, this uncompromising silence, from which no lines of logic, or of reason or of scientific and external exegesis can ever lead. It is unutterably significant to mankind but it is not rational. It can be talked *about*, the religious man might say, but words cannot approach it. It may be suggested, but translations of it are beyond all possibility. It smiles, as it were, at man's expression and activities, for they all come at last to nothing in the warm morass of silence.

But casually, there still are worlds and diversities of circumstance that absorb our different motives and approaches and our ways of action; and the efforts to resolve them into one by common sense or science or philosophy are not often satisfactory. There are pluralisms of our attitudes, if not of ultimates, and to bring them down to one by some system of logical or humane relationships is like drawing up a single code of rules for golf, chess, steel manufacture and after-dinner speaking all in one program. Eastward the world is one; but looking west it inevitably is many; it has many codes.

Scientific, practical, spiritual; there are divers paths across the plain of life, there are many gaits and ways of walking; and though common sense may say that, anyhow, they go one way, and approach all the same thing, it is not clear what that way is or what that thing eventually may be. The loose totality of interests and objects is the universe of common sense and it speaks by innuendo its persistent doubt of science, practice and the spirit and other creeds and codes and methodologies. They are

mere artifice, it says, a useful sham perhaps, but as a real
apportionment of things, more specious than profound.
It accepts the clatter and the hard stubbornness of things;
it presupposes lumps and logs, toads, thunder storms and
matter, copper bowls and wishes, shoes, thoughts and
free choices all as they knock upon the doors of its perceptions, and it blithely goes along. For the world (looking westward) may have its sinks and rivers of the reason
and its desert sands between; it may have its vagrant
codes and metaphors and organic patterns, like irrigated
patches on a plain where the sand still blows and the
winds are never tamed, but common sense, though at
heart perhaps a pluralism, will still be for one objective
world. To know that miscellaneous universe, sporadi-
cally consistent, may be hard. Reason may fail. But
common sense has various authorities; reason, knowledge,
mental discipline are not always dominant; they need
not rule.

Casually there are several worlds in general — in spite
of common sense on one hand and of the spirit on the
other — and though each one may be a method made
unduly hypostatical the fact remains that our human
operations, our world, our very building of reality itself
are involved profoundly in these several ways and worlds.
Beyond their codes and regulations only the twist and
swirl of smoke and an unappreciable chaos can be seen;
within them human questioning finds a dignity and a
consummation. Three ways at least, the scientific, the
practical, the spiritual, have found an independence in
this casual, scattered world; they have hewed three
separate trails in the jungle of experience; and a resolution
of their pluralism into one may be impossible.

It is an old schism, says Professor Moore,[6] founded long
ago in philosophic thought, that previous to pragmatism
thinkers tried in vain to close. But, schism though it be,
there are scientific, practical, spiritual approaches to the
world; there is scientific interest in some things, practical

or spiritual in others; there are world layouts on the scientific order, the success of which lies in their exclusiveness and separation; there are practical worlds upraised; there are spiritual fulfillments; and though common sense presumes that all three may pertain to one reality and the same experience, it is hard to name those realities or to designate their meaning except in terms of one code or another.

Hypostasis it may be, but it seems to be deep seated. The concreteness of things, the orders and functions of things, the rational systems, the imaginative as well as the formal reality of our world seem involved in codes and old conventions. And when we ask what lies beyond, what is the aggregate, the answer is usually to install one of these approaches as the basic order of reality — according to our aim and prejudice — and to treat the rest as glistenings and lustres on its surface. For the scientist "matter" and order are primary; for the practical man, action and utility; for the lover, the artist and religious man, spiritual being. One comprehensive world for all is hard to find, and the search perhaps is frivolous and needless. In this casual aggregate of things the three worlds remain rather stubbornly insulated.

They are in effect aspects of a universe. But the sad proviso of some philosophers that the world beyond our ways of looking at it might as well be nothing cannot be entirely ignored. Within the scientific point of view the world of matter and descriptions seems well organized and consistent. Within the practical point of view the world of action and utility is convincing and beats with the heart of reality. Within the spiritual point of view the world is profoundly in the deeps of being. They are real worlds while we are in them. They have — within their own conventions — a full authority.

Men swim like fish in vari-colored bowls, green, red, blue; are they a pose and color that we cannot see beyond? Are they but nearby moods? Is there no final countenance of the world beyond these shifting gestures and expressions? From within these points of view the world's realness is in any case significant. Perhaps there is no world from no point of view at all.

In humanistic terms the worlds of science, of practice, of art have been called knowing, doing, feeling, and these no doubt are human correlates of those three fields. But pragmatists, humanists and anthropologists notwithstanding, it remains that the validity of those worlds from their own point of view is not founded on those terms. They reach beyond their psychological and human correlates to a realm of realness for itself. Without that presumption their authority would be lost.

For we presume of this world diverse things. We read it several ways; we create it, as it were, miscellaneously; and failure to correlate our propositions in regard to it may be more a failure of the reason in such matters than an error in presumption. "In formal logic," says Whitehead,[7] "a contradiction is the signal of a defeat: but in the evolution of real knowledge it marks the first step in progress towards a victory. This is one great reason for the utmost toleration of variety of opinion. Once and forever, this duty of toleration has been summed up in the words, 'Let both grow together until the harvest.'" And this applies perhaps to worlds as well as to theologies and politics.

Reason is but a helper to philosophy, and a world that does not coagulate under its laws may not be after all a hopeless chaos. Like a snow storm or a sun dial or an Easter hat the world has diverse aspects and presumptions. For the hat may be described scientifically, its size, its shape, its texture, its material causes and effects recorded. It may be considered in its practical utility and function, its protective function, if any, noted, its use to keep the head from getting cold accented. It may be taken æsthetically, as a thing of beauty and a joy for three weeks. It has this trinity of aspects, and no doubt

others, but what (of hats as well as worlds) is the real
hat? It is hard to say, for reality is a shifty word hard to
confine to any system. It is presumed of things from this
or that or all points of view, and when that presumption
is abandoned the real hat goes. And it always is abandoned in surveying critically all points of view together,
for no matrix or container is apparent. The points of
view are lost, with no Kant to save them. They are left
disparate and floating, and there is no replacement. How
they are juxtaposed in our experience is hard to say, and
no one point of view provides a way to tell. They lose
their realistic connotations, even the material of the hat
becomes a hypothesis, and its general unity only a three
part aggregation in our minds. It all comes — so the
mystic at least would say — of trusting reason. It all is
criticism — and all rational criticism is nihilistic — which
denies the real presumption on which the aspects of the
hat are based.

Read the world crosswise and there is one answer,
practical utilities and actions; read it vertically and there
is another answer, science; read it in the line of direct
penetration and there is a third answer, spirit. What
further philosophical dimensions the universe may have
need not be sought; three are enough to show the facets
of it and the shifting glitter. Perhaps there are no more.
The veil of things, the Indic book might say, has silk and
silver strands and error and woven dreams across its
web, and there are diamonds and illusions in it.

Science shows a world of matter, and things are orderly
and thus and so, like a Dutch kitchen, regardless of our
appreciations of them. It assumes a world free of our
values and experience, and whether that assumption be
finally true makes little difference so long as scientists
act as if it were. It is the world of matter, knowable in
detail and rational in structure.

Extended the world of matter becomes the star strewn sky on one hand and the electronic vivacities of the atom on the other. It is impersonal. It turns by its own law. And whether it extends in infinite successions of incorporated galaxies, as Moulton says, or whether it is a curved universe, boundless but finite, as Einstein says, does not affect its scientific character. It is objective by presumption. And the scientist, *per se*, usually treats another world convention, for example the world of practice and of use, as if it were imposed on more basic orders of scientific law.

But this subordination is founded mostly on professors' prejudice. Only by presumption is the world of science final and external. "The right of science to deal with the beyond of sense-impression is not the subject of contest," says one of the more philosophical among scientists, Karl Pearson,[8] "for science confessedly claims no such right." The absolutes of science, classic as they are, are founded in but one dimension of reality. We know them through a red glass. They sift through our perceptions. And the humane hypothesis, the world of use, can be extended as authentically as the rational convention of the scientist.

So says the pragmatist. The rigid truths of science become relative to human action in his hands, for action is his final world. The delicate draughtsmanship of the world of matter, its sharp dichotomies and outlines melt under his new, warm world, for it has humane attributes. It may not be monistic; it may be pluralistic. It leaves Democritus and his atoms. It takes up Protagoras and his "Man is a measure of all things."

And the world of spirit has validity and completeness. For the particularities of matter are after all inadequate and limited, and the makes and breaks of action are only endless change and dying. Being somehow must lie beyond casual and conditioned things. There is a wish in the heart for completeness.

These three, it may be, are aspects of the world in general. But is there a world in general? Can some cosmic counterpoint be found wherein these voices sing together in one song? Would each be virtually complete but for the others? Is each conditioned by the others' outlooks on the world? What is beyond? Deepest of all of them is the world of spirit. It has finality in its eye, but provides for no particulars. It leads to God but provides for no return.

High on its bright hill burns the world of spirit. It consumes all; it is high and low; it is near and far. It is deep in universal depths; it is the solvent of all mundane minerals.

Though scientists and men of action may interpret it according to their own routines, it remains its own. They may involve it, as it were, in material things or make of it an element in the field of use and social progress, but they cannot justify it or condition it. James [9] tells of the utility of the absolute. But these interpretations, valid enough in their own fields, cannot be the source of spiritual validity. Mysticism may be subject to psychological research, and a behaviorist like Watson would no doubt call it visceral. Love and beauty may be placed on a biological and glandular basis. But none of these external explanations can provide the authority of love, of beauty, of the spirit in itself.

In the natural sciences and industries it never occurs to any one to try to refute opinions by showing up their author's neurotic constitution, says William James.[10] Opinions here are always tested by logic and by experiment, no matter what may be their author's neurological type. It should be no otherwise with religious opinions, he says; their value can only be ascertained by spiritual judgments; immediate luminousness, in short, reasonableness and helpfulness are the only available criteria.

With calm assurance a hard headed young student of today will probably interpret spiritual aspects of the world in terms of Psychology B2, Sociology A3, Anthropology C3, and like externalisms. And it is not surprising in a world where spiritual reality is wordless and implicit and scientific phenomena are explicit and rationally organic. But for all that the young man in accepting educational rationalism or business as his basic code is merely missing the point spiritually. Such interpretations are valuable and valid in science or in practice; but they make no contact with the world of spirit.

In his own unmeditated life the young man has a different way. In his love affairs, in games and laughter, at the dance or loafing in the shower room, in the æsthetic interests that enrich all youth, in his religious thought and wonder, he asks no genetic interpretation to authorize his interest, and Sociology A3 is not needed to persuade him that being in love has a value and authority of its own. In implicit life, in direct experience, in immediate intuition he gets the point of view without an argument. It may be undemonstrable; it is no less sure.

What is the spiritual point of view? "The created soul of man hath two eyes," says the Theologia Germanica [11] in old and piquant symbolism. "The one is the power of seeing into eternity, the other of seeing into time and the creatures, of perceiving how they differ from each other as aforesaid, of giving life and needful things to the body, and ordering and governing it for the best. But these two eyes of the soul of man cannot both perform their work at once; but if the soul shall see with the right eye into eternity, then the left eye must close itself and refrain from working, and be as though it were dead. For if the left eye be fulfilling its office toward outward things; that is, holding converse with time and the creatures; then must the right eye be hindered in its working; that is, in its contemplation."

The unknown saint and aristocrat who wrote the Theologia Germanica knows man's momentum towards eternity and separates it from affairs of time, of reason and of matter. He appreciates this deeper flame of life. It yearns towards timeless being; the other is busy in the field of science and of action. And a survey of this cosmic amphibian called man, a study of his history and motivation, shows beyond denial that the spiritual point of view, whatever it may be, is of great import in his life. In any Weltanschauung it cannot be denied.

The spirit is oneness of all being. It is beyond the obvious frontiers and reasons, and it finds in breaths of spiritual illumination what no mind can analyze nor reason explicate. For reason makes the world seem finite. That is its method and its function. Its principle is limitative; it must always separate what some things are from what other things may be. But the limitative order the spirit never will accept. It is not concerned with the *what* of reason but only in the *that* of being.

There is a deep difference there, and though the power of language to say it has grown up slowly in men's minds, as Royce says,[12] and still is technical and abstract, and heavy like a lumber wagon more with the burden of its own construction than with the load it carries, the difference in human thought between the sense of being and the scientific analysis and separation of the objects of perception, between the ultimate *that* and the multiplicity of *whats*, persists throughout our mental history. Science is indomitably centrifugal. The spiritual point of view always is centripetal.

Men want release from these dispersive things and they call it the eternal. They are equipped with discontent; they press for freedom against the explosions and the push of circumstance. Once the play world of childhood was enough for freedom. Then imaginations and adventures, of poets and of adolescents, then free activity and the finalities of love and of religion offered them fulfillment. They come seeking what the dispersed things around them cannot give. Their life overflows the cups set out for it; they seek an ultimate place.

For men divine the ore of being in them. They feel its weight and warmth. It is within them the fulfillment of all their acts and relativities, though inarticulate and still. It takes no impress; it is alien, somehow, to the limits and restrictions of the things about; it is strange among them, but most intimate. Being burns in men with a red glow that is hard to touch. It lies alone like hot, red iron amid a clutter and a waste of things. Its burning is all being and fulfillment.

These eternities are ever sought by human kind, and finding them in beauty, in love, in religion is as sound a thing in this world as an analysis of matter and of object or system of utility and human action can ever be. For Plato they transcend discursive reason and its manyness, and may be found sometimes only in madness and incandescence. It is high madness, he says,[13] and a divine release of soul from the yoke of custom and convention. It has four kinds, prophetic, initiatory, poetic, erotic madness, and four gods preside over them. There is Apollo, Dionysus; the third is inspired by the Muses, the fourth by Aphrodite and Eros. It is a "madness," called intuition, that inheres as a valid element in all men's thinking. It is the spiritual approach to the world.

For Plato, to be sure, as well as for Plotinus, reason stands at the final frontier of being, but it is wordless reason, transcendent and unlike the separative principle of science. It has escaped the gesturing of words and found fulfillment. And the soul at her height, says Plato,[14] "beholds knowledge absolute in existence absolute." Thence it can return in peace to the mundane life of reason and utility, for it goes home now, says Plato, and the charioteer of the soul puts up his horses at the stall and gives them ambrosia to eat and nectar to drink.

The wordless reason of the "soul" that Plato knows is not finite-making; it is not separative. It is integrative and immediate. It transcends differences, and, in Plato and the thoughtful mystics of his type, is identity with being.

For the spiritual world is a release from many things into the primordial one. It seeks the divine morass where objects are engulfed and self merges with the grateful darkness. Beyond and before and throughout derivative things lies being, and in it things and selves eventually are lost.

"As the bees, my dear, prepare honey by collecting the essences of different trees and reducing the essence to a unity, as they are not able to discriminate 'I am the essence of this tree,' 'I am the essence of that tree' — even so, indeed, my dear, all creatures here, though they reach being, know not 'We have reached being;'" so speaks the Chandogya Upanishad.[15]

"These rivers, my dear, flow, the eastern toward the east, the western toward the west," the mystic book of India continues. "They go just from the ocean to the ocean. They become the ocean itself. As there they know not 'I am this one,' 'I am that one' — even so, indeed, my dear, all creatures here, though they have come forth from being, know not 'We have come forth from being.' Whatever they are in this world, whether tiger, or lion, or wolf, or boar, or worm, or fly, or gnat, or mosquito, that they become. That which is the finest essence — this whole world has that as its soul. That is reality. That is soul, That art thou, Svetaketu."

Whether it be transcendent as in Plato or immanent as in this passage from the Upanishads makes little difference: the spirit is concerned with being. It is concerned not with difference but with "identity in being."

The line is long of men who have found the real beyond

the bounds of reason; all men join it at times and places
in their lives. Schopenhauer [16] after finding space and
time dispersive principles in the universe, forms of our
thinking, and after casting all differences of things and
their repulsions, attractions, decompositions, combinations, gravitations into the realm of mere phenomenal
existence, says that in their inner nature things are
identical and directly known. For phenomenal existence
is idea and all idea and object is phenomenal existence,
says this dark Kantian, but the "will" alone is a thing in
itself. "As such, it is throughout not idea, but *toto genere*
different from it; it is that of which all idea, all object
is the phenomenal appearance, the visibility, the objec-
tification." And so the gaunt philosopher struggles on to
tell with pomp and technicality the wordless being of
the spirit. The deep unreason beyond reason, the identity
of all things is his theme,[17] as it is the theme of medieval
monk and Indian mystic.

There is endless testimony: the spiritual is valid in
our human thought. In the stones and waves and love
of life there is testimony, and for those who do not
recognize the light inherent in all men, there is the
testimony of men. "Always our being is descending into
us from we know not whence," says Emerson.[18] "We
live in succession, in division, in parts, in particles.
Meantime, within man is the soul of the whole; the wise
silence; the universal beauty, to which every part and
particle is equally related; the eternal *One*. . . . The
soul circumscribeth all things. As I have said, it contra-
dicts all experience. In like manner it abolishes time and
space. The influence of the senses has, in most men,
overpowered the mind to that degree, that the walls of
time and space have come to look solid, real, and insur-
mountable; and to speak with levity of these limits is,
in the world, the sign of insanity, yet time and space are
but inverse measures of the force of the soul. A man is
capable of abolishing them both."

"And what I assume you shall assume," says Walt
Whitman,[19] poet of spiritual identity; "And every atom
belonging to me, as good belongs to you."

To these lucent intimations of the seer and poet there
is bound to be a sturdy, common sense reaction. It
comes brusquely on a man, more perhaps than on a
woman, that the world still batters at his gates. It is a
massive world of fierce energies and actions, of vivid
thrusts and living and huge things that lumber into his
experience like unasked motor trucks in a portrait
camera's field. It is a world pleasingly automotive. It
surges on without his will, and the joy of being in its
giant stream of traffic captures the average man and
holds him with a specious import. The average man is
something of a quietist, for he is glad to merge himself
in its activities and torrents and be swept on by its
direction. He loves its fighting and its action, its particularism and risk, and he accepts it, in many moods,
passively as enough.

But there are right ways and wrong ways even in the
world of common sense. There are strange bents for
goodness; there is duty; loyalties lay their hands upon
the carefree man. And though nine tenths of morals
may be practical, and what is right is what works best,
the prejudice for working best is harder to explain.
The raw taste for goodness over evil, the preference for
living over not living, the choice of pleasure over pain,
for social perpetuation over nothingness, for being over
not being, carries back beyond utilities to basic affirmations of the spirit that no linked system and no instruments can give. Neither common sense nor reason can
initiate the interests, the motives and the meanings of
our lives. They cannot authorize belief in anything of
deep significance. Morality itself is no doubt practical;

it is the best way to get on; but the deep impulse to get on, the will to live itself is spiritual.

To the biologist morality is based, first, on intelligence as to what in aggregate will give more happiness than pain; second, on our natural preference for what we recognize as the greater happiness; third, on the adjustment of our natural responses entailing pleasure or pain to the physical and developmentary requirements of our biological organism. And all that is true enough — biologically. An intelligent preference every hour for happiness would be biologically enough for good morals and civilization. It is a moral thesis based on faith in nature and an optimistic confidence that what in general makes this impulsive creature, man, happy is the most adequate and useful moral system. In this morality finds a scientific ground in instinct and a practical basis in utility. That is nine tenths of morality; but it is not spiritual.

Reason can justify; it can expound and clarify, as James[20] or Robinson,[21] for example, eloquently insists; it cannot create a moral point of view. Practical utility can make of morals a significant element in this busy world; but it cannot initiate a moral affirmation. There is a poetic impulse in all morality. There is an æsthetic preference somewhere — beyond, more than in morality — for what seems good and is not bad, and it is simple, immediate, deeper than rational moralities. The still authority of the spirit — our only ground of freedom — is there. An insight enters that defers neither to the volubilities of reason nor the stark, blind impetus of instinct.

But morality is practice, for the most part; it is good works, and though good will spiritually underlies it, morals themselves relate to conduct. They are miscellaneous and objective; they are mainly common sense. They sit roughly on the subtle structures of rational idealists such as T. H. Green; [22] and though they may be forced like spaghetti into a complicated twine of abstractions and remote relationships, they remain rather bluff matters of action. They are set massively on conglomerates of rubble and uncut stone, on brick and on carved marble, on the raw morainal drift left by glaciers of a past age and broken plinths and friezes and delicate screens of arabesque. They are of the world of common sense, and like that world in general are aggregative and unsystematic. Their authorities are diverse.

Theories of morality are many. Based on reason a type of theory is forthcoming that has had exponents from Socrates on down. Based on bodily response, and biologists and psychologists rise to tell the world what morality may be. Based on æsthetic intuition, and the poets and the mystics take a leading part. Plato with his oneness of the good and real makes morals metaphysical. Churches are organized, and earnest souls build huge structures of institutional religion to tie morality, or right conduct, to the absolute. Be its pattern scientific, practical, spiritual, biological, traditional, psychological, institutional, hedonistic, metaphysical, æsthetic or any other, moral theory is an effort to find an ultimate sanction for good deeds and to tell why we sometimes undertake them. But morality is not itself so consistent or so systematic. It is aggregative. It is eclectic. It is common sense.

To the world of the spirit morality is often juxtaposed. The youth who falls in love will be no doubt a better social creature for it, and he will lean towards good deeds that may have no organic relation to his romance. The spiritual elevation of a human being incidentally may raise the moral level. For having found the spiritual realities he may be a better man in a world of action; but that is not why he found them nor is it their justification. Good works are usual concomitants of a deeply spiritual interest, but they need not be the same. Close to the winning strategy of the battle of Austerlitz is Napoleon's good health; but the result at Austerlitz hardly can be called a function of his digestion, nor the loss at Waterloo a complication of his growing bladder trouble. The one is strategy; the other is physiology. They belong in different universes of discourse, and they illustrate the difference that lies between practical morality and the spiritual world. The spirit bears significantly but only indirectly on the moral world; it is intrinsic; and to say that the ground and meaning of spiritual experiences is its effect on practical conduct is to ignore the spiritual point of view.

Institutions may incorporate moral codes and impose them on society to the benefit of mankind. But the spirit accepts no mundane harnesses and secular organizations that would capture it. It never can be dogmatized socially or institutionally. It can be used only speciously for enforcement and for mundane sanctions of external codes of conduct. The spirit is non-relational, non-social, non-practical, non-moral.[23] It is an inner authority. It is no outer dogma.

A man "who studies for himself the ominous and the friendly aspects of reality and gives them the truest and most adequate expression he can is repeating what the founders of religion did in the beginning," says Santayana.[24] "He is their companion and follower more truly than are the apologists for second-hand conceptions which these apologists themselves have never compared with the facts, and which they prize chiefly for misrepresenting actual experience and giving it imaginary extensions."

For the spiritual approach to the world is a way that each human being must tread out for himself. It is not accumulative, as scientific knowledge may be. No reservoirs of human experience can supply the fresh wonder and insight that mark it. Nor can tradition here have the compelling influence that worlds of action and practice always accept. Spiritual reality cannot be shown or taught or passed on from mind to mind in the general commerce of ideas and objects. It must be found in each human life *de novo* and for itself.

More surely than all this other world do we know its implicit being within us. It is the naïve spring, and the taste of its waters is the taste of all the universe. Somehow we find the world real; every man is inspired with a notion of its substance; but the whole impressive mass of its reality is only a presumptive copy of reality within. Without that sense of being nothing could seem real; no idea of being could arise. The seriousness of all thought and of all meaning rests on that intimation.

The spirit is profound and original within us. It lies incommunicably deep in our selves and to define it rationally and to thrust it into our social currency is but a smoke cloud and delusion. It remains implicit, deeply personal. Our intuitions find it ultimate; but our reasons find it not at all.

For science is by nature external and impersonal and has no tools to dig it out. Science is abstract and specific — it is existential; religion is concrete and general — it is ontological; and a predisposition towards the one or the other is not a proof that one or other is more true. Religion refers to the concrete identity of the self with all being. In science self is carefully abandoned; in religion it is always a profound concern. From the spiritual point of view science is an abstraction, thinned out and clear, from a rich liquor of which religion is a basic part. Science is common and communicable, and by that fact incomplete and schematic; it is shallow and detached from the fulness of being.

The spiritual way to the world is not a public highway. Though all men travel it, each travels it alone on a path no other man can tread. It is personal and religious. It pertains, says William James,[25] "to individual men in their solitude, so far as they apprehend themselves to stand in relation to whatever they may consider divine." Within their own being men find a primary confidence in the real that inspires all the attitudes of their lives and their outlook on the diverse world. It is religion.

But the person, spiritually, is not the diverse person of things and troubles. It is not this social unit, this man of circumstance and affairs, the man of practice and the focus of individual action. It is not the pragmatic self, asking finite aid and suffering mundane worries, who has spiritually found being. It is not man externally considered, subject of science and utility; it is the "inner" person. It is inner meaning.

In general the mystic knows only internal meanings, says Royce,[26] "precisely as the realist considers only external meanings. But the mystic, nevertheless, condemns all finite ideas, just because they have no absolute internal meaning. He bids you look within; but he desires first wholly to transform your inner nature. He compares your heart to the Bethlehem, where God may at any instant be born. . . . The essence of mysticism lies not in the definition of the subject to which you attribute being, but in the predicate Being itself."

The self is the heart that is Bethlehem. It is deep. It is a oneness of the self and being that men know as the most intimate certainty of the universe. In that sense of being lies what is called the person; and the dignity attached to persons, their unique import, their final worth, their spirit, their divine equality, have roots deep in the certainty within us. Spiritually men reach for final being. They find being within, and they find it one. Therein is the self founded.

But this restlessness called living is after all impressive. It is a surf and rhythm that pounds on endlessly. It

makes uneasy contours and its crests are often steep and
desperate. It always is impressive, and though the sea
beyond it may be more profound, this surf and movement
are more often what we see. The unique experience
called living is a flux and restlessness so far as science and
society are concerned. It is structurally unstable. Only
the spirit looks to the final sea beyond.

For life materially is founded in an unstable compound
called protoplasm and it lasts in time only by ceaseless
change. It moves on always to new raw stuffs, and it
discards the old. Assimilation, the change of crude and
latent energies to action, excretion, go on in endless
rhythm so long as life goes on. Across the thresholds of
life matter moves like the long chain of a ferry boat.
It enters and it leaves and the boat somehow moves on
across a river. Biologically life is a restlessness. It is a
function of the continuing chemistry and process of
protoplasm.

And the life process is but an advertisement and an
accentuation of all the material world. It is a Heraclitean
flux, and the gloomy Greek who said, "you cannot step
twice into the same river; for fresh waters are ever
flowing in upon you," spoke for the modern restlessness
of atoms and of suns and of utilities and of people.

That is impressive, but all men, even Heraclitus,
reach for finalities of being beyond this restless edge of
things. In the arts, in love, in religion they find ways to
command 'time and the creatures' and to identify
themselves with the one world of their vision. Philosophy, critical though much of it must be, still knows the
import of that naïve insight. "The greatest men who
have been philosophers," says a philosopher,[27] "have
felt the need both of science and of mysticism: the attempt to harmonize the two was what made their life a
greater thing than either science or religion." In the
ecstasies of the sports, in war and fighting, in building
and in laughter there may be consummation. In love and

art and dancing, in hunting and in singing men may find realization. But religion, called by James [28] the total reaction on life, religion more than philosophy, more than the arts and love, takes the oneness of the world and the identity with its inner being as an end and interest. "Its quintessential core — which is the art of finding our emotional relationship to the world conceived as a whole," says Havelock Ellis,[29] "is best termed 'Mysticism.'"

It is a turning to the only "realism" that the world can give — that found within — and there phenomena and change which science and society must offer are less impressive. Being is the persistent enthusiasm of the mystic and religious man; and the difference between science and the spirit is not in validity or correctness but in this point of view and primary concern. Words after all are only words; they are fixed symbols; they are empty bottles, glass abstractions, shells; they stand in pompous rows, "identity," "absolute," "inner," "outer," "ultimate," "predicate," "unity," "subject," "object," "person," to tell what words can never tell; the shells themselves are meaningless; the world of the spirit is Being consummate.

Science deals with relations; the spirit is concerned in being. And though the channels to it in this world may be emotion or instinct, alcohol, or trance, girls or chloroform or prayer, the glitter of a glass, sorrow or meditation or sleep, or what not that is psychological or biological; its meaning never is in these, but always deep in being. It is insight, not a vehicle to ride on.

But it has human consequences, and to many that is its sole meaning. A way to the world down an inner path will carry with it webs of human need and spun silks that stream across the inner self. "Religion," says James,[30] speaking from this humanistic point of view, "deliberately bases truth on value and makes God subject to approval." And here, as Dean Inge [31] suggests in pointing to Eckhart as transitional from medieval to modern

Christianity, here is the divide where religion may leave the upward slope of purely spiritual and "ontological" interest and begin the descent into broad valleys of human values and practice.

Humanly speaking man wants one world; he wants peace within and emotional adjustment to his universe; he wants practical unity in his field of operations; he wants inner realization somehow of the being that he longs for, and in the arts, in love, in religion he hopes profoundly to attain it. All his human wishing may have not much to do in truth with spiritual reality; it is the human pasture at any rate in which the spirit sits, and by contiguity if no more is made significant.

Only by silence, says Meister Eckhart, purest of spirits,[32] can we describe being. God is deeply in the self, and no intermediaries of words or priests or hierarchies or forms can intervene.[33] Man finds within himself all being. That is a simple thought that incidentally is the ground of the Protestant reformation and of other human movements in the grand style.

Spiritual problems are not evolutionary and the insights of two thousand years ago still illumine man's thought. Six problems here, as old as thinking, have been turned about briefly like jewels under the casual light of attention. First, does man want one world; second, three general conceptions of or approaches to the world; third, what is the spiritual approach to the world; fourth, what is the relation of morality to the religious life; fifth, mysticism and the ontological problem; sixth, human affairs and the spiritual life. They are endless problems and endlessly worth while.

The Descriptive Approach
to the World

A WELL mannered scientist rarely speaks of being. His reticence in that respect is profound and unadulterated, and neither being nor Being has in him the least encouragement. He can tell a metaphysical decoy at a thousand yards, and he is always prompt to change his course from there to places of less peril. The modern scientist is being-shy. He looks upon the wrecks and fatalities of science about him, upon Theosophy, Spiritualism, Christian Science, upon four fifths of modern theological effort to give God a membership in the American Association for the Advancement of Science, upon miracles and new thaumaturgies; he sees herds of well intentioned human beings charge over these cliffs into the sea; and he says, "Not for me. This scientist will keep out of metaphysics. Being shall remain unmentionable."

He calls that "scientific phenomenalism," a long name meaning that he asks not what things are ultimately but only how they behave. He wants physics but no metaphysics. He will study things as they appear to his senses, but he refuses to speculate on their ultimate being. That is his policy; and it is the best policy, no doubt, for the security and peace of mind of science. But the temper of his repudiations is not precisely scientific.

Being is bad medicine for science, but the retching and reaction against it, though necessary perhaps, has not the calm, dispassionate dignity of the scientific mood. It is a basic dogma of science to reject ontological considerations; it is a fundamental matter of point of view;

but basic dogmas are alike the world over: their validity is more metaphysical and passionate than scientific and rational. Through its pugnacity and innocence science slips backward now and then into metaphysical considerations. And this is more true of modern science than of the old. In surveying new frontiers, in realizing rational limitations, modern science needs less of the conventional contempt for problems beyond its borders and more of wise and considerate studies of its field and categories as they have developed in the new light of recent research. Without such study all post-Einstein science, all trans-atomic science is bound surely for confusion.

For science is still a protestant against the spiritualistic and sentimental excesses of an earlier age. It is the advocate of a negation; it is anti-absolute, anti-ultimate, anti-ontological. Ernst Mach preludes his famous Analysis of Sensations with "Introductory Remarks: Anti-metaphysical." Karl Pearson fulminates viciously at the thought of metaphysics in the earlier pages of his Grammar of Science. They "are built either on air or on quicksands," he says.[1] "There is no short cut to truth," he justly continues, "no way to gain a knowledge of the universe except through the gateway of scientific method. The hard and stony path of classifying facts and reasoning upon them is the only way to ascertain truth." And with this fine denunciation of all things metaphysical he proceeds to more and more unconsciously metaphysical positions throughout the rest of the great book. The scientist's passionate rejection of all that sort of thing was adapted well to the reactionary needs of the nineteenth century. It is less well adapted perhaps to the new syntheses of the twentieth.

Today the demand on science is for a more mature point of view than these naïve bigotries and protests indicate. Metaphysical in the classic sense, science by right will never be, but it must know the problem of ultimate being and appreciate its significance in order to tell intelligently where the limits of science should lie. It must develop a metaphysical base and understanding far more mature than the innocent positivism of its past. It must resurvey its frontiers, and fix its new place in the universe. "Einstein has told us," says J. B. S. Haldane,[2] "that space, time, and matter are shadows of the fifth dimension, and the heavens have declared his glory. In consequence Kantian idealism will become the basal working hypothesis of the physicist and finally of all educated men, just as materialism did after Newton's day." It may not be Kant; it probably will not be Kant; but there will be a greater metaphysics at any rate, at the base of the new science, and more consciously recognized, than has ever been the case heretofore. "We appear to be witnessing," says a recent reviewer in *Nature* commenting on new Einsteins,[3] "not so much the birth of a new theory, for there are already half a dozen or more species of relativity theory . . . as the birth of a new branch of knowledge — *mathematical metaphysics*."

Ultimate being, which metaphysical reasoning tries to find and spiritual insight, at least to its own satisfaction, does find, is not the proper domain of science. To that philosophers, theologians and scientists in their better moments all agree. As the end of the road and final resting place of all things, being is not scientific. But to call unknown areas of investigation and unfamiliar continuities, that still may be subject to scientific research, metaphysical merely because they are strange, unusual and generally upsetting, is to exclude from science things that belong there and to delay progress in fields, such as certain regions of psychology and a good deal of Einstein, that need strictly scientific attention. Nor is the tendency to repudiate problems that lie beyond the proper reach of natural science, and, because they are metaphysical or spiritual, to deny entirely their significance any less unfortunate. The latter is a fault common among scientists that becomes increasingly dangerous to clear thinking and to science itself. For in denying rights to these ultimate problems the scientist is himself taking a metaphysical position, and a very immature one, that will inevitably react unfavorably on the development of his scientific ideas. "Each," says a philosopher,[4] referring to the practical, the mystical and scientific attitudes, "each becomes fallacious when it tries to extend beyond its proper sphere," and this is no less true of science, though less often recognized, than of any other point of view. Beyond science, the scientist as such has no more right to deny than to affirm. He cannot rightfully judge spiritual interests and realities by scientific criteria, and he would do better to go on a vacation to these foreign lands, and as a human being to try to understand them. He could return to science then, accept its limitations thoughtfully, and lay out its proper place in the world.

For being is the concern of spiritual life, and science by its own profession refrains from entering. It is an interest that penetrates profoundly through our human aggregate of actions and experiences, but it is not scientific. It is involved in the deep sense of life's significance, and this world's final meaning; it is that meaning; but it cannot be described by formulas or by scientific record. In a sensitive passage in Scepticism and Animal Faith, George Santayana hints at this remoteness of being — which he here calls substance — from the scientific comprehension and at the same time the immediacy of being to the spiritual insight: "All knowledge," he says,[5] "being faith in an object posited and partially described, is belief in substance, in the etymological sense of this word; it is belief in a thing or event subsisting in its own plane, and waiting for the light of knowledge to explore it eventually, and perhaps name or define it. . . . It is impossible to eliminate belief in substance

so long as belief in existence is retained. . . . Each phenomenon in passing is an object of intuition, all absent
phenomena, and all their relations are objects of faith;
and this faith must be mediated by some feature in the
present phenomenon which faith assumes to be a sign
of the existence of other phenomena elsewhere, and of
their order. So that in so far as the instinctive claims and
transcendent scope of knowledge are concerned, phenomenalism fully retains the belief in substance. . . .
Belief in substance is. . . identical with the claim to
knowledge, and so fundamental that no evidence can be
adduced for it which does not presuppose it. . . . It is
as if Substance said to Knowledge: My child, there is a
great world for thee to conquer, but it is a vast, an ancient, and a recalcitrant world. It yields wonderful
treasures to courage, when courage is guided by art and
respects the limits set to it by nature. I should not have
been so cruel as to give thee birth, if there had been
nothing for thee to master; but having first prepared the
field, I set in thy heart the love of adventure." The net
of scientific reason cannot encompass being. Beyond
all that, being remains spiritual.

The tools that science uses to describe this world
cannot apply to being, and the scientist is right in refusing
to treat as a descriptive problem what primarily is not
amenable to descriptive method. "Science," says a critic
of the reason,[6] "is a synthesis of reason and sensation;"
the facilities that it offers for penetration beyond those
frontiers are quite untrustworthy. Being is nameless in
words and to try to predicate it definitely only raises
fakes and ghosts of what lies beyond all definition.
Subject-predicate definements are after all, by their own
admissions, only a special shaping and a limitation devised by human use. They are dogmas of scientific
measurement, but being is the dogma of enthusiasm and
insight. They are a waffle pattern for the world, but the
world somehow does not all conform. Not all of it ac-

cepts the pattern. There is an ultimacy in being and there is a concrete, connotative intent, an imaginative depth in it that repels descriptions, outreaches definitions, and invincibly raises the scientist to its surface, as the waters of the Great Salt lake lift swimmers trying to explore their depths.

By hypothesis science is finite. It creates the finite, as it were; it selects the finite factors of the world from a chest where many other things may be available. That is all that reason and sensation are equipped to do. That is the kind of world that they must build. That is all they should try to do. The world is mixed nuts and candy for the holidays, and science picks only the filberts out. Science deliberately is not ultimate in significance. And this deliberate and methodical limitation that it places on itself prohibits the scientist from criticism — at least by scientific means — of other valid aspects of the world. To deny or to affirm those things beyond his field is not his right; and the current tendency of amiable scientists, moved by impulses for the social good, to prove by science, or to try to prove, purely spiritual theses that they may desire is as unjustified as to disprove them. It is as unjustified as the efforts of religious bigots and politicians in Tennessee and elsewhere to apply theological criteria to scientific facts.

What are the tools of science? With what instruments does it approach the world? They are different, it is sure, from the ways of the spirit. The one is intuitive and agglutinative; the other is rational and classificatory. The one realizes the self in things; the other distinguishes the self from things. The one fuses value with all data of the world, and through that fusion and transcendence of rational schisms comes to the "stille Wüste," the divine desert and fulfillment taught by

Eckhart; the other abstracts objects from all value in the effort to reveal a residual fact.

The tenets of mysticism, according to Russell,[7] are four: First: There are two ways of knowing, which may be called respectively reason and intuition, and of these intuition is that beside which all other knowledge is like ignorance. Second: All plurality and division are illusory. Third: Time is unreal. Fourth: Reality is good; evil is illusion.

And the tenets of rationalism, and of science, hold "that all our beliefs ought ultimately to find for themselves articulate grounds." Those grounds, according to James,[8] must consist of four things: definitely stateable abstract principles; definite facts of sensation; definite hypotheses based on such facts; and definite inferences logically drawn.

Different and no doubt contradictory as these two sets of rules for the game of the universe may seem, it is far from safe to say that both may not be true. For the world may tolerate more orders and dimensions than we know; it may be that kind of a universe; and what the spirit finds from the point of view of being may not hook up organically with what the reason finds from the point of view of knowledge. Hook-ups mean relational organizations, and that can only abrogate the meaning and identity of the spirit.

From the descriptive point of view the world is what the tenets of rationalism listed by James, or something like them, make it. They are creative in a selective, simple way, if not in the Kantian way, and the world, from the point of view of scientific rationalism, is just what scientific rationalism says it is, and no more.

It is a world deliberately relative. In detail and in general it is relative by postulate, and the newer relativities introduced by Einstein, Lorentz, H. Poincaré, Whitehead, Russell and others of recent science and mathematics, only apply to specific theory or to experiment what has long been inherent in the general method of science and long demanded. Modern relativity in science is really its increasing purification. Leftover absolutes from a pre-scientific era, incongruous infinities are being expelled. Science is building up a consistently descriptive approach to the world.

For science is recent, and the matter, energy and the like that it assumes is a frail sophistication never thought of in the sturdy days when reason was still a crude and uncertain tool easily mishandled in the hunt and in war and love. They were thick days then, gelatinous spheroids of living that rolled along one after the other, for memory was less codified than now, the tests of sense experience, dreams and the carefully articulated furniture of the modern mind were never made, and science was only a latent pattern in human experience that men had not yet isolated. Attention to things for their own sake, the long scrutinies of experiment and curiosity upon them was unheard of and impossible. Facts remote from human color, cold, objective, unassailable had never been invented. The abstractions on which modern science rests had not been made.

Only twice in history has this precipitate of science come down from the solutions and mixtures of human interests. First, the Greeks with their discovery of free reason; second, the moderns with their postulate of independent matter; and though reason never can be wholly free nor matter independent, the assumption of their self-sufficiency was enough to change human directions and to found western civilization. It took five thousand years or more of civilization to abstract reason from the mother stock of mental life and to learn its laws and continuities. And it took two thousand more to abstract from experience what the senses touch, to call it matter, and to learn its kind of order by experiment. Reason and sensation, and their synthesis in science, were slow to be realized in human history.

To separate an object from the colors and emotions of the "self" required long training in analysis and definition and a discipline not easily fitted on the human animal. The idea of inanimate matter, external to one-self, is the result of a complex and highly evolved method of thinking with which man became familiar only in recent thousands of years. That the so-called "objects of sensation" should be abstracted and classified apart from the rest of the general situation of living and experience is clearly artificial.[17] The materialistic approach to the world is not primitive. It is not natural animism. Unbiased observation is a difficult and sophisticated operation depending on extreme abstraction and selection.

For the materialism of science is different from the materialism of common sense. Scientifically it is matter and appropriate mechanism; to common sense it is concrete situations and actions. It is world mechanism to science and as abstract as an architect's blue print. It is a structural outline of things with a number and a formula and a line for every concrete thing, but with no concrete thing. It handles matter in terms of atomic numbers, differential equations and the like, and it handles the mechanism of matter in the same utterly descriptive way. To science that is matter and mechanism. But to common sense it is a sure way to lose all contact with them and to substitute what it contemptuously calls "theory" for the "practical."

Nor is common sense entirely wrong. It is invincibly anthropological and the effort of science to abstract data and laws from that rank background arouses a good deal of resistance. Science is a clearing in the jungle, and the neat rows of rubber trees can be protected from encroachment only by strenuous artifice. There are elements in common sense of instinct and mysticism, of practice and utility and rough, uncritical demands of living that would soon corrupt and overwhelm pure science and materialism. For pure materialism is rather thin, and the objectified, classified data of science are less convincing to the man of "common sense" than the forceful but less analytical material of his everyday life. Conceptions of matter or of "outside things" are based on abstractions from actual experience, but the assumption that this abstraction describes the real things because it shows order and logical stability is not always persuasive to common sense. The concrete materialism of common sense often bears more weight than the abstract materialism of science. The one is personal; the other is not.

In the scientist's catalogue of reverences there is no goddess more honored than the Goddess of Impersonality. She stands carved in utterly transparent crystal and though no one can see her, her form and features have a classic abstraction that repels familiar glances and undue camaraderie. She is the scientist's ineffable mistress and her vitreous affections shield him from the raw life and prejudice of mortal flesh. He looks upon the place where she is, and through her lucidities sees a world screened from the colors of personal projections and shining in the light of pure science. She is his abstracting lens, and what was the boisterous chaos of "common sense" materialism through her is seen cool and orderly, serene, unprejudiced. Without his glass goddess the scientist could never draw those limitations of his field in which he makes his progress.

But man found her late. Impersonality is rather a new thing in human thinking. It is derived, secondary, like a set of parliamentary rules drawn up, after long experience, to make the business of knowing more feasible. The job of objective knowing is rather a special one. It has its own technique, its own peculiarities, its own rules of order, and impersonality is one of them.

For science is ascetic. It is a discipline and a control of personal impulse that could arise only in a relatively mature civilization. Its endeavor to examine this world through self-imposed restrictions of method, through a regimen far removed from the rough aggregate of human ways of acting, is possible only in an era that has profited by long accumulations of moral experience. Its objectivity and indifference are highly developed sophistications essential to its progress, and though social, personal, human needs may indeed determine its direction and its selection of material, as Dewey and others point out, these are extraneous not scientific influences. The descriptive approach to the world finds its validity as well as its value within science itself. Its disregard for outer things is well nigh monastic. Progress in its own order is pure science. No Trappist monk, telling his beads, was ever more devoted.

The plenipotentiary of science to the world is reason, and reason makes its own terms. It is a point of view limited by its own nature; it is an ordering of things that is carefully impersonal. Where the mystic finds identity with the world in an intuition of being; the scientist carefully abstracts objects from those identities and describes the world by the rational ordering of sense impressions. Description by nature is separative. It abstracts what it describes from the general situation. It is impersonal, for that is reason's method. Description is implied in reason's cool way of objectifying things, and if there were no world but the world of pure science, Kant's Critique of Pure Reason would be about the only metaphysics necessary. Description is involved in impersonality, for impersonality means reason's first abstraction, the rise of objective facts, the creation of the scientific point of view.

The descriptive approach to the world rests on the faith that we can abstract from the concrete aggregate of living certain elements called independent things that can be known in common. It assumes that the logical pattern of this abstraction is more or less necessary and that logical criteria apply to the "external" things in that pattern. It assumes that these "external things" are "measurable," or comparable with each other in certain specific ways, and that sense data in reporting these measurable aspects of things are somehow co-ordinated accurately with them. Russell would have it, that the sense data involved in all descriptions are probably a part of the actual substance of the physical world. Others find other ways to explain the ambiguities in the statement that: Description is the effort to report "facts." But none can escape the primary faith and presumption involved in the descriptive method. Science as the development of this descriptive method of dealing with the universe cannot be called the preëstablished order of the "real world;" it is a kind of experiment in presumptions, an hypothesis justified by the kind of results that we get from it.

Science is always saying, "Let us pretend." In spite of metaphysical scoldings administered by Auntie Mach, Grandma Pearson and others, it keeps on saying it. If Science knows it is only playing, it is good science; but if it thinks its presumptions of substance must be "really real" that is very different. "In the history of the science of matter," says Soddy,[9] "two main types of mind can, in general, be distinguished, one of which has developed into the modern type of scientific mind, although the other type is by no means non-existent. . . . The older type of mind regarded all the forms of matter as a combination of certain elementary qualities, the newer type as a combination of certain elementary substances. . . . The modern habit of thought recognizes things as having a real existence apart altogether from the particular qualities or properties by means of which the things make themselves known to the five senses. The acceptance of this habit of thought among scientific men has been due mainly, not to formal proof, but to its fertility and to the undoubted value of the results which follow from it." "Let's pretend" seems to be a pleasant game.

On "real matter" science was founded. The pretense to being is its basic hypothesis. Science acts as if it described real things, not abstractions; and that pretense, lacking all proof, is the core of its seriousness. The descriptive approach to the world is founded in abstraction and analysis, in descriptive finiteness; but no less important is the hypothetical being that gives it seriousness and significance. Facts that are common and verifiable rest on the assumption of persistent substances. Science is in the somewhat anomalous position of knowing it to be an assumption, but acting as if it were true.

Whether that candid pretense of materialism in the English mode must also give way, as the part of non-Euclidian geometry, Einstein, the new logic, supersensory physics and continental psychology gain in popular recognition, remains to be seen. Today the general significance of science and its main motivations hangs on that irrational belief in objective substances. It is non-science dominating science; it is a wilfully accepted pretense, a faith impossible to prove that things observed are the *bona fide* world. That hypothesis is involved in the descriptive method itself; and when that hypothesis is abandoned, it is not impossible that the prestige and significance of science will go with it. There is a parallel between the authority and faith of theology in the middle ages, its rise to power and prestige as a world order, its decline with the decline of its primary presumption and faith in its reality, and the modern age of science and its basic presumptions. When a pretense of reality is dropped who knows what can happen? Perhaps it is happening now.

The liquefying touch of modern thought that has left a wet trail through art and society, morals and chemistry, philosophy and music has also brought upon the laws of nature a strange deliquescence. Their firm and quartz-like edges no longer stand stiffly against the horizon of our thought. They have melted down like mounds of ice cream on a hot day, and what was the formula for accurate reality is now the rough approximation of a complex and massive set of data that may have no ultimate formulation. Hypothesis has replaced law in modern science.

It is a stencil laid tentatively on the universe, and what we see through the apertures we call matter and motion, and what we don't see we call scientifically nothing. As an hypothesis the scientific approach to the world is justified not by material evidence, for that is part of the hypothesis, but by the way it gets along, its consistency, and its capacity to give general satisfaction; and Mill's [10] statement that "It appears, then, to be a condition of the most genuinely scientific hypothesis, that it be not destined always to remain an hypothesis, but be of such a nature as to be either proved or disproved by comparison with observed facts," can hardly apply to the basic supposition and the assumed order of scientific method.

Nor does it apply drastically in modern science to any hypothesis. Observed facts remain as ever the test of scientific validity, but the growing up of little hypotheses to big laws is not the foregone conclusion that it once was. They remain hypothetical and approximate; they are faced with no scientific necessity of becoming finished statements. For the scientist, as such, has come to doubt the ability of objective phenomena to provide that finished statement or of reason to find it. The statement of scientific law today is a Zeno paradox. It gets always closer; it struggles on ambitiously as if there were a defined goal at which natural law and scientific formula would be in sharp edged unanimity; but it knows there is no defined goal and that objective phenomena offer no scientific evidence that there may be a finished formula possible.

A guess reaching out its hand for confirmation, receiving many, but never enough to give it final stability, that is the hypothesis. Sense data, isolated by experiment or by other means, are brought to its support, and so long as they go with it reasonably and it works, it is called a sound hypothesis. It is an approximation and averaging of behaviors of things; it is schematic; but the glut of things that we call the objective world makes constant readjustment necessary. "The conception of the 'working hypothesis,' provisional, approximate, and merely useful, has more and more pushed aside the comfortable eighteenth century conception of 'laws of nature,'" says Bertrand Russell.[11] "Even the Newtonian dynamics, which for over two hundred years had seemed to embody a definite conquest, must now be regarded as doubtful, and as probably only a first rough sketch of the ways of matter." To Mill's [12] remark that we are not sure that any of the uniformities with which we are yet acquainted are ultimate laws; but we know that there must be ultimate laws; and that every resolution of a derivative law into more general laws brings us nearer to them, many modern scientists would reply, "We have no way of knowing scientifically that there must be ultimate laws. Perhaps we must pretend that there are ultimate laws in order to get along, but some of us are inclined to give up even the pretense."

But giving up the laws of nature is a serious business, and the red anarchies of matter and motion that might be supposed to result cannot be taken as a joke where science is concerned. The meticulous orderliness of nature would seem to be impugned, and perhaps it is. Contemporary thought suggests it.

Theories and systems, no matter how elaborate, must

be regarded as hypotheses; says John Dewey.[13] They should be accepted as bases of actions which test them, not as finalities. "To perceive this fact is to abolish rigid dogmas from the world. It is to recognize that conceptions, theories and systems of thought are always open to development through use. It is to enforce the lesson that we must be on the lookout quite as much for indications to alter them as for opportunities to assert them. They are tools. As in the case of all tools, their value resides not in themselves but in their capacity to work shown in the consequences of their use." And even matter, he continues, "is that character of natural events which is so tied up with changes that are sufficiently rapid to be perceptible, as to give the latter a characteristic rhythmic order, the causal sequence." It is all very alarming to staunch minds of a constitutionalist temper.

To it some scientists would offer naïve resistance. They would insist that science is working directly on a fixed order of reality and that complete statements of some of the forms and behaviors of those real things are theoretically possible. For them the significance of an hypothesis is its presumptive conformity with the real thing, and if there is no definite formulation and order of real things most of the discoverer's instinct and motivation in science is nullified. And science is indeed made important to the human imagination only by the assumption that it discovers "real" things and their relationships. It can never operate successfully on a purely pragmatic or a phenomenalistic basis.

There is one reconciling answer: "That saving pretense." Within its own order science can provide no ultimate being nor use, but the assumption of these underlying strata justify and authorize it. It is an unverifiable hypothesis involved in the descriptive approach to the world. Description assumes something to describe, though science cannot prove it. Like life in general, science has its presumptions of being worth while in its

own right. Scientists act as if they were discovering
material substances and eternal laws. Their whole
psychology is adjusted to that presumption. "And
having acted so," Dewey, Poincaré, the relativist schools
and others would say as an aside, "they should keep their
eyes open for a further approximation." Some fixtures are
necessary no doubt, and so is a constant flexibility, and a
tacit and practical readiness to reapproximate it.

Be they pragmatist, like Dewey, or largely neo-realist,
like Russell, or naïve materialist like Soddy, or classic
rational empiricist like Mill, or Kantian, like Pearson,
they all have some measure both of fixture and flux in
science. The question is, how much? Even Karl Pearson,
though not quite welcome in that company, can join the
chorus heartily enough: "There are two distinct meanings
to natural law," he says,[14] "the mere routine of perception, and the scientific law or formula describing the field
of nature. The 'reason' in natural law is only obvious
when we speak of law in the latter sense, and it is then
really placed there by the human mind. Thus the supposed reason behind natural law does not enable us to pass
from the routine of perceptions to anything of the nature
of reason behind the world of sense impression. . . .
Of the world outside sensation, science can only logically
infer chaos, or the absence of the conditions of knowledge;
no human concept, such as order, reason, or consciousness, can logically be projected into it." The modern
scientist tends more and more to take his hypotheses
approximately, and he asks little more of matter than
an endless occasion to readjust those approximations.

Approximations to what? Science, as science, never
answers ultimately. Its world is not built that way; it is
not of an ultimate pattern. Reason is relative; matter is
finite; description is definitive; by hypothesis science
carries no ultimates. It must rest on finalities not of its
own order. Science is not interested in ultimates. It is
concerned with the next approximation.

For science itself the world is fairly simple, penetrable and amenable to order. The terrors and ambiguities of the moon's other side are open to guesses, but this side is all that can be seen, and it is not so bad. In his own dimension of the universe the scientist finds things rather bright and lucid; he flagellates the thin waters of his world, like a paramœcium in a film of wet between two glass plates, and explores staunchly the wonders of it.

Science, says Ritchie,[15] in his study on Scientific Method, "is the process of exploring the external world." And on that naïve basis most of the advancement of scientific learning has been made. It is a tight little world in its way, as mythological almost as the ecclesiastical cosmogony of the middle ages, but nowadays far more useful.

First of all there is space and time. They have been, until recent years at least, respectively "out-thereness" and "going-alongness." They have been conceived by science as "really there"; and we, the people, the earth, etc., are thought of somehow in the interior of an infinite cube of space, and immersed somehow at a specific spot in an infinite stream of time. Then there is (or was) matter in lumps, filling space in places; and motion, which is matter moving in time. Then there are (or were) natural laws, basic dogmas whereby the many things in that material world relate themselves together.

These things can be observed through our senses; they are measurable; they are related in a rational order, and thus the two instruments of scientific discovery, reason and sensation, are universally applicable. But our experiences of that material world do not easily reveal that order. We must test them to find by repetitions, uniformities and other cues what are the more general behaviors of things and what are the more incidental. We must classify those things. We must place them in artificial isolation, or experiment, to see if our hypothesis of their rational relationships is verified by repeated observation of facts. We must observe, observe, observe, and come to general conclusions from the data involved. Thus we discover, or uncover, the rational structure of the seeming confusion of things. The world in short is a great mechanism, and the skilled scientist is a chief mechanic.

It is a neat world, as all machines must be, and it is a tidy, housewifely idea with which the scientist approaches it. If inspection of his idea shows huge interstices and blind spots, unrealized problems, and a simple trust in common sense where the plan fails, it should not be too harshly criticized. His heart has been right, if his universe hasn't; he has been no fanatic; the scientist has been willing to trust a working hypothesis; he has trusted common sense and approximations with a blind courage and industry that has yielded great results for civilization. It cannot be certain that even the most subtle intellects can carry science beyond those same authorities.

With a bit of French common sense Henri Poincaré — the greater one — may be trusted to indicate the ways of science as scientists travel them on the hard soil of everyday fact. "Trying to make science contain nature is like trying to make the part contain the whole," he says; and that is enough to restore science as a limited terrestrial program among a large number of terrestrial facts.

For all its monasticism of temper, its rigors, its repudiation of the flesh and the devil and unverified generalities science falls back a good deal on plain, unsystematic common sense. From the depths of his dungeon of specialization the scientist sometimes sees that the importance of his effort often has its ground in common sense as well as in pure science. He does not count the lady bugs on earth as his specialty — see Tolstoi and Poincaré — for two good reasons: it would not be common sense; it probably would have no general significance to science; the number of lady bugs, as Poincaré says, is capricious. The ascetic motif in science, for all its importance, must be modified now and then, if not inspired, by common sense choices.

Common sense may be characterized by an interest more in result than in method, by a confusion of categories and a success in practice. Intellectually its determining principle may be acceptance of the mode, so far as relations between sensations and reality, object and subject, phenomena and noumena and other threadbare problems are concerned. Common sense never exasperates problems, it assuages them. It is the humane compromise, and a philosopher of common sense would say that, after all, it is as near to finality as we can get by any other means. To accept the scientific world of atoms, electrons, vibrations, laws of gravity and the like, as in real relation to the sensations of sound or color through which we observe them, is a *coup d'état* of common sense that no amount of rational elaboration can verify.

On this first problem of science and of common sense, and perhaps the last, Bertrand Russell says: [16] "Physics is said to be an empirical science, based on observation and experiment. It is supposed to be verifiable, i.e. capable of calculating beforehand results subsequently confirmed by observation and experiment.

"What can we learn by observation and experiment? Nothing, so far as physics is concerned except immediate data of sense: certain patches of colour, sounds, tastes, smells, etc., with certain spatio-temporal relations.

"The supposed contents of the physical world are *prima facie* very different from these: molecules have no colour, atoms make no noise, electrons have no taste, and corpuscles do not even smell.

"If such objects are to be verified, it must be solely through their relation to sense-data: they must have some kind of correlation with sense-data, and must be verifiable through their correlation *alone*.

"But how is the correlation itself ascertained? A correlation can only be ascertained empirically by the correlated objects being constantly found together. But in our case, only one term of the correlation, namely, the sensible term, is ever found: the other term seems essentially incapable of being found. Therefore, it would seem, the correlation with objects of sense, by which physics was to be verified, is itself utterly and for ever unverifiable."

It is a long passage and none too easy to read, but it illustrates so poignantly the problem of verification that assails all science and that must be answered at last by realist, materialist and phenomenalist alike only by a common sense push, that the quotation will continue. There are two ways of avoiding this unverifiability of science, says Russell; first "We may say that we know some principle *a priori*, without the need of empirical verification. . . . It may be necessary to adopt this way to some extent, but in so far as it is adopted physics ceases to be empirical or based upon experiment and observation alone. Therefore this way is to be avoided as much as possible.

"Second: We may succeed in actually defining the objects of physics as functions of sense-data. Just in so far as physics leads to expectations, this *must* be possible, since we can only *expect* what can be experienced. And in so far as the physical state of affairs is inferred from sense-data, it must be capable of expression as a function of sense-data. . . .

"If physics is to be verifiable we are faced with the following problem: Physics exhibits sense-data as functions of physical objects, but verification is only possible if physical objects can be exhibited as functions of sense-data. We have therefore to solve the equations giving sense-data in terms of physical objects, so as to make them instead give physical objects in terms of sense-data."

He closes this essay on Sense-Data and Physics [17] with the conclusion that "no valid objection exists to the view which regards sense-data as part of the actual substance of the physical world, and that, on the other hand, this view is the only one which accounts for the empirical verifiability of physics." It is a passage vivid with the primordial problem of science and is answered by Russell, perforce, by a common sense fiat, by practical necessity, by unproved acceptance of the situation as it is.

And on similar common sense and practical grounds much of the selectivity and ordered regimens of science must be built. The basic economy of thought, the Occam's razor of science, has its common sense authority. Says Poincaré, [18] "that economy of effort which according to Mach is the constant tendency of science, is a source of beauty as well as a practical advantage. The buildings we admire are those in which the architect has succeeded in proportioning the means to the end, in which the columns seem to carry the burdens imposed on them lightly and without effort, like the graceful caryatids of the Erechtheum.

"Whence comes this concordance? Is it merely that things which seem to us beautiful are those which are best adapted to our intelligence, and that consequently they are at the same time tools that intelligence knows best how to handle? Or is it due rather to evolution and natural selection?" The selection of facts, though it may have deep reasons, also has its common sense interpretation. To this Poincaré [19] says, "The most interesting facts are those which can be used several times, those which have a chance of recurring. We have been fortunate enough to be born in a world where there are such facts. Suppose that instead of eighty chemical elements we had eighty millions, and that they were not some common and others rare, but uniformly distributed. Then each time we picked up a new pebble there would be a strong probability that it was composed of some

unknown substance. Nothing that we know of other
pebbles would tell us anything about it. Before each
new object we should be like a new-born child; like him
we could but obey our caprices or our necessities. In such
a world there would be no science, perhaps thought and
even life would be impossible, since evolution could not
have developed the instincts of self-preservation." And
later he adds, "Method is precisely the selection of facts,
and accordingly our first care must be to devise a
method."

Thus arise the regimens of science whereby the scientist guides his steps on his approach to the world. One of
them, by Pearson [20] is typical: "The scientific method is
marked by the following features: — careful and accurate
classification of facts and observation of their correlation
and sequence; the discovery of scientific laws by aid of
creative imagination; self-criticism and the final touchstone of equal validity for all normally constituted
minds." And Professor Henry Crew [21] uses a five step
march to truth: "The establishment of the facts: The
proper pigeonholing of the facts: The elimination of
self; the impersonalization of the facts: The formulation
of the facts: The prediction of new facts." There are
other careful credos to hold humanity on this narrow
path; but they all mean about the same thing. They are
partly disciplinary, partly explorative, partly classificatory. They must include reason, sense and common sense.

The result is tall hierarchies of facts, and a world
regimented with all the strictness of a thirteenth century
theology. "Scientists believe," says Poincaré,[22] "that
there is a hierarchy of facts, and that a judicious selection
can be made. They are right, for otherwise there would
be no science, and science does exist. One has only to
open one's eyes to see that the triumphs of industry,
which have enriched so many practical men, would never
have seen the light if only these practical men had existed,
and if they had not been preceded by disinterested fools

who died poor, who never thought of the useful, and yet had a guide that was not their own caprice. . . . What these fools did, as Mach has said, was to save their successors the trouble of thinking." It is a hierarchy of facts that they built which supplies in a measure that external authority and channel to popular action that the church supplied before it. Modern science, in some of its aspects, has not a little similarity to the ecclesiastical and theological systems of another age.

Order in science has reverberations in social order, and hierarchies of facts that lay a pattern on human work and life for men to follow may be harmonies and rhythms to the man of science quite regardless of their outer value. "Our mind is frail as our senses are;" says Poincaré,[23] "it would lose itself in the complexity of the world if that complexity were not harmonious; like the short sighted, it would only see the details before examining the next, because it would be incapable of taking in the whole. The only facts worthy of our attention are those which introduce order into this complexity and so make it accessible to us."

From these orders and correlations of the facts of matter and motion comes the assumption of universal mechanism, and that after all, and in spite of metaphysical cavil, is the persistent image of the world that the scientist carries with him. "A retrospect over human experience," says George Santayana,[24] "if a little extended, can hardly fail to come upon many interesting recurrences. The seasons make their round and the generations of men, like the forest leaves, repeat their career. In this its finer texture history undoubtedly repeats itself. A study of it, in registering so many recurrences leads to a description of habit, or to natural history. To observe a recurrence is to divine a mechanism. It is to analyze a phenomenon, distinguishing its form, which alone recurs, from its existence, which is irrevocable; and that the flux of phenomena should turn out, on closer inspection, to be composed of a multitude of recurring forms, regularly interwoven, is the ideal of mechanism." But mechanism must remain a divination, an unverified assumption. And so science lies sandwiched between an unverifiable hypothesis of external reality below and an unverifiable hypothesis of mechanism above. Science *per se* is definite and rational, but it is bounded by irrational beliefs.

What is science? What is the descriptive approach to the world? Where the solid rock is too far below the surface it is the habit of engineers in some cities to build rafts of concrete and pilings on which to erect their skyscrapers. Great mats of artificial stone are laid deep in the marshland clays and slime of towns such as Chicago, and on those floating platforms buildings stand.

Science is like that. It is a platform laid on primeval mire. It is a raft resting on bottomless ooze. It is sure, sound, real on the raft, and fine buildings stand there. Where the wild onion grew over the prairie and the marshland there is now a great town. But the fertile mud oozes up between the members and the principles of the raft, and the marsh grass grows around the town's periphery. Science is impressive. It is real in a most significant sense. But the wild onion grows between its beams and its stony sleepers.

Modern civilization is the town built on that concrete platform. It is a great thing, and it designates man as a constructive power. It has found precision in the ooze; it has articulated the morass. To do that is a great part of man's creative function. And what part of the world's structure he makes and what part he finds is after all an academic question. It must be considered, but it need not determine the issue.

Great problems, someone has said, are not answered,

they are forgotten. That is true of much of the shift and change of philosophy, of science and of life. The goal is reached by detour, once the problem, answered or unanswered, is no longer significant. Problems show curious deflations; their life goes. The new age will leave behind it a cemetery of dead, unanswered problems. Every age does.

Science is a creed for our thinking; it is a schedule for our world; it is a guide to living; it is an order of civilization. But the wild marsh grass still grows between the pilings.

The descriptive approach to the world has been inspected here from six angles: the ontological, science and being; the epistemological, science and knowledge; the anthropological, science in human history; the nature of description; science and hypothesis; methods and credos of science.

Science is a selective approach to the world. It is complete within its own order as the series, say, of odd numbers is complete in its order. But the odd numbers are not all of mathematics; nor is science able to accommodate the entire universe. It is but one dimension.

The Practical Approach to the World

IF MEN were motor trucks the world would be fairly simple. It would be a matter of moving or not moving. The good and the true and the real would be the moveable. The bad and the false and the unreal would be the unmoveable. One category would satisfy the motor truck. One dimension of the universe would be all there is. Explanation in a world where men were motor trucks would be an exotic groping, strange and senseless. Love would be only the insane buzzing of a car that is stalled. Thought would be motor and instinctively directive down the black line in the middle of the road. If people were motor trucks the world would be activity. It would be a field of operations and the giant stutterings of five ton cars.

Men are motor trucks. All machines are abstractions from human nature. They are specialized facilities and instruments that natural men possess. Trucks are legs for running and backs to carry burdens, and they do — and they do nothing else — what all men do some of the time. Machines are what men are, only more so, or men could not invent them. They are the ways that man works; they are specializations of himself; and the world is work for them to do.

On the eastern borders of Chicago they are mobilizing for a big job. The trucks march down from the city to the lake and countermarch upon the shore. They come out of the west side, the south side and the north side loaded with yellow soil. They go where the dredges work and their guttural grumbling is a sign of great activity. They make savage noises, sudden howlings, that clear the jungle of the streets and make a path for them to the big job.

The job is an outer boulevard, staked down a hundred yards or so from shore for miles along the city's rim. The boulevard is for more cars to go on. It will release more activity, and that in turn will need more room for operations. Huge areas of chaos are dragged into the world by motor trucks and there mobilized. The yellow dirt is piled high, and action begets more action. The truck carries a world on its back, and it makes that world by carrying it. It is many things. Its action is founded in the totality of human work.

The motor truck is steel; it is rubber; it is wood and wiring. It is timber; it is the forest and mine; it is petroleum and coal and the ancient swamps of the coal ages. It is the oil well and sunshine and stock gambling. It is concrete to travel on and hunger and war. It is Mr. Gary and the newspapers and the big job on Chicago's lake front. It is the mill and immigrant labor; it is electricity and paint and the Massachusetts Institute of Technology. All of those things are hauling dirt to the lake front today. All of those hands are pulling at the big job. This crowd of things have hit upon existence casually and with no self-questioning. Their activity is rough and uncritical, but they all are part of the truck's working power. They aggregate here in the truck's work.

Doing things is the universe from this point of view. It is motile man fusing the chaos of things into the amalgam of his nature. He is getting in his work. The world turns by his operation. What he does is what it is.

But doing has no grammar. Language is prejudiced, and telling is itself a didactic limitation of the world that is not adequate for action. Words weight the scales with their own constructions and the stuffs that they carry, if spiritual or practical, are mere suggestions in them. As a field of action the world could be realized better by a dance or by football, by making a boat or hoeing corn; and turning somersaults at this point would give the reader more accurate news of the world of action than reading ever can. Words are sedentary, but the world as a field of action permits no sitting down.

Through the reluctant medium of words the practical approach to the world suffers distortion; it is obscured, as the world of the spirit is obscured, by the rationalism of language; and the vivid toil of doing things is lost in balances and classification. If the spiritual life is being what we love and find beautiful, if science is knowing things and exposing their logical uniformities, then the practical world is working on things. It is impulse and adjustment; it is change; it is red action.

The concrete active thing that common sense calls "doing something" and boys call "something doing" runs wild in our experience. It burns with an engrossing flame. It is savage and predatory in our lives. We take it as a woman takes her cave man: it overwhelmingly is, and we don't explain it. It is all action. As an approach to reality it is not descriptive, and the scientific camera turns out only a static picture of it. Lattices of space and time are raised to catch this movement of the world, and they have value, but they remain alien nevertheless to that movement. This mobilized reality goes too fast for our descriptive schedules.

Acting on the world implies, not primarily a set of fixed fact data as in science, but a world plastic and shifting, where reality is more the action and the ends in action than the facts involved in their attainment. Acting finds a new dimension of the world and of experience. It warns us, says Dewey, "against the tradition which makes the objects of a certain kind of experience, the cognitive, the fixed standard for estimating the 'reality'and import of all other kinds of things.[1] "

It is the native activity of this highly moveable creature called man that is involved. It is impulsive restlessness deep in the nature and instability of protoplasmic things. It is not explainable, for explaining is something else again. It may be forsaken and lost in the spiritual life but its unity is never spiritual. It hangs together, as James says,[2] by space and motor continuities, by influence or acquaintances, but in its heart it has no structural organization after the order of science. In its own nature it is explosive, urgent, irrational. That is the practical approach to the world.

In the Soudan twelve thousand men are working on the Makwar dam. They are going deep into native rock for its foundations. They will make it deep and tall to hold the Nile for a few months each year. The dam will save the floods for the slow rinsing of the roots of cotton plants that will grow there. It will be a million tons of masonry placed tenderly in the strategic place. It will provide for 855 kilometres of small canals and 90 kilometres of large ones. They will reach fingers of water into the desert and bring back cloth and spinning mills. It all is significant work. The lives of many human beings will find through it a redirection.

The Soudan dams are stones laid in an African river bed, but every stone there will lie on Louisiana; every rivulet will wash away a cotton plant in Alabama. They say to England, "Independence in cotton," and to America, "diversified farming, smaller plantations, more farm owners and more skill in southern agriculture." The first is the teleology of the dam, its pragmatic cause; the second, whether planned or not, should follow as a consequence.

Reality, whatever it may be, is involved in purpose for the practical man, and truth to his common sense, is significance. What he believes is what he can test in operation, and the feeling of belief, as Charles S. Peirce says, "is a more or less sure indication of there being established in our nature some habit that will determine our actions." [3] For the practical man the world has the plasticity of things that are more or less adjustable to his interests, and the indifferent absolutes of reason have small cogency. For him truth is plastic; reality is plastic. The one may be made, unmade, remade by the shift and exigency of his need, and change is ever re-stating the other according to the flux of human purpose. Truth in the abstract, and relative to no purpose, is plainly unmeaning, says F. C. S. Schiller, in his essay, The Making of Truth.[4] "For it never becomes even a claim, and is never tested, and cannot therefore be validated." From the point of view of action the world is based on teleology. It always looks beyond. That it looks just beyond, that it is a mediate teleology, not ultimate, makes it no less purposive by nature.

This motorized universe hangs always on the mile just ahead. It is always rolling into the just beyond. Its sufficiency in this minute can hardly be realized without reference to the next minute. Its uniformity is change itself, and its significance lies in utilizing that change, or selecting it, and coördinating it with human need. Needs are vague symbols of man's biological instability. They never are far from the cosmic shift and change that we call process, organic and inorganic. They are a falling forward like a baby walking; their present is impossible; their future is a hope; but they never fall down. A world that moves on is always real in the next moment.

Presumably the process of adjustment to the world is what we mean by action, and if the world significant to the practical man is just that action, one term, i. e., the world adjusted to, would seem to be ignored. That is a sophistry no doubt that common sense and pragmatists can scorn, but it leaves a question of some size for those who do not accept "action" with the naïve and ecstatic confidence that some pragmatists possess.

Ours is an action intelligence, says Delton Howard

with pragmatic staunchness, "and thought is immersed in struggle." It is the shift and thrusting of a constant readjustment, and it finds in action all man's needs and meaning, the realization of his purpose, the working out and evolution of his natural design. Beyond the froth and storm of man's multiple activities, say pragmatists, all things are insignificant and to that degree unreal. They freeze. They are abstract and static. For life lies in the adjusting process, and reality is the bearing and significance of things upon that vital dynamism.

That there may be a "primary reality" even for pragmatists and their allies, the humanists, is admitted, however, by Schiller. Fact in the wider sense, he says, covers everything. Its existence is undeniable. It is the starting point and final touchstone of all our theories *about* reality. It may be "called 'independent of us,' if that comforts any one. For it is certainly not 'made' by us, but 'found.' But as it stands, we find it most unsatisfactory and set to work to remake it and unmake it. And it cannot possibly be taken as 'real fact' or 'true reality.' For, as immediately experienced, it is meaningless chaos, merely the raw material of a cosmos, the stuff out of which real fact is made. Thus the need of operating on it is the real justification of our cognitive procedures." [4]

But these reluctant subtleties come from the pragmatist not in the true spirit of the men of action whose philosophical delegate he is, and the pragmatist prefers not to display them. Activity simply taken is enough. It is adjustment to the world, and the adjustment of the world to him. It involves a set of proximate ends, a concern in the use of things within the scope of his action with no concern in the eventualities of the final result. That is the attitude of the practical man towards the world. It is a world without logical completeness for it is set not on a rational plane but on a plane of action. But the fulness that he finds in continuous action compensates for intellectual indifference. As an attitude to-

wards the world it is as legitimate as any other. The
spirit, science, action: fulfillment, discovery, creation;
they are three ways of human experience and three
dimensions of a rich and pregnant reality.

A German shepherd dog is as restless as water. His
ears are cocked and his stride up and down the beach is
lean and wolfish. He spatters through the ebb of a wave
and hurdles a high timber; he is going somewhere. And
then, for no reason other than his own activity he turns,
and is going somewhere else.

Business is business for the German shepherd dog. He
allows no outside criteria, sentiments, ultimate ends, rewards to complicate his clean activity and running. Action for action's sake seems to be his interest, and to treat
that action merely as a preface to an ultimate arrival
impugns its wolfish beauty and worth-whileness, and it
approaches drudgery. It is here that the German shepherd dog and the man of action verge upon the spiritual
life. They find immediacy of value in action.

This restless beauty is usually ignored in critical accounts of western civilization and of America. The
consummations that shepherd dogs and business men
find in activity itself are not noted. Only the purposive
aspect of action, adjustment and more adjustment, is
apparent to the casual critic. And that to him is life
imperfect and unfulfilled, subjected to utilities and
spiritually unfinished. To him it all is either progress or
perfection, and he is likely to hold with Count Keyserling [5] in the Travel Diary of a Philosopher, that a per-
fected lower form is nearer to God than a higher imperfect
one. The Westerner, says the philosophic Count, "has
abdicated his life in favor of a means to it."

This is true, and Keyserling's extenuating remark
that the magnitude of western effort, the attempt to

extend higher perfections to the masses of men, renders
our incompleteness less odious, cannot soften the raw
tin edges of our civilization and the savageries of many of
our points of view. And when he says, "The more I
see of the East the more unimportant the type of modern
Westerner seems to me," there is no answer, if it seems
that way.

As a self-denying civilization our democracies of the
West have not been all that was once hoped of them.
They have denied high perfection to the few, and for
the love of human kind they have extended to all men
the hope of a higher consummation of life than any other
system offered. They sacrificed the perfections of the
few to chaotic progress of the many; and they assumed,
perhaps rightly, that the loss of those perfections was
less a loss in absolute civilization than a deprivation in
comforts, prestige and personal expression of a few
individuals. It was levelling a few persons and upsetting
others for the sake of many; it was done for love of men
and free activity, but the results are less lovely and less
free no doubt than the founders hoped. With the growth
of standardized industrial production and the concentration of capital it is a question whether democracy will
not be devoured by its own offspring. The threat to
human liberty and love is real, and what many other
systems gave up at the beginning, the West may be forced
to give up by its own development. Can free activity for
all men be maintained? The West at least still tries to
answer.

It is this free activity that Westerners find beautiful
in their life. It is the simple joy of action, nomadry and
adventure. It is the restless sense of living that the
shepherd dog, the cowboy, the bond salesman, the
structural steel worker, the business man find worth
while. And it is this consummation in activity that
critics rarely note in western civilization. It is primitive;
it has few sublimities perhaps; it has unquestionably

instrumental implications; it is pedestrian and massive; but to Westerners it does have that worth while aspect. Observers should see that Westerners do find finality of a sort in their civilization. That finality is action.

But their action nevertheless is based tacitly on the assumption that there is an end of action. Within itself action may attain finality of being in a sense, but it never can escape wholly its external implications and becoming. It is plainly designed for ends beyond itself and an aimless wagging of a tail or a violent but function-less trotting about by dog or business man is rarely the consummation most desired. Action hangs on a hook. It has an end beyond itself. And in the practical world the end of action is more likely an opportunity for more action. The ultimate universe for the German shepherd dog is more release in action. It pyramids, and the world becomes a system of tacit or articulate instrumentalities in which fixed perfection or completeness would destroy the need for action and be evil.

Biologically there can be no fixed adjustment of living things to their environment. Routines may develop, it is true, and new problems every day may be very like the old. Monotonies and ease may settle tropically over living things; but fixed adjustment is impossible. Life is assimilative; it must move or die, and the pragmatists, shepherd dogs, business men and men of action generally, know it. The practical approach to the world is found in the essential mobility of living things — perhaps of all things.

"Progress," "onward and upward," and many of the idealizations of "evolution" current in the nineteenth century, are founded on these eternities of action. They assume that actions are adjustments to this world that leave immortal residues of success behind them and build up slowly a delta of human triumph that is there to stay. Actions build for good and all, and they always keep on building. That is pleasant to believe and it is partly true. It is an hypothesis that justifies achievement, and it satisfies in some measure man's persistent yearning for finality. Even if it be a gracious trick to stimulate activity, it is not so bad; for pure activity may have æsthetic and final worth in the dance, in sports, in other actions, but it can hardly be a permanent and continuous aim in the practical man. "Progress" and such war cries as a "bigger, better town" provide ulterior authorities for action that no doubt are necessary in the long grind of years. They are virtual compulsions, and their truth is obvious in various fields limited in extent but many in number. They enforce continuous action.

This restlessness of life, warped by Americans into "progress" and other optimisms and by Hindus, Schopenhauer and others into vain and dismal pressures of illusion, blind, morose will and like unpleasantnesses, has a basis deep in nature. Animate things survive only by persistent encroachment on the frontiers of their natural neighbors, and when an individual or a species no more expands its field the omens for its survival are none too good. Behind the restlessness and action of human beings is this biological imperialism.

Living creatures command what things they can, animate and inanimate, within their reach. And they reach for all that they can assimilate. "When a restaurant concern sells over 42,000,000 griddle cakes a year," as an advertisement claims, "it means something:" It means that man is commanding his environment, including griddle cakes, to his own uses. It means that his demands are great and continuous and that the "turnover" in the process of physical and social metabolism is rapid. It means that the activities involved in providing griddle cakes and other human necessities must be continuous and on a large scale. They reach out and conquer. They utilize the conquest. "Progress," continuous action, the practical life in general are never far from expanding frontiers and the elemental thrust of nature's imperialism.

The gang's job is to fill barrels with pitch, pass them by two men who nail the hoops in place, and roll them into position in the storage yard. The place is an oil refinery, and one of the workers, Whiting Williams, says, "Hour after hour in the hottest sun of this summer my job was to roll every barrel — hundreds of them, each weighing about 500 pounds — over the rough gravel; then worst of all, to 'bung it up' — turn it and twist it and tug it into its place, always with its freshly inserted bung up to prevent leaking. The job is no snap for a beginner and his bare hands — there is a lot of knack in it which no one can get the first day. When my temples began to drum hard and my mouth to fill full of cotton so that I felt a few minutes in the shade might barely save me from sunstroke, I asked my Polish foreman about changing places with one of those in the shade at easier jobs. In a surly voice I was refused any change and any rest — the barrels would pile up and stop the line even as I spoke." [6]

This average job is a kind of activity hardly measurable in terms of "vital release," "expression in activity" and the like. Billions of men have worked at jobs like these through all the ages and have found life endurable under them if not happy; reality unquestionable though harsh; and truth a grim pressure on their lives like a hard and heavy rider on a tired horse. They have gone the slow route of work. Their action is set to a rigid channel and the course of it is not in their control. It is not easy, day in and day out, to find æsthetic value in rolling barrels of pitch, but this is the life of action and its meaning to most men in the world. To those suited by training and by heredity for a lifetime of action such as this it is tolerable no doubt though tiresome. It is an

approach to the world under the pressure of a problem —
survival — that lays on them harsh compulsions.

This is the world of action to the uncritical man of
common sense. It is doing something that must be done.
It is a muscular universe; it is kinæsthetic; and the problem to be answered states itself in simple terms of things
to be changed somehow to suit somebody's purpose.

Problems of action rest on our confidence in these
naïve categories of the practical life. There are things to
be done and there is pay (other things done) for doing
them. Faith in human responsibility is here uncritical.
Although the job of rolling barrels of pitch is externally
directed, there is still the assumption that the action
of the man who takes the job and rolls the barrels is
internally directed in so far as he stays on the job. That
naïve confidence in a man's freedom to solve his own
practical problems is a real ingredient in the modern
industrial and social system. It is assumed that the man
who prefers survival and rolling barrels to starvation
and not rolling them is making a free choice. It assumes
that a man who has an inherited wealth, educational
experience or hereditary equipment sufficient only to roll
barrels and who persistently chooses to roll barrels to
keep alive is responsible for his place in life. His hardships are rated somehow as penalties justified by his
failure to choose to be better off than he is. That sentiment underlies most of the "hard boiled" moral philosophies of our day. A purely biological approach to
the problems of practical life would be different. It
might be more predestinational, but it would assess
no blame. It would accept all effort and aspiration, but
it would lay the cause for widespread human hardship
and failure less to man's choice and blunder than to a
complex of environmental and physical factors. It would
lay the cause largely to the system in which it is implicated. Behaviorism would introduce strange complications into the world of "common sense."

But behaviorism notwithstanding, it is doubtful if far reaching scientific uniformities can ever be discovered in human affairs. They are found in a measure in the psychological laboratory and insurance tables, and their application to human problems is important; but a thoroughgoing, scientific de-humanization of human activity would seem to be impossible. Factors are involved not subject to organization or measurement. The movement of industry towards de-humanization, towards quantity production, piece work, scientific management, absentee ownership, control by financiers, impersonal organization has its advantages and its production value, but it has also its human limits of toleration. History shows that the external direction of human action has limits of toleration that often are disastrously abrupt.

The practical problems of life are many and various, and work for a living is not the only one in which men are concerned. In a normally happy life there must be much free activity directed by interests other than direct economic necessity, and rules moral and otherwise are devised for the protection of it. The conflict between science and religion that rages here and there from Tennessee to Burmah is neither a religious nor a scientific problem but a practical question in regard to the suppression of free activity. Morals are problems of free practice. Government, eugenics, foreign debts, birth control, questions of practical policy march by, day after day. They are common sense problems. They are things to be done or not to be done. They relate to action. They are all kites in one wind.

On the restless shifting of human activities, interests, diversities, there is a persistent effort to impose a traffic system. Through streets, stop-go signs, one way lanes, safety islands, and traffic control officers seem to be necessary in these anarchies of action. Governments, social institutions, codes and conventions are formed — presumably not from above but from within — in order to protect so far as possible the freedom of human action from internecine conflict and destruction. Symmetries of action are developed, order and social rhythm, that save human effort and free activity from mutual nullification. On a planet too small for the human race, a people bred through the ages to a semi-isolated life — a life roughly in family groups with a well nigh infinite periphery of wilderness to absorb their excess life and action — finds itself suddenly constricted to a small sized satellite of the sun, growing hugely in numbers and crowding in vast herds upon more favored sections of the earth. It raises a comparatively new problem for the race to answer. It is a new test of survival. And it remains something of a question whether man, equipped with the instincts and conventions of an old and thinly settled world, can meet it.

Can man maintain a modicum of free activity in this crush and restlessness of life? Power, modern or ancient, demo' or autocratic, rests on this demand for free activity. Whether it be the president of the steel trust or a mob of peasants with their scythes, whether it be Napoleon or Tim Murphy of the gas workers' union, the drive for power is for free activity. And the problem of this much congested human race and of practical civilization is to correlate the activities of all men and to control and redirect the activities of some men so that a maximum of free activity for all people will be preserved from mutual anarchy and predatory individuals. Society is stronger than Napoleon; it should use that gentleman but keep him, like all good servants, in his place.

The chaos and "turnover" of experience, the turmoil of concrete things and complexities is the natural field of human power and action. Into that field man carries a motley assortment of weapons, instruments, instincts and the like designed at some time or another to help him out. In his knapsack he has love and a garden rake, joy and a piebald horse, a Winchester and a stink bomb, a spectroscope and a book of Byron. It is a great battle that he fights with them, and he somehow muddles through.

For action after all is what the practical man wants most, and action he can get with diverse instruments. The practical man and his world are an operative unit. They are, so to speak, one operation.

Florida's real estate not long ago became interesting. The white shell sands of her beaches began to clink and rattle with gold. The cabbage palms raised fronds, as green as bank notes, to the sun. Miami, Tampa, Myers, Lauderdale and others climbed close to big business, and "realtors," and "estators," as they call themselves, began the day in Fords and ended it in Lincolns. "Turn-over" was the big idea, action and more action, and lands that sold for $100.00 an acre three years before went for $3000.00 an acre and more. As an operation the world of Florida's practical men became highly successful.

This rather frantic clutching, this pyramiding of operation on operation, is often called the world of common sense. It is a world largely of things that "just are"; and though belief obviously has a part, as it must in all operations of any complexity, the unremote things dominate the situation. "Some things," says Dewey, "things of action and suffering, are not matters of belief at all, they just are." [7] That at least is the practical man's point of view. Whether it be Florida real estate or the battle of Manila, that directness is characteristic of all fields of action.

"Why should we smile at the inscription in West-

minster Abbey which calls the inventor of the spinning-
jenny one of the *true* benefactors of mankind?" says
George Santayana.[8] "Is it not probable, on the whole,
that he has had a greater and less equivocal influence
on human happiness than Shakespeare with all his plays
and sonnets? But the cheapness of cotton cloth produces
no particularly delightful image in the fancy to be compared with Hamlet or Imogen. There is a prodigious
selfishness in dreams: they live perfectly deaf and in-
vulnerable amid the cries of the real world."

In the long warfare between dream and reality men
of action are consistent workers for reality, and they
rarely note, perhaps, that the main difference between
dreams and the real world is in perspective. To the man
of action the pertinency of things, their nearness in
perspective, is their reality, and what affects his action
is most pertinent. For him reality is wrought on the
anvil of action, and whether it be the spinning-jenny or
Imogen, that is the test. "The real external world,"
says F. C. S. Schiller, "is the pragmatically efficient
parts of our total experience, to which the inefficient
parts such as dreams, fancies, illusions, after images,
etc., can for most purposes be referred."[9] We create
reality, he says, as a consequence of making truth. And
we make truths in the red forge of action and human
need.

To be told that his job, among other industrial pur-
suits, is to manufacture truths and to build realities may
cause some protest on the part of the practical man who
accepts one cosmos officially and puts it away like a
diploma, and who acts in quite another. For reality in
the practical sense is pertinent reality. It is the next
thing to do, or something near it. It is the thing that
bears on action. And in action he recognizes it simply
enough and takes it without question. But he is more
than likely to reserve a corner in the parlor for a framed
and glass covered diploma written in stately terms and

relating to remote and static absolutes that affect him little and interest him not at all. It is furniture; he does his work outside.

Effective reality — and to the practical man why suggest more — is whatever relates to his action. It means that the "knowing" of descriptive science, is not the sole authority for the real, nor perhaps the best authority. For "*being* and *having* things in ways other than knowing them, in ways never identical with knowing them, exist, and are pre-conditions of reflection and knowledge," says Dewey,[10] and "all cognitive experience must start from and must terminate in being and having things in just such unique, irreparable and compelling ways."

The effective test of reality for the man of action is not in knowing and analysis. For him reason is not an ultimate criterion; it is functional and is right if it works. "Any idea upon which we can ride, so to speak; any idea that will carry us prosperously from any one part of our experience to any other part, linking things satisfactorily, working securely, simplifying, saving labor; is true for just so much, true in so far forth, true *instrumentally*," says James.[11] And that, the working of a true idea, is its validity.

For the man of action, including advertisers, the truth would seem to be a practical matter. Every judgment, says Schiller,[12] is essentially an experiment, which to be tested, must be acted on. And even perception, for these humanists, is implicated in man's mobility. "By perceiving the same," says Schiller,[13] "I mean only perceiving in such a way that we can act together." They go all down the line: Truth, perception, judgment, reality, belief, all refer to action as their test and authority. In that world action rises like Popocatepetl above the Aztec plain. For the man of action, action is as ultimate as anything may be in this non-ultimate world. And beliefs themselves, says Charles S. Peirce,[14] are rules for action; the meaning of a thought, the function of reason is in the conduct it is fitted to produce.

The brothers Van Sweringen, railroad mixers, reported profits of $16,000,000 not long ago on the proposed, and later prohibited, Nickel Plate line merger. They anticipated the federal plan for railroad group consolidations and made one of their own. They built a railroad block of lines from Michigan to Norfolk. They absorbed the Pere Marquette and the C. and O.; and though they cut across the scientific federal plan for merging, it is not unlikely that their work had some worth, if not $16,000,000 worth, to American transportation. It was activity, and like all human and purposive activity, it was in some sense creative.

To the man of action, and to all men in their active moods, this is a world that will not take care of itself. It is a world that may go wrong for him; it may fall out of adjustment; and only his action remains to set it right. There is risk behind all action. There is a presumptive uncertainty in all situations that makes action significant and hypothetically worth while. And in this the man of action finds his zest and pertinacity.

This situation need not be universalized, as it is so effectively by John Dewey in Experience and Nature, to persuade the common sense of its cogency. Action always probes an incompleteness; it rides on risk, and its outcome, if worth while, is something that we were not sure to have before. "The conjunction of problematic and determinate characters in nature renders every existence, as well as every idea and human act, an experiment in fact, even though not in design," says Dewey [15] in his essay on Existence. "To be intelligently experimental is but to be conscious of this intersection of natural conditions so as to profit by it instead of being at its mercy."

To the man of action the world is the organization of human success. It is under him, like a pyramid on which his life may succeed in laying one new stone. He must take much uncritically; for what he uses and the instruments that he works with must be left to unanalyzed common sense; but the pyramid is somehow under him. He works in the confidence that successful action is cumulative, and that things once made to suit human purpose will in a measure stay made. His conquests of risk are measurably permanent. The practical approach to the world is creative, relatively, in its ever new adjustments to liquid human purpose and in its building out of risks and gambles and necessities what was not sure before. If the spirit, in humanistic metaphor, is fulfillment; if science is discovery; then action in this sense is creative. The man of action organizes success. With the world as his raw material he creates to suit his need.

The world of action is discrete and separative. It is an aggregate of problems, and its realities vary according to the problem uppermost. Here five problems have crowded to the top of the discussion. They are: the world as a field of action; the essential mobility of human adjustments; the naïve world of human problems; the imposition of system on shifty events; reality to the man of action. But action after all is only action. It is no orator, though it speaks louder than words. It is inarticulate, and efforts to explain it are rightfully thankless. A few hand springs by the reader would be more persuasive than any amount of printed paper put before him.

CHAPTER SEVENTEEN

The World in General

THE compass dips and whirls aimlessly in a new steel ship and good navigators never trust it. They know its taste for iron things, and they have learned to doubt its steadfastness for the finalities of the pole when local iron is about. They study its inconstancies, and they define its errors by careful collaboration with the stars. In port they turn the ship on every bearing, sight with their peloruses at landmarks, and write down rows of figures. They fix large compensating balls of iron in exact places nearby to hold the needle right.

The philosopher in man tries the same thing, for man is an iron ship, full of new wiring and dynamos and strange machinery, and a compass must be well adjusted to escape his various deflections. For ages philosophers have tried to set the needle on the pole. They have assured us that there is a pole and that the needle yearns to point there. They have asked dramatically, why otherwise the compass, why the voyage, and why the problem of a world in general? And everyone in his capacity as a philosopher has tried to solve it for himself. Theologians have tried it. Scientists have tried it. The Greeks set reason free from man's deflections — or tried to — Euclid organized geometry; the moderns set matter free. Regardless of the twists and turns of man's course, here are logical and mechanical systems, they said, that are constant. But their constancy is artificial. It is abstract, and nature does not wholly justify it.

Those endless processes of fission and separate development whereby man has built up intellectual institutions have been justified no doubt in great results. By abstracting them from human context men have solved problems, but they have made them too. Specialization, of which science, logic, mathematics, mechanics, are examples, has never helped him much in his primary problem, the world in general. For the human context, after all, is not entirely escaped by them. Man cannot get off the ship, no matter what machinery he builds down in the hold and on the decks; and the world in general must be somewhere on the ship's horizon. A perfect philosopher man can never be, for such a perfect one, presumably, could observe reality from no point of view at all. He could see things perfectly in general; he could take them from all sides. That for god or man would seem to be no view; and it would still remain a question whether reality from no point of view at all would be reality.

What is the problem of the world in general? It is an attitude more than a demand for answers. It is a situation, on which our interest impinges concretely, and that still bears within itself what we call reality and the stuff of things in general. It is man inarticulate, looking east against the sun, facing the waves on open water or a thundrous wind, far more than an equation and a matter of proof. The "problem" of the world in general is a rather wordless affair, less of knowing than of intimation.

For the conventional continuities of philosophy and science, of cognition and observation, cannot be very useful in integrating fields, like science, action, the spirit, which either include those continuities as structural parts or exclude them as alien to their natures. Continuity is itself a specific kind of order, and the neat arrangements of things into universal wholes so common among philosophers and scientists take no account of worlds to which progressive order is a stranger. The problem of the world in general is not mainly one of continuity; it is a problem of reality.

Not the relativities and tools and continuities of the world so much as the nuclear stubbornness of things that we call real, their importunities and assertion, is the prob-

lem of the world in general. For reality is a grand word,
but only a word, so long as it remains a kind of grand-
mother of all symbols, or a queen piece in the chess of the
universe. It must forego those formal restrictions and
equations. It must accept the inflations and the depths,
the harsh possessiveness of real things. It must leave the
exchange counter and the clearing house and debate
directly with the soil and the winds of being. Then the
word, reality, will be more adequate.

For that is the nature of the problem. It is concrete
and informal. It presses an undefined mass upon us. It
is turgid with possibilities. The problem of the world in
general is a problem of the real, but reality is no terse
word set up for definition. It cannot be spelled in a
spelling book. It is a lifetime of meaning, and the problem
that raises it may well be the situation that exposes its
nature and significance in each man's life. For problems
are like chemical combinations; their ingredients are
diverse and sometimes accidental but their results may
be the exposure, if not the creation, of things hitherto
unknown. They raise realities, and the problem of the
world in general is no exception. "By the union and conflict of two very different human impulses, the one
urging men towards mysticism, the other urging them
towards science," says Bertrand Russell,[1] "the attempt
to conceive the world as a whole by means of thought
has been developed." That haphazard synthesis is metaphysics, and for us the outcome of the situation is wonder
and reality. It is everyone's problem and the meditations
on reality inherent in it inhabit every mind.

The thickness of that problem, its primordial significance in all affairs is its justification. It is limited for
us by human definitions. It is involved in a human
context, like the sea in our nets, and its reticulations are
important to us, but wherever the nets may reach there
will be always the sea and more sea under them. "Reality " says Santayana [2] "is being of any sort." And though

the poet-philosopher defines one word in terms of another his meaning is clear: Reality is no lone abstraction. However the problem of the world in general may develop, wherever the compass at last may point, reality will not be failing to enforce it.

The search for a field of reference whereon the shifting elements of human experience, things, contingent events may be placed and coördinated has led many a philosopher to labor on this world in general with a good deal of hope. It is a problem in philosophical location, and the classical demand for external absolutes, ultimate organizations, supreme laws and monitors is inspired by the same locative needs that move the physicist in another field to demand absolute space, time, an absolute "now," a fixed world stuff.

But an absolute point of reference for the philosopher is perhaps no more within hope than it is for the physicist, and whatever metaphysical location the philosopher may have will hardly be expressed in terms of relations to an ultimate point or reality. For reference and relation are possible only in a special field of logical hypotheses. They are mediate terms and a world of ultimate relations or of references to absolutes destroy themselves with their own weapons. The philosopher's impulse to locate himself metaphysically is sound, and his impulse to build a world in general for that purpose is praiseworthy; but his instruments are inadequate and his ultimate notion of a neat universal organism is hardly commensurate with the wild intensity and scope of being and the deserts and disorder, the burning and pressures of real things.

Men are impressed by their own insecurity and listlessness; they are aware of the contingency and flight of things that they observe; and they ask: Is there nothing in terms of which we can express all these relative things? Is there no way of determining a point beyond our own gyrations? Is there no monument of finality and courage fixed in the middle of this city square?

The answer is: No, so far as external ultimates are
concerned. Time has no goal. Space has no focus.
Organized personality has no final consummation.
Events in philosophy as in physics are only relatively
measurable; and the affairs and importances of living,
the flux of experience, the things and importunities that
we name this, that and the other cast no shadows on the
eternal walls of the universe; for there are no walls.
Those comprehensive absolutes that some philosophers
like to build are buildings only of words. They are huge
cellular systems that toil not nor spin; they are useless
supernumeraries in the worlds of action and of science;
they are abhorrent to the spirit. They rise like vague and
wasted steam from the workings of reason, for their
futility and failure as a final standard of reference is
guaranteed by the nature of the rationalism that produces
them. They come at a wish for stability, but they have
the wrong answer. They are asked somehow to ease a
restlessness, to find fulfillment; for the world always
wants it. But the unsymmetrical series, the progressions
to eternity, the Aristotelian climaxes, the theocratic
organons of Aquinas, the various systematic compre-
hensions of the philosophers cannot fulfill anything but a
depleted vocabulary. Being is fulfillment, and being
cannot be fully comprehended in a rational process. It
overlaps process and organism; it breaks through fences.
Real things have many categories, of which rational
and scientific hypotheses are only one.

Life, says Santayana,[3] is the fixation of points of interest in the flux of things. It is the establishment of
preferences. It is the creation of points of view. And so
far as points of reference are concerned this is about all
man can rightfully find. The sweeping and inclusive
absolutes that philosophers and theologians manufacture
are synthetic goods. They lack the sting and authority
of the real thing.

Reality is not an organized corporation, and the

problem of reality and of the world in general is not a bartering in logic or the proving of a mathematical proposition. "Completed" worlds are not fulfillments of activities and research, but their death. Perfect being, as Dewey suggests,[4] is in this sense the fruit only of our desires. It is an hypothesis deeply involved in the mechanics of activity and of science, and were those workings once "to arrive," and to stop in the arrival, the hypothesis as well as the "perfection" would be no more. External absolutes, perfections, ultimate organizations, final fields of reference may be well forgotten. They are quaint unrealities. What of the real?

What the real is may well be forever unknown; for problems rise — as Moore says — local and specific, to question vivid findings made already by another path. *That* the real is can hardly be less than our confidence in living, nor less than the ground of all our acts, assertions and thinking. It is a presence and an authority in things that cannot be denied. It abides somehow like coolness in the air, like life in a young body, and though the skeptic says, "I cannot touch it; I cannot fix it here alone for further notice," all persons, skeptics included, admit its validity. Through it the skeptic gazes innocently, as through a pane of pure glass, and says, "It is not there"; and the purer the glass, the more assured is his remark. For in applying his category of doubt to all things — doubts systematic and progressive, doubts persistent and doctrinaire — the sceptic is not ungearing the universe; he is merely shifting it into reverse; and the gears mesh, the pistons dance their old rhythms, the carburetor takes its small drinks of gasoline and air quite as before. The machinery of skepticism is rather complicated. It is built on naïve faith in doubt. It is built on faith in the power of reason to penetrate and perhaps discredit reality. It rests on hypotheses and presumptions. It assumes orders and methodologies for the sake of getting somewhere (backward) that it cannot prove, and dare not doubt, if it means to continue doubting. Carried far enough skepticism can be only silence. It must close its eyes and be nothing, for that is the only resistance possible against the pressures and command of real things. Silence is the skeptic's only ultimatum.[5] The things that are real ride in and know him not at all.

For all experience means reality; all thought looks towards it, and human knowledge tangles and festoons across its shoulders like cobwebs along an early morning path. Some call it objective, independent; some, experimental. Dewey says:[6] "An experience is cognitional, which is contemporaneously aware of meaning something beyond itself. Both the meaning and the thing meant are elements in the same situation. . . . One is present as not-present-in-the-same-way-in-which-the-other-is. . . . We may say that the smell of a rose, when involving conscious meaning or intention, is mental." But real things break through fences and definements like goats through woven wire. They are impressive, stubborn. They are resentful of halters and guide ropes. They are capricious inwardly, and their assertions and their whims for being have no rational design. Their sole authority is themselves.

The real is the commandment in things. It inspires their eagerness and expectation; it is their consummation and the end of reason, of common sense, of activity, of uses and natural process. In Mr. Dewey's terrifying cognitional rose that smells not-present-in-the-same-way-in-which-the-other-is there is the bud of completeness; in the roar and threshing of the Twentieth Century Limited on its way to New York there is a kind of consummation. In the inarticulate realness of things there is, rightly or wrongly, the sole answer to their subjections and uncertainties. There is fulfillment sought. Experiences wait like flowers for its fertilizations; all meaning and significance rest in it.

Under the knife of analysis reality seeps away like life blood. Under the prod of questions it has no answer. It is silent, though its voice is the only sound in the world. It says nothing, though every person hears it. It roars forever like the waves; it says all that has been said or ever will be said; it is as still as the sky. In a single silence ultimate assuredness and ultimate doubt can sit down together and make no conversation. Complete insight by either way is the same silence.

What reality is may well be beyond our knowledge. But here it is. It is eternally present. It is profoundly here. Questions and doubts ripple over it like small waves on the sea.

What things are increases our museums of facts, but these aid none too much in the problem of reality and the world in general. They are the infantries of system and analysis, and they capture only collective and antique absolutes. They are specifications and methods; they are science and use, reason and relativities, but they are not fulfillments. "Methods may be turned into metaphysics by accepting them as ultimates," says F. C. S. Schiller.[7] And if he means that the defining activity by which we determine methods and specify *what* things are cannot be made an ultimate and adequate occasion for reality, he said, as the boys of late say, something. For methods are functional. They are instruments that make poor metaphysics. Their eternities are hardly adequate.

But it remains, no less, that well travelled approaches to the world, science, the spirit, action, which in part at least are founded on method and categorical orders, are adequate as methods only to the extent that they accept themselves as ultimates. To take them, from within, as contingent methods might well disintegrate them, for their authority depends much on their inner completeness, or the assumption of it, and their self-determination.

To themselves they are world orders; but the "within-ness" of their finality may save them from ancient failure and philosophical artifice. For if methods become metaphysical by accepting them as ultimates, it is no less true that ultimates may be dehydrized like dried apples by specifying them as methods. It counts both ways, and both are dangerous. Applying creeds of any sort from the outside is unsafe, and the abiding reality in things, their inner authority and presence, may be befogged by rituals and methodologies and too much asking, *what?*

Thought corrupts reality, and when a man, as A. E. Taylor, says [8]: "The work of thought or knowledge in making our world more intelligible to us essentially consists in the progressive analysis of a content or *what*, considered in abstraction from the *this* to which it belongs," he names in that abstraction the executioner of reality and spirit and designates the date, place and method of the execution. Silence is nearer the real than words and analysis, and on ontological and spiritual grounds alone there can be no reason adequate to excuse discussion of it. Though poetry may suggest reality and music bear the burden of it on its shoulders, sounds and symbols are inadequate. Silence is nearer, as death is nearer than life to birth and eternal creation.

Where reality is the problem, truth, an amanuensis, and knowledge, a maid servant, are not first in interest. Real things are many; we may know what they specifically are; we may find truths and diverse things. But the reality of them is not many: no substance, says Spinoza,[9] is divisible. Reality is gratuitously here; but no one can say what it is. It is the world in general.

Reality like Gaul has three parts, says William James[10] in a heroic effort to complete his conquest of truth, absolute and relative, and to send back a victor's terse report. The first part of reality is the flux of our sensations. They "are forced upon us, coming we know not whence. Over their nature, order and quantity we have as good as no control. *They* are neither true nor false; they simply *are*."

The second part of reality is the "*relations* that obtain between our sensations or between their copies in our minds." They also require our beliefs obediently to take account of them. They have two sub-parts: the relations that are mutable and accidental, as those of date and place; and those that are fixed and essential because they are grounded on the inner natures of their terms. "Both sorts of relations," says James, "are matters of immediate perception. Both are 'facts.' But it is the latter kind of fact that forms the more important sub-part of reality for our theories of knowledge. Inner relations namely are 'eternal,' are perceived whenever their sensible terms are compared; and of them our thought — mathematical and logical thought so-called — must eternally take account."

The third part of reality, says James, is the previous truths of which every new inquiry takes account. It is a less obdurate part of reality and often ends by giving way. But "however fixed these elements of reality may be," says James in outlining the structure of his pragmatism, "we still have a certain freedom in our dealings with them. Take our sensations. *That* they are is undoubtedly beyond our control, but *which* we attend to, note, and make emphatic in our conclusions depends on our own interests; and according as we lay the emphasis here or there, quite different formulations of truth result. . . . What we say about reality thus depends on the perspective into which we throw it. The *that* of it is its own; but the *what* depends on the *which;* and the which depends on *us*."

And such is the usual fate of good men who abandon

for one reason or another the spirit's intuitions of the
real and attempt to analyze it and tell *what* it is. For
whats and other queries are not easily applied to it, and
the blithe decisiveness with which the pragmatists
abandon the attempt and substitute a line of human
choices and practical interpolations deserves credit at
least for candor. With it they abandon metaphysics and,
in many cases, reality as it is generally imagined. Modern
theories of knowledge, says Dewey,[11] with their rival
materialistic, spiritualistic, dualistic doctrines, and
rival realistic, idealistic, representational theories; and
rival doctrines of relation of mind and matter, occasional-
ism, preëstablished harmony, parallelism, panpsychism,
etc., have a single origin "in the dogma which denies
temporal quality to reality as such . . . this denial of
change to true Being had its source in bias in favor of
objects of contemplative enjoyment, together with a
theory that such objects are the adequate subject-matter
of science." The pragmatists make a drastic sacrifice
to clear the world of rational artifice and false façades.
Thought works within reality, they say, where it harms
not; analysis is inside the real and but one phase of it:
Reason is not the real. Theirs is a harsh purgative.
They throw aside full many solemn things. But they
drop reality too.

For philosophies multiply with dreadful rapidity, once
the gate is opened and reason and classification like he-
goats enter the pasture. There is classic rationalism,
which asserts that "all real or scientific knowledge is
derived from reason," and over against it is its arch
enemy, empiricism, such as that of James, which holds
that "all knowledge springs from perception." There
is another pair called realism and idealism: The one
says[12] that the "character of that which really is, as
distinguished from that which is only imagined to be,
is to be found in its independence of all relation to the
experience of a subject. What exists at all, the realist

holds, exists equally whether it is experienced or not."
The other says [12] that "all reality is mental."

Upon these Paulsen [13] pounces; and promptly combines
them into four philosophic groups. They are: 1. Realistic
empiricism: It asserts that "we know things as they are
in themselves by perception." This is nearest to the
popular conception. 2. Realistic rationalism: It asserts
that "we know things as they are, not by the senses, but
by reason." It is a view "common to the great metaphysical systems. Plato, Spinoza and Hegel all claim
that an adequate knowledge or reality is reached by
reason." 3. Idealistic empiricism: It asserts that "we
know of things only by perception, which, of course, gives
no adequate knowledge. This is the view of the epistemological criticists of rational-metaphysical systems."
Hume is its best example. 4. Idealistic rationalism: It
asserts that "we can know reality *a priori* by pure reason;
however, not as it is in itself, but only as it appears to us,
and only as to its form." This is Kant's philosophy.

Then there are the four conceptions of being outlined
by Royce.[14] They are : First, mysticism, which says that
"to be means, simply and wholly, to be *immediate;*"
second, realism; third, critical rationalism, which says
that to be real means "to be valid, to be true, to be in
essence the standard for ideas"; fourth, a Roycean
synthesis of the three, "what is, is other than the mere
idea, yet not because it externally corresponds thereto.
but because it completely expresses, in a form that is
ultimately individual, the very meaning that the finite
idea consciously, but partially and abstractly, embodies
in its own general form."

And so they go. Good men come on one after another,
age after age, and toil upon the perennial blossoms of
reality. Some find fulfillment in the imaginative exercise
but others cut and slice with their various instruments
and according to their diverse methods, and at the end,
with petals and leaves and broken stems about them say,

"Now at last *here* is this flower. It is — say — Malus angustifolia; Family 12. Pomaceae; Order 18. Rosales; Series 1. Choropetalae; Subclass 2. Dicotyledons; class 2. Angiospermae; Subkingdom 2. Spermatophyta, of the vegetable kingdom." The value of their dissections for certain purposes is unquestioned, but the real wild crab apple blossom in April is rarely caught on a scalpel's point.

The struggles of systematic philosophers, of Greek thinkers and Hindu, of German and Latin and Anglo-Saxon, have not brought them much closer to reality. They have lost their innocent eyes. They have inter-jected endless structures that push reality away. They have given up the intimate realizations of youth; for the young girl, the child, the athlete, except when they try to think, may be nearer, as Paul suggests, than the philosophers. No one can deny their effort or the value of their work for other purposes — chess and arabesque are worth while too — but reason has not found reality and it is not likely that it ever will.

Reality leans against us like a wall of wind. It is there always, always blowing, but a sample of it under a microscope turns out to be only air. It is a pressure, an immediate significance; it is an inflation of things with being. It is not here nor there, this nor that; it is not definable. It is the presence of things, their gratuity, their assertion.

"The sense of existence evidently belongs to the intoxication, to the *Rausch*, of existence itself," says Santayana; [15] "it is the strain of life within me, prior to all intuition, that in its precipitation and terror, passing as it continually must from one untenable condition to another, stretches my attention absurdly over what is not given, over the lost and unattained, the before and after which are wrapped in darkness, and confuses my breathless apprehension of the clear presence of all I can ever truly behold." The tellings are always different, yet the same. Be it Santayana or Schopenhauer or Emerson, Shelley or William Blake, Eckhart or Plato or Çankara they tell somehow of the same thing in different words.

With the real most mystics identify the one, and for almost all men, mystic or rationalist, business man or polo player, oneness of the world is the first requisite of a well behaved, dignified and satisfactory universe. Only insurgents stick for pluralism, and they would be embarrassed no doubt, if not humiliated, by more than a few worlds. Why we want it one is not so clear. Perhaps a fear of tariff walls and difficulties of mental transportation is behind it; perhaps our sense of mastery is threatened; perhaps our own self-unity hangs on one world, or sex and food hungers in us drive us on to metaphysical acquisitiveness. At any rate we want world properties and leaseholds in perpetuity. Man votes frequently nowadays for annexation of any outside worlds. He wants his world in general one.

Close to reality for him is usually the amendment, "one reality." It soaks into his thinking like oil into a lamp wick. And though his detailed life is surely pluralistic in deeds and pleasures, in loves and personality, in the segregated specialities of learning and the diversities of interests and hopes, still he wants one world and only one.

There are of course objections: Russell says [16] that universal oneness is a relic of the days before Copernicus, of notions anthropocentric and naïve, and that "apparent oneness of the world is merely the oneness of what is seen by a single spectator or apprehended by a single mind." James says [17] that oneness may be "merely a name like 'substance' descriptive of the fact that certain *specific* and *verifiable connections* are found among the parts of the experiental flux." But the real world still says, "one world" to most persons. It is one in its reality, it would seem, if not in its appearances.

Across the diverse fields of discourse, of worlds of action, of spirit, of science, oneness is more difficult to trace and even more important. The worlds bounce apart like tennis balls; systematic unities break down; external ultimates are futile; and what oneness there may be among them it is clear is not like these. Dewey takes it up profoundly but not altogether adequately in his Experience and Nature: [18] Their disunities are found in the fact that traditional thought regarded knowledge as complete possession and penetration of reality while modern thought, he says, regards the objects of science as orders of relations which serve as tools to effect havings and beings. We think traditionally of science as a grasp of reality in its final form, but we see that modern science deals only with a mathematico-mechanical world; and in confusion we ask, "Can it be that this mechanical world of science is the final world? Is there no span between the world of cause and of appreciation? Are there several orders of existence?" All that, says Dewey, is a confusion. We must give up the traditional notion that science can incorporate all reality in itself, and then the antithesis between the worlds of description and appreciation, between mechanics and ends will disappear.

Other philosophers in their various ways have sought through proof and rational compulsions to expose the unity of worlds and the oneness of their fields of discourse. But proofs are not available and there is no compelling in these things, for proofs by their nature never can apply. In the primary insight into being, which is neither reason nor external observation, in the inner oneness of real things, which we find spiritually within ourselves and in the "yes" of all things in our world, lies the sole certainty of world oneness. External pluralisms and disconnections may well obtain, but within reality, as we spiritually see it, there cannot well be many.

James names eight kinds of world oneness in his lecture on The One and the Many [19] and then decides like a true rebel for pluralism. Those onenesses are: 1. one subject of discourse, 2. continuity, 3. lines of influence, 4. causal unity, 5. generic unity, 6. unity of purpose, 7. æsthetic unity, 8. one knower. But what of them all? They are incidental to the simple sight of oneness in the real, the first certainty of living.

For the realness of things is one realness. The command to be is one command, and though the wild pressures and anarchies of experience and things may defy external regimentations and outer combines, their urgency and thrust is one and can well be only one. Their authority is concrete and lonely. Their voice is one voice saying many things. Real things are spiritually one; for pluralisms hardly belong in that dimension of the universe. It is a profound question, but it has the simplest of answers.

When the winters are hard and the fodder in the ricks and mows is surer than the undergrowth of the forest a stag will sometimes leap the bars of a westerner's corral and spend the colder months with domestic cattle. He accepts an artificial and, to him, unreal order of living to solve a problem that presses overbearingly upon him. He takes a taming and a limitation, he is content with an abstraction for a time in order to find within it a continuation of the realities that were too harsh for him outside. And when March comes he leaps the bars again and goes back to the raw being of things and the fulfillments that he is used to finding there. The world as it comes in avalanche upon him is too much. He will accept corrals and special fields of discourse when he must.

Man is domestic. He lives in a reassembled world, and what the forest is like in its natural entirety he per-

haps can never know. The wolves and other raw realities
of the woods, the burdens of the cold and loneliness, the
utter pathlessness are too much to pay for freedom, and
man finds within the orders and limitations of special
fields of discourse a freedom and perhaps fulfillment that
the reckless world beyond those categories denies.
Limitation and the evolving difference between the worlds
of action, of spirit, of science is his answer to a problem.
He makes defense and adjustment. He creates a schism
between those worlds for the sake of consistency and life
within them. He raises artifice, fences, corrals because he
humanly must.

It is man's fate or fortune to see the world in general
from special points of view. They are his limitations, and
in some measure he creates them; in some measure, he
finds them. He cannot observe the world in general from
no point of view at all. He feeds in a secure corral. He
takes what comes through the gate. It is significant
however that these points of view, these worlds of action,
of spirit, of science are within themselves "complete."
Each is general, or presumed to be, within itself, and
though several worlds may knock around incongruously
together in our lives, each within is sincere and profound.
For when they cease to take themselves seriously they
are worthless worlds; their heat has died away and their
significance has gone. Their reality, and it may be all
reality, lies in that "withinness" and meaning. They are
wells drilled towards the living rock and cold water.
They tap their respective eternities; they may be spirit-
ualized; and — to put them all in terms of the world of
spirit — they may well be one eternity.

"When the flux manages to form an eddy and to
maintain by breathing and nutrition what we call a life,"
says Santayana,[20] "it affords some slight foothold and
object for thought and becomes in a measure like the ark
in the desert, a moving habitation for the eternal. . . .
The absolute flux cannot be physically arrested;" the

philosopher continues beautifully and with an accurate vagueness, "but what arrests it ideally is the fixing of some point in it from which it can be measured and illumined. Otherwise it could show no form and maintain no preference. . . . The irrational fate that lodges the transcendental self in this or that body, inspires it with definite passions, and subjects it to particular buffets from the outer world — this is the prime condition of all observation and inference, of all failure and success." Living itself, as Santayana suggests, is the first of all our points of view. On that primary issue and its problems we find and create the others.

It is a question more than anything of how we take them. We may say, at least of science and of action, that they are answers to our problems. That is an instrumental view, and of it James says [21]: "Ought not the existence of the various types of thinking . . . each so splendid for certain purposes, yet all conflicting still, and neither one of them able to support a claim of absolute veracity, to awaken a presumption favorable to the pragmatistic view that all our theories are *instrumental*, are mental modes of *adaptation* to reality, rather than revelations or gnostic answers to some divinely instituted world-enigma?" And in respect to the external situation the correctness of this view can hardly be denied.

But it remains that science, the spirit, the world of action are natural monopolists. Within itself science is presumably a world order. It sits on an hypothesis that is a throne and to look beyond it would be to abandon science. To complicate that hypothesis with the pragmatic doubts of Dewey and James, the skepticisms of Santayana, or the indifferentism towards it of the spirit would corrupt its value and reality to the scientist. To break the man of action's faith in the finality of his world would make it not worth toiling for. To accuse the world of the spirit of unreality and abstraction would destroy

it. That world is intimate with being, and if it merely is
a point of view for certain purposes, reality is a point of
view. It all becomes a very different matter from the
instrumentalities of James, Dewey, Santayana and
Schiller. The inner authority of the worlds of action,
of spirit, of science is another way to take them.

We have numerous types of experience, says R. G.
Collingwood,[22] "each claiming not only to give truth, but
to give the absolute or ultimate truth concerning the
nature of the universe, to reveal the secret of existence, and
to tell us what the world really and fundamentally is. But
surely there is in the last resort only one world, and there
can be only one type of theoretical activity which is
really adapted to solve the problem of its ultimate
nature." It is an old and difficult problem, and though
this suggests a solution that seems to use instruments
already repudiated in the statement, the problem at
least is there, as old as civilization and as impenetrable.

In the older philosophies the problem of the realms of
being was less synthesized than today, but no less pertinent; and in Democritus, the materialist, Protagoras,
the humanist, and Plotinus, the mystic, at least three
worlds of discourse, the worlds of science, action, the
spirit, respectively found representatives. They are type
philosophers. They spoke only of the universe and in
terms of the universe, and they recognized no other
than their own. They are repeated and recombined like
elements down through the history of our thought, and
after each effort they fall radically apart again, complete,
persuasive and final each in his own way.

To Plotinus the world is wholly spiritual and the real
is one and immediate. He abjures reason and the senses
and discrete personality, and where Greek philosophy
before him had known the soul only as one of nature's

products side by side with many others — for him the whole of nature is real only so far as it is soul.[23] Like his more logically minded predecessors, Parmenides and Heraclitus and like the great Plato in many of his rôles, Plotinus finds his primary problem in the real, in the one and the many, in finality and change, and like many others of his spiritual brethren the world over he answers it in terms of the ineffable one and the progressive unreality of the many. His is the spiritual way. It is the Plotinean dimension of the universe.

To Protagoras this world may be known not as it is but only as man at the time perceives it.[24] Change and motion is the ground of our perceptions, and an opinion or a truth that is final and universally valid cannot be. For man is the measure of all things, and the real is relative to his vicissitudes. For Protagoras, as other great sophists including even Socrates, the primary problem is the human problem. Man is the sole focus on which we can found a universe. His is the humanistic approach to the world. It is the Protagorean dimension of the universe.

To Democritus the primary problem is to explain nature.[25] He tries in the manner of modern science to reduce all qualitative relations to quantitative relations. He starts with the atom as the last minimum of that which is. It has body; it fills space; it has motion. Atoms in various arrangements and motions constitute the entire physical and psychical phenomena of the universe. The world is materialistic in the scientific way. It is the Democritean dimension of the universe.

Matter, spirit, human action: the crucible may pour into many moulds but we are built for three. The world may have dimensions over and beyond but it is hard to know them. They are formulating principles, if the logician will insist, but their forms do not cohere and their authorities respectively are within. They are dimensions, Plotinean, Protagorean, Democritean, but dimension is a metaphor. It suggests: it cannot formulate. It must awake reality within; it cannot describe it from without. It is basic poetry, not prose.

For all presentations of the universe must be metaphors in some sense, human or otherwise; they must focus in a situation that has a concrete meaning to the human mind; and though the universe itself may not be focused in any situation or tied to human images, its presentation must be made somehow in that language. For Democritus matter is a metaphor; for Protagoras the metaphor is human life; for Plotinus it is God. They execute through these figures a lien on reality. They establish foci there for the concretion of a meaningful world. They realize in their metaphors something of the threats and enthusiasms with which the world besets them, the exuberance and push of real things, and their philosophies are impulsive articulations, native points of view, like telescopes pointing at one sun.

To say that "worlds" of science, of the spirit, of action are dimensions of the universe is more a metaphor than an accurate proposition. But the world in general can only be suggested, and dimensional analogies will come as near to saying it, no doubt, as all the ghosts and legends and the trying of philosophers and scientists will ever come. The world may have dimensions, many of them; these at least are three.

To critical defense and to stout paraphrase in logical and learned terms a world like that is easily amenable, but it would gain no truth from them. It would find no further being, and the clank and rattle of its iron load of exegesis would only drown its voice. It is a living voice, though it speaks sometimes in different tongues.

That is the world in general. It is a metaphor perhaps; but all things that are not this flaming now, this crushing presence of reality may well be metaphors. They are metaphors — unless we accept their instant presence and their being in our souls.

Speculative problems do not flourish greatly in the shadows of immediate being. The purely spiritual approach to the real — or reality *per se* — makes philosophy a minimum and very simple. Here seven issues have been raised and passed on, as they always must be passed on, to the endless searchings and imaginations of humankind. They are: the problem of the world in general; reality; how some philosophers analyze the real; the problem of the one; the three worlds and the one; three type philosophers; the dimensional view of the world. In some ways these problems of the world in general summarize this book; in some ways they begin it.

APPENDIX

TABLE OF KEY IDEAS

There are as many worlds no doubt as there are observers; and the new universe discussed in the preceding chapters can be only a selection and an emphasis on what seem the dominating continuities and problems of contemporary thought. The key ideas developed in these chapters are *in part* as follows:

CONCEPTIONS OF COSMIC STRUCTURE:

Chap. II: Light and the new universe. Relativity of space, time and motion. Events and reality. Electrical structure of matter. Matter in terms of energy. Quantitative conceptions of the elements. Transmutation of the elements. Quantum theory of energy. Conservation, old and new.

CONCEPTIONS OF COSMIC PROCESS:

Chap. III: The dynamic factor of process. Irreversibility of process.
Inorganic Identities of process and evolution. General scope of evolutionary process. Stellar and galactic evolution. Solar evolution. Planetesimal hypothesis. Types of geological process. Land and sea and air. Geochemical basis of life.

CONCEPTIONS OF COSMIC PROCESS:

Chap. IV: Is the appearance of life inevitable? Life as a term for
Organic (chemical) behavior. Metabolism. Life and the sun. Reproduction. Sensitivity. Evolution as a type of continuity in living material. The Weismann theory and its opponents. The value of diversity and the function of sex. Function of the individual. Trial and error method in nature. Types of value involved in evolution and life.

CONCEPTIONS OF COSMIC PROCESS:

Chap. V: The biology of "consciousness," behavior. Development
Psycho- of sensitivity. Behavior and mechanism. Nerve systems:
logical mobility; coördinators. Their control of "distance" in space and time. Wholeness of behavior versus psychic atomism. Stimulus and response. Unconditioned and conditioned responses. Emotions, visceral reactions. Freud, dreams, wishes, and modern inhibitions. Words, thoughts as behavior. Intelligence as condensed trial and error.

411

CONCEPTIONS OF COSMIC PROCESS:

Chap. VI: Mechanistic order contrasted with other types of value
Social, Pre- Correlated origin and development of society and the
historic individual. Instruments and their relation to human development. Prehistoric division of labor, specialization, social organization. Races of man. Trinil, Neanderthal, Cro-Magnon. Early art, ritual, religion, morality, society. Prehistoric industry; creative woman. Society as a living continuum. Modern races and the new stone, bronze and iron ages.

CONCEPTIONS OF COSMIC PROCESS:

Chap. VII: The break-down of Nature's balance of the species. Writ-
Historic ing; its relation to trial and error method. Settlement and new mobility. Despotism, a simple control. Unity versus freedom. The super-natural intervention. Power captured from nature. Gunpowder. Coal. Man's anatomical and biological climaxes. Growth of inner control. Man's evolutionary continuity with all process. Dangers of teleological ideas of human development. Civilization today.

DOMINANT CONCEPTIONS IN MODERN LIFE:

Chap. VIII: Man's inventiveness as an emphasis on nature's trial and
Applied error method. Basis in liberalism of all science. Sources of
Science modern power. Man's control over materials. Social control of applied science. Democratizing science, and its endurance. The next age; superpower.

DOMINANT CONCEPTIONS IN MODERN LIFE:

Chap. IX: The power of life. Standardized life. Unstandardized
Industrial currency. The tendency towards specialization. Increas-
Society ing separation of production from consumption or enjoyment. The denotative gain; the connotative decline. Separation of gain from service. Inherent tendencies in industry, social organicism. Proposed forms of control, communism, individualism. The need for distributive society. The future evolution of machines.

DOMINANT CONCEPTIONS IN MODERN LIFE:

Chap. X: Business: The dominion of the abstract. Its contrast with
Social engineering, farming, etc. City life, child of business and
Situations machines. Crime, failure of city government. Standards of
of Today living, population governors. Decline of sex instinct as a factor in population growth. Birth control: population growth dependent on social need. Industrial population

margins, unbalanced societies. Immigration flow, and its
control, race values. Future union of city and country,
environmental values. Education, press, public opinion,
expression values.

DOMINANT CONCEPTIONS IN MODERN LIFE:

Chap. XI: Politics: the great defeat. Ghandi, revolution, agrarian
Social   reaction. Lenin, industrial evolution. Mussolini, violence
Situations and the *status quo*. Wilson, democracy resurgent, liberalism,
of   political failure. Ways to internal democracy and external
Tomorrow strength. Russia, America, China, Europe, four powers.
           Newer nationalisms. Race, channels of human development.
           Social solvents. The state, the family and new woman.
           Marriage and divorce, morality. Institutional religion.

ULTIMATE VALUES IN LIFE:

Chap. XII: The world as a thing enjoyed. The transition from means
Man's   to ends. Intrinsic and extrinsic aspects of things. The arts
Arts and are inseparable. They are life. Language values; poetry
Ends   suggestive, prose informative. The songs of being, poetry.
           New music, the world forsakes old forms and rigidness.
           New art, from outer to inner authority. Building, the dance,
           theatre.

ULTIMATE VALUES IN LIFE:

Chap. XIII: Man's consummations, the timelessness of every step.
The Final- Beauty. Love. Religion. What is worth while? Various
ities of Life doctrines.

GENERAL IDEAS OF THE WORLD:

Chap. XIV: Does man want one world? Spiritual, scientific, practical
The   aspects of the world. *Knowing* allotted to science; *being*
Spiritual allotted to the spirit. Have they a cohesive element? The
Approach spiritual; the world as being; innerness. Morality is only
           contiguous to the spirit. The mystic in all men, and being.
           Is the spirit related to human affairs?

GENERAL IDEAS OF THE WORLD:

Chap. XV: The scientist's retreat from being. Science is a synthesis of
The De-   reason and sensation. Science is finite. Science and mysti-
scriptive cism. Can the world tolerate both? Science is deliberately
Approach relative. Science is impersonal. Scientific materialism, com-
           mon sense materialism. The mentalism of absolute science.
           Science is ascetic and abstract. The rise of objective facts
           from abstraction. Natural laws as approximations. The
           origin of method in science. Scientific codes.

GENERAL IDEAS OF THE WORLD:

The *Practical* *Approach* Chap. XVI: The world of doing things. The action dimension of the world. The mobility of human adjustments. Consumma- tions in action. Purpose, blame, in action. External, internal direction of action. Dehumanization of action by specialties. System imposed on events. Reality to the man of action.

GENERAL IDEAS OF THE WORLD:

The *World in* *General* Chap. XVII: The search for a point of reference. Is there no absolute point of reference? Reality, as philosophers see it. The one. Three worlds and the one. Protagoras, practical, humane. Democritas, scientific, material. Plotinus, mys- tic, ontological. Doing, knowing, being: World dimensions.

This is not an outline of the book, but a selection of certain ideas that unlock, as it were, important chambers of the world.

The ideas of a new universe have not always the same intrinsic difficulty for different persons. The graph below is an estimated table of difficulty for three types of persons. The reader might well draw here his own curve of trouble.

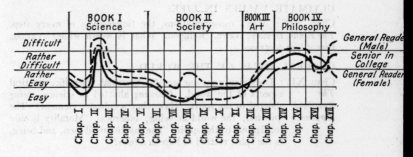

References and Reading List by Chapters

Books starred (*) are suggested for the general reader or for collateral reading in Orientation courses, survey groups and the like. The list is larger in periodicals and popular books than is ordinarily necessary; this is in order to give the general reader and the college student leads to further reading in fields that may be of interest.

CHAPTER II
THE COMPONENTS OF THE MATERIAL WORLD

1. DE SITTER: *See* M. Luckiesh: Foundations of the Universe. N. Y., 1925. P. 97.

2. JOHN DEWEY: Changing Intellectual Climate. *The New Republic*, Feb. 17, 1926.

3. * BERTRAND RUSSELL: A. B. C. of Relativity. N. Y., 1925. P. 57, 67 ff.

4. * A. N. WHITEHEAD: Science and the Modern World. N. Y., 1925. Pp. 111, 142, 155, 102, 168.

5. * KARL PEARSON: The Grammar of Science. London, 1911. P. 220. See note on this page also.

6. RUSSELL: work cited. P. 226. Also * RUSSELL: A. B. C. of Atoms. N. Y., 1923. P. 151. Also A. N. WHITEHEAD: The Concept of Nature. Cambridge, England, 1920. P. 195. 7. RUSSELL: A. B. C. of Atoms. P. 153. Also WHITEHEAD: Science and the Modern World. Pp. 51, 144, 152, 154, 102, 131. 8. WHITEHEAD: Science and the Modern World. Pp. 98, 79, 77, 81, 156. 9. DEWEY: work cited. E. V. Huntington: The Continuum as a Type of Order, etc. Harvard University Publication.

10. * ALBERT EINSTEIN: Relativity, Translated by R. W. Lawson, N. Y., 1921. *See* P. 32. 11. EINSTEIN: Relativity, Chap. II. Also,* A. N. WHITEHEAD: An Introduction to Mathematics. London. Chap. XII. Periodicity in Nature. 12. EINSTEIN: Relativity. P. 65. Also RUSSELL: A. B. C. of Atoms. P. 155; A. B. C. of Relativity. Chap. VII. 13. Encyclopædia Britannica, 11th edition. (Aether). N. Y., 1910. Vol. I, p. 295.

14. * L. BOLTON: An Introduction to the Theory of Relativity. N. Y., 1921. P. 54. 15. EINSTEIN: Relativity. P. 21.

16. * J. H. THIRRING: The Ideas of Einstein's Theory, Translated by R. A. B. Bussell. N. Y., 1922. P. 24. 17. * M. LUCKIESH: Foundations of the Universe. N. Y., 1925. Chap.

VI. Also THIRRING: The Ideas of Einstein's Theory.
Chaps. III, IV, V.   **18.** *American Journal of Science.*
3rd Series. Vol. 34, p. 333 and others.

19. * HARRY SCHMIDT: Relativity and the Universe. Translated
by Karl Wichmann. N. Y., 1922. Pp. 62, 68, 69.
20. BOLTON: Introduction to the Theory of Relativity.
P. 55.   **21.** EINSTEIN: Relativity. P. 32.

22. WHITEHEAD: The Concept of Nature. P. 72 f. Also EINSTEIN:
Relativity. Chap. IX.

23. *Science:* June 19, 1925. No. 1590. Also, A. S. EDDINGTON:
The Domain of Physical Science, essay in * Science, Religion
and Reality, by various writers. N. Y., 1925.

24. EINSTEIN: Relativity. Chap. XX. Also * H. A. LORENTZ:
The Einstein Theory of Relativity. N. Y., 1920. P. 36 ff.
25. RUSSELL: A. B. C. of Atoms. Pp. 148, 170. Chap.
XIII. Also LUCKIESH: work cited. P. 74.

26. EINSTEIN: Relativity. Chap. XXXI. Also A. S. EDDINGTON:
work cited. Pp. 203–209.

27. * CHARLES NORDMAN: Einstein and the Universe. Translated
by Joseph McCabe. N. Y., 1922. Chap. VII.

28. EINSTEIN: Relativity.   Chap. XXVII and P. 113.   **29.**
LUCKIESH: Foundations of the Universe. P. 89.

30. RUSSELL: A. B. C. of Relativity. Chaps. VI, VII.   **31.** RUS-
SELL: A. B. C. of Relativity. P. 127.   **32.** RUSSELL:
A. B. C. of Atoms. P. 158.

33. * FREDERICK SODDY: Matter and Energy. N. Y., 1912.
P. 42. and London, 1923. Also * JOHN MILLS: The Realities
of Modern Science. N. Y., 1921.

34. R. A. MILLIKAN: The Physicist's Present Conception of the
Atom. *Science.* May 30, 1924., Vol. LIX, No. 1535. Also
RUSSELL: A. B. C. of Atoms. P. 116.

35. * JOHN MILLS: Within the Atom. N. Y., 1922. Chap. VIII.
Also LUCKIESH: Foundations of the Universe. Chap. XI.

36. SODDY: Matter and Energy. Chap. VIII and * SODDY: Science
and Life. London, 1920. P. 85.

37. * R. A. MILLIKAN: High Frequency Rays of Cosmic Origin.
Science. Nov. 20, 1925. No. 1612. Also *Manchester Guardian Weekly*, March 5, 1926.

38. RUSSELL: A. B. C. of Atoms. P. 62. Also LUCKIESH: Foundations of the Universe. Chap. XII for definition of *hn.*
39. RUSSELL: A. B. C. of Atoms.

The above books are worth while references in connection with Chapter II. Some other books are: CREHORE: The Mystery of Matter and Energy. N. Y., 1917. CREHORE: The Atom. N. Y., 1920. SLOSSON: Easy Lessons in Einstein. ROUGIER-MASIUS: Philosophy and the New Physics. Philadelphia, 1921. KRAMER and HOLST: The atom and the Bohr Theory of its Structure. N. Y., 1923. BORNS: The Constitution of Matter. London, 1923. HAAS: The New Physics. London, 1923. SOMMERFELD: Atomic Structure and Spectral Lines. London, 1921. * SVANTE ARRHENIUS: Worlds in the Making. Translated N. Y., 1908. LOCKYER: Inorganic Evolution as Studied by Spectrum Analysis. N. Y., 1900. EDDINGTON: Space, Time and Gravitation. London. THOMSON: The Outline of Science. This is a field in which the reader must keep in touch with new books as they appear, for ideas in physics and chemistry are changing fast.

CHAPTER III
THE FORMS OF THE MATERIAL WORLD

1. * JOHN DEWEY: Experience and Nature. Chicago. 1925. P. 72.

2. * A. N. WHITEHEAD: Introduction to Mathematics. London and New York. Chap. XII. Periodicity in Nature. Chap. XIV. Series. Also W. R. INGE: in Science, Religion and Reality. N. Y., 1925. P. 361.

3. * JOHN MILLS: Within the Atom. N. Y., 1922. P. 187.
4. * GILBERT N. LEWIS: The Scientific Meaning of Chance. *Yale Review.* July 1926. Also Encyclopædia Britannica: 11th Ed. N. Y. 1910. Heat. Vol. 13. P. 142. Thermodynamics. Vol. 26. P. 813. Also * JOHN MILLS: The Realities of Modern Science. N. Y., 1921. Chap. XIX. Pp. 267-269.

5. F. H. SEARS and P. J. VAN RHIJN: A New Determination of the Distribution of Stars with Respect to Magnitude and Galactic Latitude. *Nature.* June 20, 1925. No. 2903.

6. * F. R. MOULTON: An Introduction to Astronomy. N. Y. 1923. P. 548.

7. * BERTRAND RUSSELL: A. B. C. of Atoms. N. Y. 1923. P. 156.   8. * A. R. HINKS: Astronomy. London and N. Y. P. 169. Also * C. G. ABBOTT: The Earth and the Stars. N. Y. 1925. Chaps. XI, XII.   9. MOULTON: work cited. P. 531.   10. MOULTON: work cited. P. 425.

11. * AGNES M. CLERKE: The System of Stars. London. 1905. Chap. X. The Colours of Stars. **12.** * GEORGE ELLERY HALE: The New Heavens. N. Y., 1922. P. 53. **13.** Encyclopædia Britannica: Stars. 11th Ed. Vol. 25. P. 789.

14. * AGNES M. CLERKE: Problems in Astrophysics. London. 1903. Chap. XV.

15. A. S. EDDINGTON: The Source of Stellar Energy. *Nature.* May 1, 1926. No. 2948. Also MOULTON: work cited. Pp. 527, 530.

16. CLERKE: Problems in Astrophysics. P. 240, 213.

17. W. D. MACMILLAN: Cosmic Evolution. *Scientia.* Milan. January–February 1923. P. 104.

18. *Science.* December 24, 1925. P. X. Also MOULTON: work cited. Chap. VIII.

19. * T. C. CHAMBERLIN: The Origin of the Earth. Chicago. 1916. P. 70. **20.** CLERKE: The System of Stars. Chap. III. **21.** MOULTON: work cited. Chap. XI. **22.** MOULTON: work cited. P. 390. **23.** CLERKE: Problems in Astrophysics. Part. I. Solar Physics.

24. CHAMBERLIN: Origin of the Earth. P. 112. Also W. D. MACMILLAN: Some Mathematical Aspects of Cosmology. *Science.* July 24, 1925. Vol. LXII. No. 1595.

25. MOULTON: work cited. P. 425.

26. CHAMBERLIN: Origin of the Earth. Pp. 114, 134. **27.** CHAMBERLIN: Origin of the Earth. P. 130.

28. * T. C. CHAMBERLIN and R. D. SALISBURY: Geology. N. Y., 1906. Vol. II, p. 64. **29.** CHAMBERLIN: Origin of the Earth. P. 168. **30.** * CHAMBERLIN and SALISBURY: Geology. Vol. I, p. 5.

31. * JOHN MURRAY: The Ocean. HOLT. N. Y. P. 47. Also * HENRY FAIRFIELD OSBORN: The Origin and Evolution of Life. N. Y., 1921. P. 27. Also MOULTON: work cited. P. 360 f.

32. CHAMBERLIN: Origin of the Earth. P. 172. **33.** CHAMBERLIN and SALISBURY: Geology II, p. 119.

34. * G. A. J. COLE: Rocks and Their Origins. Cambridge University Press. 1922. P. 129. **35.** COLE: work cited. P. 109. **36.** CHAMBERLIN and SALISBURY: Geology I, p. 413. **37.** CHAMBERLIN and SALISBURY: Geology I, p. 441. **38.** COLE: work cited. P. 19. Also MURRAY: The Ocean. Chap. IX. Marine Deposits.

39. Bowditch: American Practical Navigator. U. S. Hydrographic Office. Washington. 1918. Chapter XVIII. Winds. **40.** R. S. Tarr: New Physical Geography. N. Y., 1905. P. 258. **41.** Chamberlin and Salisbury: Geology I, p. 51.

42. T. G. Bonney: The Work of Rain and Rivers. Cambridge, England. 1912. P. 117.

43. Lyon, Fippin, Buckman: Soils, Their Properties and Management. N. Y., 1916. Pp. 139, 146. Also * Milton Whitney: Soil and Civilization. N. Y., 1925.

44. Chamberlin and Salisbury: Geology. Vol. I, p. 51.

The above books are worth while as collateral reading to the chapter on forms of the material world. They in turn give references enough for unlimited study of this field.

CHAPTER IV
THE APPEARANCE OF LIFE IN THE WORLD

1. * Chamberlin and Salisbury: Geology. N. Y., 1905. Vol. I, p. 649.

2. * John Murray: The Ocean. N. Y. and London. Chapter X.

3. * T. C. Chamberlin: The Origin of the Earth. Chicago. 1916. P. 260.

4. * H. F. Osborn: The Origin and Evolution of Life. N. Y., 1921. P. 48. **5.** Chamberlin: Origin of the Earth. P. 252. **6.** Frank C. Eve: In the Beginning. *Atlantic Monthly*. May 1923. **7.** H. F. Osborn: work cited. P. 62.

8. * Lawrence J. Henderson: The Fitness of the Environment. N. Y., 1913. P. 276. (Quoted by Osborn. P. 9.)

9. * Frederick Soddy: Matter and Energy. London, 1923. P. 45. Also * Joseph Needham: Mechanistic Biology and the Religious Consciousness, essay in * Science, Religion and Reality by various writers. N. Y., 1925.

10. * Lester F. Ward: Dynamic Sociology. N. Y., 1923. Vol. I, p. 320. J. H. Parker: Organic Determinism. *Science.* June 13, 1924.

11. Chamberlin: Origin of the Earth. P. 252. **12.** Chamberlin: Origin of the Earth. P. 247.

13. * JACQUES LOEB: The Organism as a Whole. P. 23. N. Y., 1916. (Quoted by Osborn, P. 286.)

14. H. C. JONES: The Elements of Physical Chemistry. N. Y., 1907. P. 278. Nernst's Theory. P. 282. Colloids. P. 284. Also Encyclopædia Britannica: 11th Ed. N. Y., 1911. Vol. 25, p. 376. Solution. Vol. 22, p. 603. Psychology. Also ALEXANDER FINDLAY: The Twilight Zone of Matter. *Science.* August 28, 1925.

15. CHAMBERLIN: Origin of the Earth. P. 258. Also * W. J. V. OSTERHOUT: The Nature of Life. N. Y., 1924. P. 14. Imbibition and Osmosis.

16. * MILTON WHITNEY: Soil and Civilization. N. Y., 1925. P. 24.

17. HENDERSON: work cited. (Quoted by Osborn, P. 37.)

18. OSBORN: work cited. P. 67-69.   19. JONES: work cited. P. 533.   20. OSTERHOUT: work cited. P. 55-57. 21. OSTERHOUT: work cited. P. 82.   22. OSBORN: work cited. P. 21.   23. JONES: work cited. P. 285. Also G. W. CRILE: A Bipolar Theory of Living Processes. N. Y., 1926. 24. OSBORN: work cited. P. 52-57.   25. LOEB: work cited. (Quoted by Osborn, P. 286.)

26. * E. G. CONKLIN: Heredity and Environment. Princeton, 1922, P. 8.

27. * F. O. BOWER: in Evolution: A Collective Work. London, 1925. P. 163.

28. R. HERTWIG: Manual of Zoölogy (Kingsley). N. Y., 1909. P. 61.

29. * E. B. WILSON: The Cell in Development and Heredity. N. Y., 1925.

30. OSTERHOUT: work cited. P. 45.   31. OSTERHOUT: work cited. P. 45-50.   Also JONES: work cited. P. 493. Actinometry.

32. * STRASBURGER, NOLL, SCHENCK, KARSTEN: Text Book of Botany (Lang) (The Bonn Text). London, 1908. P. 220.

33. *See* S. A. ARRHENIUS: Chemistry of Modern Life. N. Y., 1925. P. 163.

34. OSTERHOUT: work cited. Pp. 67, 54.   35. OSTERHOUT: work cited. P. 62-72.   36. CONKLIN: work cited. P. 16.   37. CONKLIN: work cited. Pp. 140, 151, 153. 38. CONKLIN: work cited. P. 142.

39. OSCAR HERTWIG: Embryology of Man and Mammals. (Mark) N. Y., 1905. P. 145.

40. Conklin: work cited. P. 125. Also Evolution: A Collective Work. London, 1925. P. 241. Also Joseph Needham: work cited. P. 237.

41. Osborn: work cited. P. 24. Also F. O. Bower: in Evolution: A Collective Work. London, 1925. P. 207–209.

42. * George Santayana: Reason in Science. N. Y., 1906. P. 108.

43. Osborn: work cited. Pp. 159, 199. * Also J. Arthur Thomson: Concerning Evolution.

44. Osborn: work cited. Pp. 108, 107.   **45.** Osborn: work cited. Pp. 270, 117.

46. Charles Darwin: The Origin of Species. N. Y, 1904. Pp. 151, 6.

47. E. C. Jeffrey: Drosophila and the Mutation Hypothesis. *Science.* July 3, 1925. Also Henderson: The Fitness of the Environment. P. 282.

48. Conklin: work cited. P. 46.   **49.** Osborn: work cited. Pp. 121, 178, 256, 81, 110 ff.

50. Chamberlin and Salisbury: Geology. Vol. I, p. 659. **51.** Osborn: work cited. Pp. 214, 235, 252.

52. * Jost: Lectures on Plant Physiology.

Inspection of the above books, particularly those by Osborn, Conklin, Wilson and others will reveal a fairly complete bibliography.

CHAPTER V
MIND AND BEHAVIOR

1. * John B. Watson: Behaviorism. N. Y., 1924. P. 8.

2. * George Howard Parker: The Evolution of the Nervous System of Man. Chap. III. of the Evolution of Man by Lull, Ferris, Parker, Angell, Keller, Conklin. New Haven, 1922. P. 90. **3.** Parker: work cited. P. 87. **4.** Parker: work cited. P. 93.

5. * William James: The Principles of Psychology. N. Y., 1907. P. 12.

6. W. I. Thomas: Mechanistic Psychology. *New Republic,* Sept. 30, 1925. Also C. E. Ayres: On the Firing Line of Science. *New Republic.* Oct. 28, 1925. Also Charles M. Childs: Physiological Foundations of Behavior. N. Y., 1925.

7. WATSON: Behaviorism. Lecture IV, Part II, also Psychology, Philadelphia, 1919. P. 183. * Also WALTER B. CANNON: Bodily Changes in Pain, Hunger, Fear and Rage. N. Y., 1922. Also LOUIS BERMAN: The Glands Regulating Personality. N. Y., 1921.

8. * JOHN DEWEY: Reconstruction in Philosophy. N. Y., 1920. P. 91.

9. * E. B. TITCHENER: A Text Book of Psychology. N. Y., 1911. P. 37. 10. GEORGE HUMPHREY: Psychology Revolts Against Atomism. *New Republic*, July 29, 1925.

11. *See* WILLIAM McDOUGALL: Body and Mind. London, 1923. Pp. 357, 131. Also GEORGE MALCOLM STRATTON: Experimental Psychology. N. Y., 1908. P. 278.

12. * EDWIN GRANT CONKLIN: Heredity and Environment. Princeton, 1922. P. 56. 13. JOHN B. WATSON: Behavior. N. Y., 1914. P. 16.

14. WATSON: Behaviorism. N. Y., 1924. Lecture I. P. 1. 15. WATSON: Behaviorism. Pp. 4, 10. 16. WATSON: Behaviorism. P. 11 f. 17. WATSON: Behaviorism. P. 20.

18. *See* LEWIS M. TERMAN: Group Tests of Mental Ability. London, 1921. Also MONROE, DEVOSS and KELLY: Educational Tests and Measurements. N. Y., 1924. Also SCOTT and CLOTHIER: Personnel Management. Chicago, 1924.

19. WATSON: Behaviorism. N. Y., 1924. P. 73-79. 20. WATSON: Behaviorism. P. 99. 21. WATSON: Behaviorism. P. 122. 22. WATSON: Behaviorism. P. 107. Also W. MITCHELL: Structure and Growth of Mind. London, 1907. P. 126. 23. WATSON: Behaviorism. Pp. 113, 116. 24. WATSON: Behaviorism. Pp. 118, 122.

25. * EDWIN B. HOLT: The Freudian Wish. N. Y., 1915. P. 3. Also * VAN TESLAAR: An Outline of Psychoanalysis. Modern Library.

26. * SIGMUND FREUD: The Interpretation of Dreams. Translated by A. A. Brill. N. Y., 1913. P. 103. 27. FREUD: The Interpretation of Dreams. P. 105.

28. * SIGMUND FREUD: Psychopathology of Everyday Life. Translated by A. A. Brill. N. Y., 1916.. P. 42 f.

29. WATSON: Behaviorism. P. 177. 30. WATSON: Behaviorism. P. 186.

31. * *See* GEORGE SANTAYANA: Reason in Science. N. Y., 1906. P. 114.

32. JAMES ROWLAND ANGELL: The Evolution of Intelligence. Chap. IV. of the Evolution of Man, by LULL, etc., New Haven, 1922. P. 105. **33.** *See* Chapter IV of this book. **34.** ANGELL: work cited. P. 111.

35. SANTAYANA: Reason in Science. P. 116.

36. GEORGE HUMPHREY: Psychology Revolts Against Atomism. *New Republic,* July 29, 1925. No. 556, p. 257. **37.** HUMPHREY: work cited. **38.** HUMPHREY: work cited. Also A. S. EDDINGTON: Science, Religion and Reality, by various writers. N. Y., 1925. Pp. 195–197; 208–214 ff.; 200.

39. * KURT KOFFKA: Growth of the Mind. N. Y., 1925.

40. * GEORGE A. DORSEY: Why We Behave Like Human Beings. P. 416. N. Y., 1925.

The literature in this field is rich and pugnacious. Psychology is lively now and the reading rather vigorous. The above books will serve as an introduction.

CHAPTER VI
EARLY MAN

1. * ALEXANDER A. GOLDENWEISER: Early Civilization. N. Y., 1922. P. 235.

2. * HENRY FAIRFIELD OSBORN: Men of the Old Stone Age. N. Y., 1922. Pp. 62, 49, 72, 75.

3. * HARRIS H. WILDER: Man's Prehistoric Past. N. Y., 1924. P. 4. **4.** * OSBORN: work cited. P. 84.

5. * CHARLES DARWIN: The Descent of Man. Chap. XVIII. Figs. 72–78. **6.** OSBORN: work cited. P. 59.

7. * GEORGE GRANT MacCURDY: Human Origins. N. Y., 1924. Vol. I, pp. 314, 298. **8.** MacCURDY: Human Origins. Vol. I, pp. 311, 435. **9.** WILDER: work cited. P. 9.

10. * CHAMBERLIN and SALISBURY: Geology. N. Y., 1906. Vol. III, p. 420. **11.** OSBORN: work cited. P. 95. **12.** OSBORN: work cited. P. 130.

13. *See* ROLAND B. DIXON: The Racial History of Man. N. Y., 1923. **14.** OSBORN: work cited. Pp. 280, 23.

15. MacCURDY: work cited. Vol. I, pp. 344, 374. **16.** OSBORN: work cited. Pp. 184, 213. **17.** WILDER: work cited. P. 49, Chap. VI. **18.** OSBORN: work cited. Pp. 194, 237, 236. **19.** OSBORN: work cited. Pp. 206, 213. **20.** MAC-

Curdy: work cited.   Vol. I, p. 431.   **21.** Goldenweiser: work cited. P. 393.   **22.** MacCurdy: work cited. Vol. I, p. 145.

23. * Edward Jenks: A History of Politics, London, 1900. P. 43. Also Osborn: work cited. P. 257.   **24.** Osborn: work cited. Pp. 261, 272.   **25.** Osborn: work cited. P. 23. **26.** MacCurdy: work cited. Vol. I, pp. 74, 84.   **27.** Osborn: work cited. P. 282.   **28.** Osborn: work cited. P. 287.   **29.** Osborn: work cited. P. 298.   **30.** Osborn: work cited. P. 261. Also MacCurdy: work cited. Vol. I, p. 387.   **31.** Osborn: work cited. P. 335. **32.** Osborn: work cited. P. 308.   **33.** Osborn: work cited. Pp. 270, 271, 282.   **34.** MacCurdy: work cited. Vol. I, p. 173.   **35.** Goldenweiser: work cited. Pp. 231, 233. L. Lévy-Bruhl: How Natives Think. Translated by Clare. London, 1926.   **36.** MacCurdy: work cited. Vol. I, Chap. VII.   **37.** Osborn: work cited. Pp. 395, 414.   **38.** Osborn: work cited. Pp. 396, 432.   **39.** MacCurdy: work cited. Vol. I, p. 259 ff. **40.** Osborn: work cited. P. 450.   **41.** Osborn: work cited. P. 491.   **42.** *See* also MacCurdy: work cited. Vol. II, p. 295.   **43.** MacCurdy: work cited. Vol. I, p. 440.   **44.** Osborn: work cited. P. 500.   **45.** Osborn: work cited. P. 490.   **46.** Wilder: work cited. P. 196.   **47.** * H. G. Wells: The Outline of History. N. Y., 1920. Vol. I, Chap. XV.   **48.** Osborn: work cited. P. 487.   **49.** Wilder: work cited. Pp. 194, 65. **50.** Wells: work cited. Vol. I, p. 111.   **51.** MacCurdy: work cited. Vol. II, pp. 151, 154.

52. * Otis Tufton Mason: Woman's Share in Primitive Society. N. Y., 1920. Pp. 139, 143, 152.   **53.** Wells: work cited. Vol. I, p. 130.

54. * Franz Boas: The Mind of Primitive Man. N. Y. 1922. Chap. VIII, pp. 198–238.   **55.** Goldenweiser: work cited. Part III. Also Bronislaw Malinowski: Magic, Science and Religion, essay in * Science, Religion and Reality, by various writers. N. Y. 1925.

56. Boas: work cited. Pp. 203, 204. Also * Graham Wallas: The Great Society. N. Y., 1916. P. 77.   **57.** MacCurdy: Work cited. Vol. II, pp. 62, 92.   **58.** Wilder: work cited. P. 217 note.   **59.** Goldenweiser: work cited. Pp. 235, 265.

60. Goldenweiser: work cited. P. 239.   Also F. W. Blackmar and J. L. Gillin: Outlines of Sociology. N. Y., 1917. *See*

P. 16.   **61.** MacCurdy: work cited. Vol. II, pp. 158, 52, 149.

62. Goldenweiser: work cited. P. 268 ff. Also Fay-Cooper Cole: Lecture before class in Problems of Contemporary Thought, Northwestern University. Dec. 9, 1925.

63. MacCurdy: work cited. Vol. II, p. 199.   **64.** MacCurdy: work cited. Vol. II, p. 178.

65. Wilder: work cited. P. 246.

These and other works will open this interesting field to the reader. In the field of myth, religion and primitive culture the following books are worth reading: * Frazer: Golden Bough. One volume. * Lang: Social Origins. * Tylor: Primitive Culture. * Durkheim: Elementary Forms of the Religious Life. * Westermarck: The History of Human Marriage. * Marett: The Threshold of Religion.

CHAPTER VII
MODERN MAN

1. Encyclopædia Britannica. N. Y., 1911. Eleventh Ed. Vol. 28, p. 852.

2. * Alexander A. Goldenweiser: Early Civilization. N. Y., 1922. P. 115.

3. * William Kay Wallace: The Trend of History. N. Y., 1922. P. IX.

4. Adam Smith: The Wealth of Nations. Book I. Chap. II.

5. Henry Smith Williams: Civilization. Encyclopædia Britannica. N. Y., 1911. Eleventh Ed. Vol. 6, p. 406. Also * Edward Jenks: A History of Politics. London, 1900.

6. * James Baikie: The Life of the Ancient East. N. Y., 1923. P. 188.   **7.** * H. G. Wells: Outline of History. N. Y., 1920. I. Chap. XVI, p. 196.

8. Old Testament.   **9.** Ferdinand Schevill: Lecture before Class in Problems of Contemporary Thought, Northwestern University, Chicago. Dec. 12, 1923. **10.** * Hendrik Van Loon: The Story of Mankind. N. Y., 1921. P. 36. **11.** Baikie: work cited. Pp. 50, 60.   **12.** Baikie: work cited.   Chap. XII.

13. J. B. Bury: History of Greece. London, 1906. Chap. XVII.

14. * W. M. West: The Ancient World. Chicago. 1904. Pp. 263, 271.

15. THEODOR MOMMSEN: The History of Rome. Translated. N. Y., 1885. I. Chap. VI.

16. * ELLSWORTH HUNTINGTON: Climate and Civilization. New Haven, 1924. Also * HEREFORD B. GEORGE: The Relation of Geography and History. Oxford, 1910. **17.** WELLS: work cited. I, P. 497.

18. CHARLES SEIGNOBOS: The History of the Roman People. Translated N. Y., 1902. Chap. XVIII.

19. SEIGNOBOS: The History of the Roman People. Translated N. Y., 1902. P. 433. **20.** WELLS: work cited. I, p. 542.

21. MATTHEW ARNOLD: Essay. Hebraism and Hellenism. **22.** BURY: work cited. P. 767.

23. A. T. MAHAN: The Influence of Sea Power on History. Boston, 1898. P. 13 ff.

24. E. M. WALKER: Encyclopædia Britannica. N. Y., 1911. Greece. Vol. 12. P. 443.

25. * PLATO: Phaedrus, Gr. P. 230. JOWETT. **26.** SEIGNOBOS: work cited. P. 147.

27. * JAMES HENRY BREASTED: Ancient Times. Boston, 1916. P. 689.

28. * F. M. STAWELL and F. S. MARVIN: The Making of the Western Mind. London. P. 46.

29. * ALLAN MENZIES: History of Religion. N. Y., 1906. P. 425.

30. * WILLIAM RALPH INGE: Christian Mysticism. London, 1913. Lecture II. Also CLEMENT E. J. WEBB: Science, Christianity and Modern Civilization, essay in * Science, Religion and Reality, by various writers. N. Y., 1925.

31. HENRY THOMAS BUCKLE: History of Civilization in England. N. Y., 1870. Vol. I, p. 29.

32. JOHN RICHARD GREEN: Short History of the English People. Chap. VI, Sec. IV.

33. * FERDINAND SCHEVILL: Political History of Modern Europe. N. Y., 1907. P. 23. **34.** BUCKLE: work cited. Vol. II, p. 1.

35. CARL LOTUS BECKER: Beginnings of the American People. Boston, 1915. Also THEODORE C. SMITH: The Wars Between England and America. N. Y., 1914. Also Francis A. Walker: The Making of the Nation. N. Y., 1912.

36. SHAILER MATHEWS: The French Revolution. Chatauqua. N. Y., 1914. Also J. Holland Rose: The Revolutionary and Napoleonic Era. Cambridge, Eng., 1907.

37. * OSWALD SPENGLER. The Decline of the West. Trans. by Atkinson. N. Y., 1926. Reviewed by Lewis Mumford, The *New Republic.* May 12, 1926. Also STAWELL and MARVIN: work cited. P. 301.

38. WILLIAM E. DODD: Expansion and Conflict. Boston, 1915.

39. * CHARLES A. BEARD and MARY R. BEARD: History of the United States. N. Y., 1921. **40.** * E. E. SLOSSON: Creative Chemistry. N. Y., 1923. P. 10.

41. * FREDERICK SODDY: Science and Life. London, 1920. P. 86.

CHAPTER VIII
MAN'S ALLIANCE WITH NATURE

1. *See* W. KÖHLER: The Mentality of Apes. N. Y., 1925. Also *see* OGBURN and THOMAS: Are Inventions Inevitable. Political Science Quarterly. 37, 20, 3. Also Psychology of Invention: in Evolution. A Collective Work. London, 1925. P. 331.

2. * E. E. SLOSSON: Creative Chemistry. N. Y., 1923. P. 265.

3. * *See* A. A. GOLDENWEISER: Early Civilization. N. Y., 1922. P. 391.

4. * THORSTEIN VEBLEN: The Place of Science in Modern Civilization. N. Y., 1919. P. 2.

5. * FREDERICK SODDY: Matter and Energy. N. Y., 1912. I, and London, 1923.

6. * FREDERICK SODDY: Science and Life. London, 1920. Pp. 23, 86, 6. **7.** SLOSSON: Creative Chemistry. I.

8. * *See* JOHN DEWEY: Reconstruction in Philosophy. N. Y. 1920. P. 12. Also Experience and Nature. Chicago. 1925. P. 136. **9.** *See* JOHN MILTON; Paradise Lost. Book III. 1-20. Also *see* this book: Chap. III. Also *see* F. C. EVE: In the Beginning, *Atlantic Monthly.* May, 1923. **10.** E. E. SLOSSON: Address before class in Problems of Contemporary Thought, Northwestern University, Chicago. Jan. 9, 1924.

11. Wm. L. DE BAUFRE: Mechanical Power. *Science.* No. 1609, Oct. 30, 1925. **12.** DE BAUFRE: work cited. **13.** Compare ELLSWORTH HUNTINGTON and S. W. CUSHING: Human Geography. N. Y., 1922. Pp. 202, 192 with DE BAUFRE: work cited, and with STEINMETZ and with CHASE: work cited below. **14.** HERBERT S. PHILBRICK: Address before class in Problems of Contemporary Thought, Northwestern University, Dec. 19, 1923.

15. * *See* SVANTE AUGUST ARRHENIUS: Chemistry in Modern Life. N. Y., 1925. P. 138. (International Geological Congress in Canada, 1913. Estimate of coal above 1800 meters.) **16.** ARRHENIUS: work cited. P. 139. **17.** De Baufre: work cited.

18. *See* C. G. GILBERT and J. E. POGUE: Energy Resources of the U. S. Bulletin 102. Smithsonian Institution. Wash. Also G. O. SMITH: Industry's Supply of Energy. In *Mechanical Engineering*. March, 1921. **19.** DE BAUFRE: work cited. **20.** E. E. SLOSSON: Gasoline as a World Power, in Science Remaking the World. CALDWELL and SLOSSON. N. Y., 1924. P. 36. **21.** PHILBRICK: work cited. Also GILBERT and POGUE; and CHASE: cited below. **22.** ARRHENIUS: work cited. P. 143, *see* note.

23. C. P. STEINMETZ: America's Energy Supply. Transactions of the American Institute of Electrical Engineers. Vol. XXXVII. Part 2. P. 985. **24.** DE BAUFRE: work cited. **25.** PHILBRICK: work cited.

26. * CHESTER G. GILBERT and JOSEPH E. POGUE: America's Power Resources. N. Y., 1921. P. 13. **27.** GILBERT and POGUE: work cited. (for 1921) P. 15. **28.** STEINMETZ: work cited (for 1918).

29. RALPH BENNETT: Discussion On Power. Transactions of the American Institute of Electrical Engineers. Vol. XXXVII. Part 2. pp. 985, 990 ff. **30.** STEINMETZ: work cited. **31.** HUNTINGTON and CUSHING: work cited. P. 203. **32.** SLOSSON: address cited.

33. *See* STUART CHASE: The Tragedy of Waste. N. Y., 1925. P. 241 f. **34.** DE BAUFRE: work cited. Also CHASE: work cited. P. 12. **35.** ARRHENIUS: work cited. P. 63. **36.** DE BAUFRE: work cited.

37. N. M. FENNEMAN: A Classification of Natural Resources. *Science*. Feb. 20, 1925. Vol. LXI, No. 1573. **38.** ARRHENIUS: work cited P. 63 (for 1910). **39.** ARRHENIUS: work cited. P. 82. **40.** * MILTON WHITNEY: Soil and Civilization. N. Y., 1925. P. 37. **41.** SLOSSON: Creative Chemistry. P. 43. **42.** WHITNEY: work cited. Pp. 138, 144. **43.** WHITNEY: work cited. Pp. 258, 204, 209.

44. The Chambers of Commerce Atlas. London, 1925. P. 24. **45.** *See* WHITNEY: work cited. P. 206. **46.** *See* WHITNEY: work cited. P. 198.

47. *See* Statistical Abstract of U. S. A. 1923.   P. 176.   **48.** WHIT-
NEY: work cited. P. 116.   **49.** BAKER BROWNELL:
Editorial, *Chicago Tribune*, Dec. 1, 1924.   **50.** ARRHENIUS:
work cited. P. 138.   Also Chambers of Commerce Atlas.
51. Statistical Abstract. 1923. P. 224, and FENNEMAN:
work cited.   **52.** CHASE: work cited. Pp. 37, 257
(Little). Also FENNEMAN: work cited.   **53.** SLOSSON:
Gasoline. Work cited. P. 19.   **54.** Statistical Abstract.
1923.   **55.** SLOSSON: Creative Chemistry. Chap. VIII.
The Race for Rubber.   **56.** SLOSSON: Creative Chemis-
try. Chap. III. Feeding the Soil. P. 54.   **57.** SLOSSON:
Creative Chemistry. P. 15.   **58.** SLOSSON: Creative
Chemistry. P. 198.   **59.** ARRHENIUS: work cited.
60. Statistical Abstract.   **61.** HARPER LEECH: *Chicago
Tribune.* 1924.

62. COL. JOHN PRICE JACKSON: Policies of Future Power Development. Transactions of the American Society of Mechanical
Engineers. Vol. 42.   **63.** *See* DE BAUFRE: work cited.

64. * O. S. BEYER, JR.: Engineering, in Civilization in the United
States. N. Y., 1922. (Edited by Harold Stearns.)

65. * FOREST MOULTON: Introduction to Astronomy. N. Y., 1923.
P. 73.

66. * *See The Survey*: Giant Power issue. March 1, 1924. Vol.
LI, No. 11. for numerous social and economic aspects of
superpower.   **67.** *Survey*: cited.   **68.** Statistical Abstract. 1923.

69. * W. D. MACMILLAN: Cosmic Evolution. *Scientia*, Milan.
Jan.–Feb. 1923. P. 110.

CHAPTER IX
INDUSTRIAL SOCIETY

1. * RICHARD T. ELY: Outlines of Economics. N. Y., 1916.
Pp. 119, 123.

2. * JOHN DEWEY: Reconstruction in Philosophy. N. Y., 1920.
P. 85.

3. W. L. DE BAUFRE: Mechanical Power. *Science.* Oct. 30,
1925. No. 1609.

4. * F. W. TAUSSIG: Principles of Economics. N. Y., 1919. I,
p. 70.   **5.** TAUSSIG: work cited. I. Chap. 4. Large
Scale Production.   **6.** Some Great Commodities. Various

Authors. N. Y., 1922. P. 78.   **7.** TAUSSIG: work cited. P. 52.

8. * THORSTEIN VEBLEN: The Theory of Business Enterprise. N. Y., 1923. P. 19. Chapter on Machine Process. **9.** VEBLEN: work cited. P. 11. Also The Place of Science in Modern Civilization. N. Y., 1919. P. 2.

10. * GRAHAM WALLAS: The Great Society. N. Y., 1916. P. 210. **11.** ELY: work cited. P. 317. Also OWEN D. YOUNG in *Chicago Tribune*, May 30, 1926.

12. MAYNARD KEYNES: Monetary Reform. N. Y., 1924. Pp. 42, 181.

13. * IRVING FISHER: Stabilizing the Dollar. N. Y., 1920. Pp. 37, 104, 86, 97. **14.** KEYNES: work cited. Pp. 187, 203. **15.** EARL DEAN HOWARD: Lecture before Class in Problems of Contemporary Thought, Northwestern University. Chicago. Jan. 20, 1926.

16. * R. H. TAWNEY: The Acquisitive Society. N. Y. 1920,. P. 33.

17. * STUART CHASE: The Tragedy of Waste. N. Y., 1925. Pp. 270, 106. **18.** VEBLEN: work cited. P. 326. **19.** CHASE: work cited. Pp. 231, 21. **20.** * BERTRAND RUSSELL and DORA RUSSELL: Prospects of Industrial Civilization. London, 1923. P. 22. **21.** BERTRAND RUSSELL and DORA RUSSELL: Prospects of Industrial Civilization. P. 33 ff.

22. WILLIAM T. FOSTER and WADDILL CATCHINGS: The Dilemma of Thrift. The *Atlantic Monthly*. April 1926. P. 543. *See* also same authors: Profits. Newton, Mass. 1926. Also BERTRAND RUSSELL and DORA RUSSELL: Prospects of Industrial Civilization. Pp. 24–50.

23. * BERTRAND RUSSELL: Proposed Roads to Freedom. N. Y., 1919. P. 1. **24.** BERTRAND RUSSELL: Proposed Roads to Freedom. Pp. 3–7. **25.** BERTRAND RUSSELL: Proposed Roads to Freedom. P. 29. **26.** *See* MORRIS HILLQUIT: History of Socialism in the U. S., 1903. **27.** RUSSELL: Prospects of Industrial Civilization. Especially Chap. VI. **28.** RUSSELL: Proposed Roads to Freedom. Pp. 37, 66, 68. **29.** Quoted by Russell: Proposed Roads to Freedom. P. 73. **30.** RUSSELL: Proposed Roads to Freedom. P. 83. **31.** FREDERICK DEIBLER: Lecture before Class in Problems of Contemporary Thought, Northwestern University, Chicago. Jan. 16, 1924. **32.** CHASE: work cited. P. 266.

33. * HILAIRE BELLOC: Economics for Helen. N. Y., 1925. Pp. 136, 112, The Distributive State.

34. * See GARET GARRETT: Business: in Civilization in the United States. N. Y., 1922. P. 414.

CHAPTER X
SOCIETY TODAY

1. * GARET GARRETT: Essay on Business, in Civilization in the U. S. N. Y., 1922. P. 404. **2.** GARRETT: work cited. P. 411. **3.** E. A. ROSS: Lecture before class in Problems of Contemporary Thought. Northwestern University, Chicago. Feb. 13, 1924.

4. * E. C. HAYES: Introduction to the Study of Sociology. N. Y., 1919. P. 60. See also Bibliography in this book. **5.** W. L. BAILEY: Lecture before class in Problems of Contemporary Thought. Northwestern University, Chicago. Feb. 10, 1926. Also ADAM SMITH: Wealth of Nations. Book III. Chap. II, III, IV. Also ROBERT C. PARK and others: The City. Chicago, 1926.

6. RAYMOND B. FOSDICK: American Police Systems. N. Y., 1920. P. 13. See also CLARENCE DARROW: Crime and the Alarmists. Harper's Magazine, October, 1926.

7. HAVELOCK ELLIS: The Dance of Life, Boston, 1923. P. 291. Also RAYMOND FOSDICK: work cited. P. 4–34. Also W. H. HUDSON: The Purple Land. London, 1925. P. 335.

8. RICHARD T. ELY: Outlines of Economics. N. Y., 1916. P. 438.

9. STUART CHASE: The Tragedy of Waste. N. Y., 1925. P. 265. **10.** HAYES: work cited. P. 262.

11. * T. R. MALTHUS: An Essay on the Principle of Population. N. Y., 1895. Pp. 21, 112. **12.** HAYES: work cited. P. 264.

13. J. SWINBURNE: Population and the Social Problem. N. Y., 1924. Pp. 16, 17. **14.** SWINBURNE: work cited.

15. RAYMOND PEARL: The Biology of Population Growth. N. Y., 1925. Reviewed by C. E. Ayres in the New Republic, Jan. 13, 1926. P. 223. **16.** RAYMOND PEARL: As reviewed in the New Republic. P. 223.

17. E. B. REUTER: Population Problems. Chicago. 1923. Pp. 171, 172. **18.** See REUTER: work cited. Pp. 243, 244.

19. ELY: work cited. P. 435. Also LEWIS COREY: How is Ownership Distributed. New Republic, May 5, 1926. **20.** REUTER: work cited. P. 187.

21. *See* EDWARD A. STEINER: On the Trail of the Immigrant. Chicago. 1906. P. 369.   **22.** HAYES: work cited. P. 268.   **23.** REUTER: work cited. Pp. 191–195.

24. HAYES: work cited. Pp. 267–269. Compare however: Population Problems (Dublin) N. Y., 1926; essay on Population and Immigration. Also * E. A. ROSS: forthcoming book, Standing Room Only. N. Y., 1927.

25. *See* ELY: work cited. P. 607.   **26.** ELY: work cited. P. 619.

27. * E. A. ROSS: Social Psychology. N. Y., 1920. Crowds and Mobs. Chapters III, IV. Also *see* ISAIAH THOMAS: History of Printing in America. James Rivington.

28. *See* WALTER LIPPMANN: Public Opinion. N. Y., 1922.

29. * NORMAN ANGELL: The Press and the Organization of Society. London, 1922. Also CARROLL D. CLARK: The Small Town Press Sells Out. *The New Republic.* Jan. 20, 1926. No. 581. Also UPTON SINCLAIR: The Brass Check. Also OSWALD GARRISON VILLARD: Some Newspapers and Newspaper Men.

CHAPTER XI

SOCIETY TOMORROW

1. * CHARLES E. MERRIAM: New Aspects of Politics. Chicago, 1925. Lecture before class in Problems of Contemporary Thought, Northwestern University, Chicago, Feb. 11, 1925. Also * H. J. LASKI: Grammar of Politics. London, 1926. *See* Chap. VIII. Also * EDWARD JENKS: A History of Politics. London, 1900.

2. * HARIDAS T. MUZUMDAR: Gandhi, The Apostle. Chicago, 1923.

3. MAURICE J. HINDUS: The Russian Peasant and the Revolution. N. Y., 1920. Pp. 79, 251, 277.

4. * HENRY N. BRAILSFORD: The Russian Worker's Republic. New York, 1920.   **5.** * MAYNARD KEYNES: Economic Consequences of the Peace. N. Y., 1920. Chap. III.   **6.** E. A. ROSS: Lecture before class in Problems of Contemporary Thought, Northwestern University, Chicago, Feb. 13, 1924.

7. * *See* BERTRAND RUSSELL and DORA RUSSELL: Prospects of Industrial Civilization. N. Y., 1923. Pp. 58, 60.   **8.** RUSSELL: work cited. Also W. L. BAILEY: Lecture before class in Problems of Contemporary Thought, Northwestern University, Chicago, Feb. 10, 1926.

9. E. B. REUTER: Population Problems. Chicago, 1923. Pp. 20, 271, 272.

10. E. A. ROSS: work cited. Also, Standing Room Only; to be published in 1927. Also FLINDERS PETRIE: The Revelations of Civilization (quoted by Ellis: The Dance of Life) P. 308.   11. E. A. ROSS: Lecture before class in Problems of Contemporary Thought, Northwestern University, Chicago, Feb. 17, 1926. Also Geroid Tanquary Robinson: Racial Minorities, in Civilization in the United States, N. Y., 1922. P. 356.   12. REUTER: work cited. P. 276.

13. HERBERT J. SELIGMAN: The Negro Faces America. N. Y., 1920. P. 255.

14. REUTER: work cited. P. 24. Also A. J. Lotka: quoted by H. P. Fairchild in Population Problems. Ed. by Dublin. Boston, 1926. P. 148.

15. * E. A. ROSS: Social Control. N. Y., 1922. P. 52. Also * W. F. Ogburn: Social Change. N. Y., 1923. 16. *Science:* Science Service Section. Oct. 23, 1925. 17. Scrutator: *Chicago Tribune.* Sept. 23, 1925.

18. * E. C. HAYES: Introduction to The Study of Sociology. N. Y., 1919. P. 248.

19. F. W. BLACKMAR and J. L. GILLIN: Outlines of Sociology. N. Y., 1917. P. 429. Also W. H. R. RIVERS: Social Organization. N. Y., 1924.   20. HAYES: work cited. P. 295. *See* H. G. WELLS: The New Machiavelli.

21. * *See* Our Changing Morality: Essay by BERTRAND RUSSELL. P. 7. N. Y., 1924.   22. CHARLOTTE PERKINS GILMAN: Towards Monogamy. In Our Changing Morality. N. Y., 1924.

23. * LESTER WARD: Dynamic Sociology. N. Y., 1923. Vol. I, p. 605.   24. ISABEL LEAVENWORTH: Virtue for Women. In Our Changing Morality. N. Y., 1924.

25. ELSIE CLEWS PARSONS: Sex; and KATHERINE ANTHONY: The Family; in Civilization in the United States. N. Y., 1922.

26. * STUART CHASE: The Tragedy of Waste. N. Y., 1925. P. 68.   27. *See* WESTERMARCK'S History of Human Marriage. 28. ARTHUR GARFIELD HAYES: Modern Marriage and Ancient Laws. In Our Changing Morality. N. Y., 1924.

28. * KIRSOPP LAKE: The Religion of Yesterday and Tomorrow. Boston, 1925. P. 159.

30. *See* HORACE BRIDGES: The Religion of Experience. N. Y., 1916. P. 14.   **31.** HERBERT CROLY: Christians Beware! in *New Republic*. Nov. 25, 1925. P. 12.   **32.** HERBERT CROLY: Progressive Democracy. N. Y., 1915. P. 397. **33.** Quoted by Stuart Chase: work cited. P. 41.

CHAPTER XII
MAN'S ARTS AND ENDS

1. BRIHAD-ĀRAṆYAKA UPANISHAD. First Adhyāya. First Brāh-maṇa 1, 2; The Thirteen Principal Upanishads. Translated by R. E. Hume. Oxford, 1921.

1. ARTHUR SCHOPENHAUER: The World as Will and Idea. Book III, 33, 34. Translated by Haldane. London, 1907. P. 229.

3. * HAVELOCK ELLIS: The Dance of Life. Boston, 1923. P. 70. **4.** ELLIS: work cited. P. 330 and footnote, Pp. 341, 342.

5. G. E. LESSING: Laocoon. Chapter III.   **6.** ELLIS: work cited. P. 36.

7. *See* IRVING BABBITT: The New Laokoon. Boston, 1910. Chap. VI, p. 127.

8. * GEORGE SANTAYANA: Reason in Art. N. Y., 1906. P. 4. **9.** BAKER BROWNELL: Kinæsthetic Verse; *Poetry, A Magazine of Verse*. Apr. 1923. Vol. XXII, No. 1.   **10.** GEORGE SANTAYANA: Reason in Art. P. 87.   **11.** BAKER BROWNELL: The Code of Minority. *Poetry, A Magazine of Verse*. March 1922. Vol. XIX, No. 6.

12. BLISS PERRY: A Study of Poetry. Boston, 1920. P. 72. The poetry quoted in this section is respectively from: Starting From Paumanok; Song of Myself; Gitanjali; Essay, The Poet; Smoke and Steel; in Smoke and Steel; Adonais; Walden; Mending Wall; Look We have Come Through; Spoon River Anthology; Spoon River Anthology.

13. * *See* GEORGE SANTAYANA: Three Philosophical Poets. Cambridge, Mass., 1910. Also * LLEWELLYN JONES: First Impressions. N. Y., 1925. P. 38.

14. * AMY LOWELL: Tendencies in Modern American Poetry. N. Y., 1917. Pp. 163, 174.

15. *See* H. L. MENCKEN: The American Language. N. Y., 1921. Also GEORGE SANTAYANA: Reason in Art. P. 45.

16. JOHN ALDEN CARPENTER: Lecture before class in Problems of Contemporary Thought. Northwestern University, Chicago, March, 1924.   **17.** EDMUND WILSON: The Jazz Problem. *New Republic.* Jan. 13, 1926.

18. * GEORGE DYSON: The New Music. Oxford, 1923. Pp. 47, 70, 55.   **19.** DYSON: Work cited. P. 103.

20. DEEMS TAYLOR: Music, in Civilization in the United States. N. Y., 1922. P. 202.

21. GEORGE SANTAYANA: The Sense of Beauty. N. Y., 1908. P. 150.

22. SHELDON CHENEY: A Primer of Modern Art. N. Y., 1924. P. 68.

23. ARISTOTLE: Poetics VI. 9. Translation, Butcher. London, 1907. P. 27.

24. * ELIE FAURE: History of Art. London. 1924. Ancient: Vol. I. Modern Art: Vol. IV. P. 101. Also S. REINACH: Apollo, N. Y., 1910 — and others of the series.

25. * CLIVE BELL: Art. London, 1913. P. 172.   **26.** BELL: work cited. Pp. 122, 148.   **27.** CHENEY: work cited. P. 85.   **28.** BELL: work cited. P. 220.   **29.** CHENEY: work cited. P. 92.

30. ELIE FAURE: work cited. Modern Art. P. 456.   **31.** CHENEY: work cited. P. 100.   **32.** CHENEY: work cited. Pp. 118, 134, 136, 140, 149, 160, 172.   **33.** CHENEY: work cited. Pp. 202, 279.   **34.** *See* CHENEY: work cited. Chap. XIV. FAURE. work cited. Vol. IV.

35. ELLIS: work cited. Chap. II.

CHAPTER XIII
THE FINALITIES OF LIFE

1. LAO TSE: The Tao Teh King: Part I. Chap. XXV, 34. 1, 2. Translated by Legge. Sacred Books of the East. Vol. XXXIX. Oxford, 1891. P. 76.

2. KWANG-TZE: work cited. Vol. XL, p. 66.

3. * LLEWELLYN JONES: First Impressions. N. Y., 1925. P. 210.

4. * CLIVE BELL: Art. N. Y., 1913. Pp. 53, 57.

5. GEORGE SANTAYANA: The Sense of Beauty. N. Y., 1908. P. 127 f.

6. ARTHUR SCHOPENHAUER: The World as Will and Idea. Book III. Para. 41. Translated by Haldane. London, 1907. Vol. I, p. 270 ff.

7. * BENEDETTO CROCE: Aesthetic. Translated by Ainslie, London, 1909. Pp. 1, 35.   **8.** CROCE: work cited. Pp. 162, 161. Also JONES: work cited. Pp. 162, 215.

9. * ETHEL D. PUFFER: The Psychology of Beauty. Boston, 1905. Pp. 47, 49.

10. LYOF N. TOLSTOI: What is Art. N. Y., 1899. Chaps. I, II, III.

11. H. TAINE: Lectures on Art. N. Y., 1896. Translated by Durand. P. 60. Also *see* PUFFER: work cited. P. 54. **12.** *See* WALTER PATER: The Renaissance. Introduction and conclusion.   **13.** *See* G. B. SHAW: Prefaces to Man and Superman. Read W. H. Hudson: Green Mansions. N. Y., 1916.

14. * GEORGE SANTAYANA: Poetry and Religion. N. Y., 1905. Chap. V. Platonic Love. 138.

15. SCHOPENHAUER: work cited. Supplements, Book IV. Chap. XLIV. The Metaphysics of Love of the Sexes. Vol. III. p. 362.

16. SANTAYANA: Poetry and Religion. Pp. 120, 132, 137.

17. * PLATO: Symposium: Translated by Jowett. Pp. 210, 211. **18.** PLATO: work cited. P. 212.

19. BELL: Art. Art and Religion. P. 81.   **20.** * SANTAYANA: Sense of Beauty. P. 112.   **21.** ROBERT MORSS LOVETT: Lecture before the Class in Problems of Contemporary Thought. Northwestern University. Chicago. March 10, 1926, and his bibliography.

22. *See* CARLYLE: Sartor Resartus, Essay on Characteristics; J. S. MILL: Utilitarianism, Liberty; NEWMAN: Grammar of Assent, Apologia pro Vita Sua; HUXLEY: Evolution and Ethics; RUSKIN: Unto This Last, Munera Pulveris; ARNOLD: Culture and Anarchy; WELLS: A Modern Utopia, The Research Magnificent; BUTLER: The Way of All Flesh; DEWEY: Human Nature and Conduct; RUSSELL: Why Men Fight; INGE: Christian Mysticism.

CHAPTER XIV
THE SPIRITUAL APPROACH TO THE WORLD

1. * Theologia Germanica: London, 1907. Translated, Winkworth. Pp. 62, 65.

2. * BERTRAND RUSSELL: Scientific Method in Philosophy. Chicago. 1914. P. 10.

3. * WILLIAM JAMES: A Pluralistic Universe. London, 1909. Pp. 319, 321.

4. PAUL DEUSSEN: The System of the Vedanta. Translated by Johnson. Chicago, 1912. Pp. 210, 453.

5. DEUSSEN: work cited. P. 453.   **6.** A. W. MOORE: Lecture before Class in Problems of Contemporary Thought, Northwestern University, Chicago, May 19, 1926.

7. * A. N. WHITEHEAD: Science and the Modern World. N. Y., 1925. P. 260.

8. * KARL PEARSON: The Grammar of Science. London, 1911. P. 110. Also * Science, Religion and Reality by BALFOUR, INGE, EDDINGTON and others. N. Y., 1925. Pp. 202, 209–218.

9. * WILLIAM JAMES: Pragmatism. London, 1909. P. 273.

10. * WILLIAM JAMES: The Varieties of Religious Experience. London, 1915. P. 17.   **11.** Theologia Germanica: cited p. 22.

12. JOSIAH ROYCE: The World and the Individual. N. Y., 1908. I, p. 52.

13. * PLATO: Phaedrus. Translated by Jowett. N. Y., 1892. Gr. P. 265.   **14.** PLATO: Phaedrus. Translated by Jowett. Gr. p. 247.

15. The Thirteen Principal Upanishads. Translated by R. E. HUME. London, 1921. Chandogya Upanishad (6, 9, 10).

16. ARTHUR SCHOPENHAUER: The World as Will and Idea. Translated by Haldane and Kemp. London, 1907. Book II, 21.

17. * JOSIAH ROYCE: The Spirit of Modern Philosophy. N. Y. 1899. P. 238.   **18.** * R. W. EMERSON: Essays, The Oversoul.   **19.** * WALT WHITMAN: Song of Myself, etc.

20. JAMES: Varieties of Religious Experience. Pp. 436, 448.

21. * JAMES HARVEY ROBINSON: The Mind in the Making. N. Y. 1921.

22. T. H. GREEN: Prolegomena to Ethics. Oxford, 1906. Chaps. II, III.

23. * HAVELOCK ELLIS: The Dance of Life. N. Y., 1924. P. 224 f.

24. * GEORGE SANTAYANA: Reason in Religion. N. Y., 1906. P. 30.   **25.** JAMES: Varieties.   **26.** ROYCE: The World and the Individual. I, p. 176.

27. * BERTRAND RUSSELL: Mysticism and Logic. London, 1921.   **28.** JAMES: Varieties. P. 35.

29. ELLIS: Dance of Life.   Chap. V. Part I.   30. JAMES: Varieties.   Also JAMES: Pragmatism.   P. 299.

31. * W. R. INGE: Christian Mysticism.   London, 1913.   Lect.
IV.   P. 162.

32. Meister Eckeharts Schriften und Predigten.   Vol. I and II.
Jena, Germany, 1912.   Ed. and translated, Büttner.   Pub.
Diederichs.

33. INGE: work cited, P. 163.

Also Evelyn Underhill: Mysticism (also contains a bibliography).
N. Y., 1910.

CHAPTER XV

THE DESCRIPTIVE APPROACH TO THE WORLD

1. * KARL PEARSON: The Grammar of Science.   London, 1911.
Part I, p. 17.

2. * J. B. S. HALDANE: Daedalus.   N. Y., 1925.   P. 14.
3. Nature: F. F. P. B. No. 2893.   P. 533.   Also * A. S. ED-
DINGTON: Science, Religion and Reality, by various writers.
N. Y., 1925.   P. 206–209.

4. BERTRAND RUSSELL: Address before the class in Problems of
Contemporary Thought, Northwestern University, Chicago.
April 16, 1924.

5. * GEORGE SANTAYANA: Scepticism and Animal Faith.   N. Y.
1923.   P. 182 ff.   6. * BERTRAND RUSSELL: Scientific
Method in Philosophy.   Chicago, 1914.   Also * A. N.
WHITEHEAD: Science and the Modern World.   N. Y., 1925.
P. 209.

7. * BERTRAND RUSSELL: Mysticism and Logic.   London. 1921.
P. 11.

8. * WILLIAM JAMES: Varieties of Religious Experience.   London,
1915.   P. 73.

9. * FREDERICK SODDY: Matter and Energy.   London, 1923.   P.
38 ff.

10. J. S. MILL: Logic.   III. Chap. XIV. 4. N. Y., 1904.   P. 352.

11. * BERTRAND RUSSELL: Preface to Science and Method by
H. Poincaré.   London.   Thos. Nelson and Sons, Publishers.
P. 6.   12. J. S. MILL: Logic. III. Chap. XIV. 1. P. 345.

13. * JOHN DEWEY: Reconstruction in Philosophy.   N. Y., 1921.
P. 145.   Also Experience and Nature.   Chicago.   1925.
P. 73.

14. KARL PEARSON: Grammar of Science. London, 1911. I, p. 112.

15. A. D. RITCHIE: Scientific Method. N. Y., 1923. P. 14. Also * A. S. EDDINGTON: The Domain of Physical Science, essay in * Science, Religion and Reality by various writers. N. Y., 1925.

16. BERTRAND RUSSELL: Mysticism and Logic. London, 1921. Essay on The Relation of Sense-Data to Physics. P. 144. 17. BERTRAND RUSSELL: Essay on The Relation of Sense-Data to Physics. Also A. N. WHITEHEAD: The Concept of Nature. Cambridge, England. 1920. Chap. II. Theories of the Bifurcation of Nature. P. 31.

18. HENRI POINCARÉ: Science and Method. Translated by F. Maitland. London. Thos. Nelson and Sons. Publishers. Pp. 16, 23. 19. HENRI POINCARÉ: Science and Method. Pp. 17, 19.

20. KARL PEARSON: Grammar of Science. P. 37. 21. HENRY CREW: Address before the Class in Problems of Contemporary Thought, Northwestern University, Chicago. April 22, 1925. 22. HENRI POINCARÉ: Science and Method. P. 16. 23. HENRI POINCARÉ: Science and Method. P. 30.

24. * GEORGE SANTAYANA: Reason in Science. N. Y., 1906. P. 69.

The above books are valuable as collateral reading to the chapter on the Descriptive Approach to the World. Some others worth reading in this connection are: * POINCARÉ: Science and Hypothesis. JEVONS: The Principles of Science. CLIFFORD: Lectures and Essays. HELMHOLTZ: On the Relation of the Natural Sciences to the Totality of the Sciences. BACON: Novum Organum. MACH: Analysis of Sensations. BROAD: Scientific Thought. Harcourt, Brace & Co. HOBSON: The Domain of Natural Science. Cambridge University Press, 1923. CAMPBELL: What is Science? London, 1921. Congress of Arts and Sciences. St. Louis Exposition. Vol. I. Houghton Mifflin. 1905.

CHAPTER XVI
THE PRACTICAL APPROACH TO THE WORLD

1. * JOHN DEWEY: Experience and Nature. Chicago, 1925. P. 31.

2. * WILLIAM JAMES: Pragmatism. N. Y., 1909. P. 134.

3. * CHARLES S. PEIRCE: Chance, Love and Logic. N. Y., 1923. Essay on Fixation of Belief. P. 15.

4. * F. C. S. SCHILLER: Studies in Humanism. London, 1907. Pp. 193, 187.

5. * COUNT HERMANN KEYSERLING: The Travel Diary of A Philosopher. N. Y., 1925. Reviewed by Robert Morss Lovett: *The New Republic.* June 3, 1925.

6. WHITING WILLIAMS: What's On the Worker's Mind. N. Y. 1920. P. 177.

7. JOHN DEWEY: Experience and Nature. P. 14. Essay on Existence.

8. * GEORGE SANTAYANA: Reason in Common Sense. N. Y., 1906. P. 249.

9. F. C. S. SCHILLER: Studies in Humanism. P. 202.

10. JOHN DEWEY: Experience and Nature. P. 18.

11. WILLIAM JAMES: Pragmatism. P. 58.

12. F. C. S. SCHILLER: Studies in Humanism. P. 192. 13. F. C. S. SCHILLER: Studies in Humanism. P. 318. Essay on Protagoras the Humanist. *See* W. PATER: Marius the Epicurean. Chaps. VIII, IX.

14. CHARLES S. PEIRCE: Chance, Love and Logic. P. 41. Also JAMES: Pragmatism. P. 46. 15. JOHN DEWEY: Experience and Nature. P. 70.

The above books are worth while collateral reading to Chapter XVI. Other books worth reading in this connection are: * JAMES: The Meaning of Truth. SCHILLER: Humanism. SANTAYANA: Scepticism and Animal Faith. DEWEY: Reconstruction in Philosophy. * DEWEY: Human Nature and Conduct.

CHAPTER XVII
THE WORLD IN GENERAL

1. * BERTRAND RUSSELL: Mysticism and Logic. London, 1921.

2. * GEORGE SANTAYANA: Scepticism and Animal Faith. N. Y., 1923. P. 33.

3. * GEORGE SANTAYANA: Reason in Common Sense. N. Y., 1906. P. 43.

4. * JOHN DEWEY: Experience and Nature. Chicago. 1925. P. 63. 5. GEORGE SANTAYANA: Scepticism and Animal Faith. Compare P. 8.

6. C. K. OGDEN and I. A. RICHARDS: The Meaning of Meaning. N. Y., 1925. Quoted on P. 300.

7. * F. C. S. SCHILLER: Studies in Humanism. London, 1907.
P. 19.

8. * A. E. TAYLOR: Elements of Metaphysics. London, 1903.
P. 31. **9.** SPINOZA: Ethics I. Prop. XIII. Corollary and
note.

10. * WILLIAM JAMES: Pragmatism. N. Y., 1909. P. 244 ff.
11. JOHN DEWEY: Experience and Nature. P. 149.
12. A. E. TAYLOR: Metaphysics. P. 67.

13. * FRIEDRICH PAULSEN: Introduction to Philosophy. Translated by Thilly. N. Y., 1895. P. 341 f. Also * WILL
DURANT: The Story of Philosophy. N. Y., 1926.

14. JOSIAH ROYCE: The World and the Individual. N. Y., 1908.
I. pp. 80, 202, 386. .

15. GEORGE SANTAYANA: Scepticism and Animal Faith. P. 37.
16. BERTRAND RUSSELL: Mysticism and Logic. P. 99 f.
17. BERTRAND RUSSELL: Mysticism and Logic. Quoted by
RUSSELL.

18. JOHN DEWEY: Experience and Nature. P. 135. **19.** WIL-
LIAM JAMES: Pragmatism. P. 132. **20.** GEORGE SANTA-
YANA: Reason in Common Sense. P. 42 f.

21. WILLIAM JAMES: Pragmatism. P. 193. Also W. R. INGE:
Conclusion of * Science, Religion and Reality. N. Y., 1925.

22. R. G. COLLINGWOOD: Speculum Mentis. Oxford. 1924.
Pp. 41, 307, 309.

23. * WILHELM WINDELBAND: A History of Philosophy, Translated
by J. H. Tufts. N. Y., 1907. P. 249. **24.** WINDELBAND:
work cited. P. 92. **25.** WINDELBAND: work cited.
P. 109 ff.

The above books are worth reading in connection with Chapter
XVII. Other books suggested for collateral reading are: * PLATO:
Dialogues; Republic. Parmenides. Protagoras. Theatetus, etc.
ARISTOTLE: Metaphysics. Organon. BACON: Novum Organum.
Philosophical Works of DESCARTES, SPINOZA, BERKELEY, HOWE,
KANT, HEGEL, SCHOPENHAUER and modern Philosophers. * RUSSELL:
The Problems of Philosophy. * CALKINS: Persistent Problems
of Philosophy. * ROYCE: Spirit of Modern Philosophy.

The literature of this field is large. A reading of a brief history of
philosophy such as that by WEBER, CUSHMAN, FULLER, or by ROGERS
will orient the reader and help him to choose further readings intelligently and to his own interest. DURANT'S The Story of
Philosophy is worth while.

INDEX

INDEX

A

Absolute, 277; knowledge and existence, 330; simultaneity, 21; space and time, 21.
Absolutes and reality, 392.
Abstractionists, 295.
Acquired characteristics, 76.
Action, 14, 32; as the end of life, 369.
Adjustment to variables, 109.
Advertising, 247.
Aesthetic experience, 302–6.
Aether, 20, 24.
Aether-drift experiment, 19, 24.
Agriculture, 264 f.; foundation, 139 f.; social conditions, 245.
Alchemy, 31.
Alexander, 157 f.
Aliens, 262 f.; in America, 243 f.
Alpine stocks, compared with others, 136 f.
Aluminum age, 194.
America, 199 f., 249; dominant, 179; power control, 180; power resources, 187 f.; revolution, 174 f.; source of strength, 256.
American "progress," 377.
Analysis, and reality, 394.
Anarchism, 226.
Angell, 109.
Aquinas, T., 391.
Arboreal man, 121.
Archipenko, 296.
Architecture and dancing, 308.
Aristotle, 85, 291, 391; imitation, 307.
Arnold, M., 313.
Arrhenius, 64, 188.
Art, 291 f.; and capital, 308; and

mobility, 308 f.; and reason, 296 f.; and science, 276 f.; as activity, 307; of Cro-Magnons, 134.
Asceticism of science, 352.
Aspects of reality, 325.
Âtman, 320 f.
Atom, 28; for power, 192.
Atomism in psychology, 95, 112 f.

B

Bach, 290.
Bacon, 28, 171, 173.
Bacteria, 83.
Bailey, W. L., 234, 257.
Baker, 264.
Bakunin, 226.
Bankers, 216.
Barnard, G. G., 296.
Beauty, 302 f.; and hierarchies, 305.
Beethoven, 174, 290.
Behavior, 88 f.; at birth, 101.
Being, 282, 301 f.; and reason, 331 f., 391; and science, 342 f; beyond reason, 331 f., 391; immanent or transcendant, 331; spiritual, 329.
Bell, C., 292, 302 f., 303, 312.
Bennett, R., 191.
Berlach, 296.
Berlin, I., 289.
Berthelot, 112.
Bill of rights, 173.
Biology and morals, 334.
Birth control, 240 f.
Bismarck, 174.
Boas, F., 140 f.
Body, 13, 27.

445

Erosion, 55 f.
Eternal beauty, 311.
Eternity, 15, 329 f.
Euclid, 9, 387.
Eugenics, 265.
Europe in the ice ages, 130 f.
Events, 11, 12, 26 f., 391.
Evolution, 11, 79, 376; and teleology, 85; as process, 59; mechanically irreversible, 78; of death, 77; of music, 289 f.; of man's thinking, 140 f.; of the individual, 77; of stars, 41; of the universe, 38.
Existence, 399.
Experience, 16; and reality, 393.
Experimentalism, 385 f.
Experts, 4 f., 6.
Expressionism, 295 f.
External world and science, 359.

F

Family, 144 f.; size, 240; system and state, 266.
Farm earnings, 245 f.
Farmers in America, 245.
Faure, E., 293.
Feebleminded, 265.
Fenneman, N., 194.
Fermented liquors, early, 146.
Fertility of women, 241.
Field of reference, 390.
Fields of discourse, 401.
Final being and reason, 311 f.
Finalities of life, 299 f.
Finite standard, 23.
Fisher dollar, 217.
Fletcher, J., 285.
Flint, and its technique, 131.
Florida, 382.
Forests, 201.
Form, four dimensional, 293.
Fosdick, R., 236.
Foster and Catchings, 222.
France, revolution, 174 f.

Free activity, and life, 381; and the West, 375.
Freedom, of Greeks, 319.
Freud, 103 f., 183 f.
Frog, pioneer in intellect, 110.
Frost, R., 285.
Futurism, 294.

G

Gandhi, 251 f.
Gary, E., 369.
Gaudier-Brzeska, 296.
Gauguin, 293.
Genesis (star), 48.
Geologic conditions of life, 61; eons and eras, 51 f.; fluidity, 57; triumvirate, 50.
German shepherd dog, 374 f.
German tribes, 165.
Germany, of 1870, 174 f.
Germ plasm continuity, 76.
Gershwin, G., 289.
Gilbert and Pogue, 190.
Gilman, C., 266 f.
Glands, ductless, 93 f.
God, 310 f., 312, 314, 318 f., 342.
God's democracy, 312.
Goldenweiser, A., 119, 133, 143 f.
Good, 334 f.
Greece, 156 f.; and matter, 184 f.
Greek culture, 163 f.; freedom, 319; free reason, 349; primitives, 292; Weltanschauung, 318.
Green, T. H., 334.
Guild socialism, 227.
Gunpowder, 170, 186, 207.
Guyon, 308.
Gravitational fields, 24.
Gravity, 24, 26.
Galaxy, 39.
Group cities, 234.

H

h, the quantum theory, 32.
Haldane, J., 344.